ALDEN SPRINGER CRAFTS, born June 25, 1897, at Fort Collins, Colorado. A.B. University of California 1927; Ph.D. Univ. of California 1930. National Research Council Fellow 1930-31 at Cornell University. Asst. Botanist, Calif. Agri. Expt. Station, Davis, 1931-36; Asst. Botanist and Asst. Prof. of Botany, Univ. of Calif. at Davis 1936-39; Associate Botanist and Assoc. Prof. of Botany 1939-46; Botanist and Prof. of Botany 1946- —. Guggenheim Fellow July 1 to December 31, 1938; Research Fellow in Biology, Harvard University July 1 to December 31, 1938; Fellow AAAS 1940- —. Member A.A.A.S.; Bot. Soc. Amer.; Amer. Soc. Plant Physiol.; Calif. Bot. Soc.; Amer. Soc. Range Management. Sect'y Western Sect. Amer. Soc. Plant Physiol. 1937-39, Vice Chairman 1939-40, Chairman 1940-41. Visiting Professor, Puerto Rico Agri. Expt. Sta. July 1, 1947-June 30, 1948. Honorary Societies, Sigma Xi, Phi Sigma, Alpha Zeta, Phi Beta Kappa, Gamma Alpha.

HERBERT BASHFORD CURRIER, born Oct. 16, 1911 at Richwood, Ohio. B.S. Ohio State University 1932, M.S. Utah State Agric. College 1938, Ph.D. Univ. of California 1943. Teaching Asst. in Botany, Utah State Agric. College 1937-38; Teaching Asst. in Botany 1938-39, Associate in Botany 1939-42, College of Agric., Univ. of California, Davis; Research Chemist, Basic Vegetable Products Co., Vacaville, Calif. 1942-46; Asst. Botanist, Calif. Agric. Expt. Sta. and Asst. Prof. of Botany, College of Agriculture, Univ. of Calif. 1946- —. Member A.A.A.S., Bot. Soc. Amer., Amer. Soc. Plant Physiol., Sec'y Western Sect., Amer. Soc. Plant Physiol. 1948- —. Honorary societies: Sigma Xi.

CLIFFORD RALPH STOCKING, born June 22, 1913 at Riverside, California. B.S. Univ. of California 1937, M.S. Univ. of California 1939, Ph.D. University of California 1943. Teaching Asst. in Botany, Dept. of Botany, Univ. of Calif. 1938-40; Associate in Botany, College of Agric., Univ. of Calif., Davis, 1940-42; Food Chemist, Puccinelli Packing Co., Turlock, Calif. 1942-45; Asst. Botanist and Asst. Prof. of Botany, College of Agric., Univ. of Calif., Davis, 1946-. Member A.A.A.S., Bot. Soc. Amer., Amer. Soc. Plant Physiol. Honorary Societies: Alpha Zeta, Phi Beta Kappa, Sigma Xi.

CHRONICA BOTANICA
NEW SERIES OF PLANT SCIENCE BOOKS

edited by Frans Verdoorn

Volume XXI

WATER

in the

PHYSIOLOGY

of

PLANTS

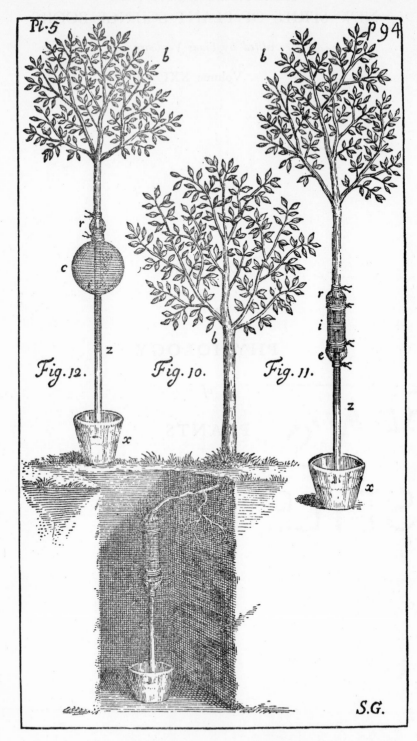

Plate illustrating HALES' "Experiments, whereby to find out the force with which trees imbibe moisture."—*From his* "Vegetable Staticks" (ed. 3, 1738).

WATER

IN THE

PHYSIOLOGY

OF

PLANTS

BY

A. S. CRAFTS
Professor of Botany
University of California,
Davis, California

H. B. CURRIER *and* C. R. STOCKING
Assistant Professor of Botany   *Assistant Professor of Botany*
University of California   *University of California*

The Ronald Press Company • New York

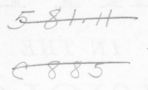

First published MCMXLIX
By the Chronica Botanica Company

PREFACE

In writing a modern scientific monograph, the writers must choose between a detailed treatment of the literature and a brief exposition of the facts and principles of the subject. In this volume, we have attempted to cite most of the relevant literature; in Chapter 1, the broader reviews; within the subsequent chapters, the more specialized papers. From these, we have repeated the minimum of material essential to a connected discourse on the subject, feeling that interested students will refer back to the original papers for details.

Thus, whereas this is intended as a reference work, it is hoped that its reading will not be so tedious as to preclude its use in the classroom. If any part seems needlessly long, it is because we deem the material of particular concern to certain workers in the field, or because it pertains to our own research. For this, our only excuse is that one usually reports most accurately that subject in which he is personally interested.

One further choice that must be made in treating so broad a subject is that of vocabulary. One could use the loose and rather indefinite terminology of two or three decades ago; or he may employ the more accurate wording of the modern plant physiologist; or he might adopt the highly technical language of the physical chemist. Again we have compromised. This volume has been written for use by present day botanists and plant physiologists; hence, we have used their language. At the same time, we have cited several recent treatises that employ, almost entirely, the vocabulary of physical chemistry. We realize the need for more accuracy in the definition and use of technical terms; also the desirability of a universal language for all scientists. On the other hand, the writing of a monograph for a certain group in a language with which they are not familiar is futile.

If the language of physical chemistry is to be adopted by physiologists, and most modern students will agree that it should be, two changes must be made. First, physical chemistry must become a required course for all undergraduates in physiology, and its terminology should be introduced and used relatively early in their careers. Second, physical chemists must develop a deeper appreciation for certain fields of physiology which, up to the present, have been somewhat or even totally neglected. Although many of the living systems with which the physiologist deals may be so complex as to offer little hope for thermodynamical analysis by present methods, their tremendous importance with respect to the well being of man, both through his own physiology, as well as that of the plants and animals upon which he depends for food and clothing, demands constant and sympathetic study. And the exact vocabulary of physical chemistry must be adapted to these complex functions if it is to be of use in their study. Though the thermodynamicist may be content to treat only the initial and final states of a system, the physiologist is interested in every mechanical detail of its operation, and his studies must deal with the description as well as the mathematical aspects of its functioning. Ultimately, all these problems must submit to analysis in terms of the molecular mechanics of the systems involved.

With regard to the above problem, we hope that this volume will serve two purposes. For plant workers, we trust that it will develop an appreciation for the exact analytical methods of the physical sciences. Much of the progress in the field of water relations has resulted from use of such methods. For the physical chemist, on the other hand, we hope to have presented a challenge to broaden, if need be, his view of the physical universe to encompass those many living systems upon which his very existence depends. There should be some common ground where these two may meet to work out their common problems for the mutual benefit of all. And if such cooperation between fundamental and applied scientists will lead to a warmer feeling of appreciation by both for their common interests, much good will have been done. The field of plant water relations presents many problems upon which such cooperative effort may be profitably spent. We hope that our volume may present these problems in such a way that many workers will be stimulated in their study.

In conclusion, we would like to express our appreciation to our many friends who have contributed to the writing of this monograph. Through conferences, discussions, and, in some instances, almost daily contacts, they have helped clarify some of the intricate problems involved in plant water relations. For reading parts of the manuscript we are especially indebted to Dr. L. E. Davis; for use of manuscripts, which at the time of writing were not yet published, we thank Dr. B. S. Meyer and Mr. T. C. Broyer; for counsel and advice in the development of the concepts of osmosis and osmotic pressure we express our appreciation to Drs. N. E. Edlefsen, F. A. Brooks, Max Kleiber, H. A. Young, H. G. Reiber and R. B. Dean. Translations of many foreign papers were kindly put at our disposal by Dr. F. J. Veihmeyer and Mr. T. C. Broyer. For encouragement throughout the preparation of the manuscript and aid in its final organization we are grateful to Dr. W. W. Robbins.

* * *

This book has been produced during troubled times. Because publication has been delayed, many current papers are not cited in the text. Some of these we are reporting here in an effort to bring our Bibliography up-to-date.

Workers on the properties of liquids and solutions are in general agreement that the unusual behavior of water results from coordination of its molecules by hydrogen bonding. Assuming a bonding energy of 4.25 K cal. per mole, Taft and Sisler (1947) calculate that, of the energy absorbed upon heating, 11 per cent is utilized in breaking bonds during melting of ice, 16 per cent is used raising the temperature from the melting to the boiling point, and 73 per cent goes in the vaporization process. Weissler (1949), using the velocity of sound at different temperatures to determine coordination, concludes that water undergoes a decrease in association of about 7.2 per cent between 0°C. and 100° C. Sound waves will detect molecular aggregates that are stable for 10^{-6} seconds. A previous value of 13.2 per cent was found using Raman spectrum analysis. The difference is due to the fact that the latter method detects aggregates that are stable for only 10^{-14} seconds.

In contrast to Taft and Sisler, Searcy (1949) calculates a value of 6.4 $\pm$ 0.5 K cal. for the H-bond energy in water. He concludes that repulsive as well as attractive forces contribute to the dipole energy.

Using a new formula to determine an index of association in liquids, Parshad (1947) has calculated values between 240 and 325 for a series of non-polar compounds;

values of 403 to 745 for some common associated organic liquids; and a value of 5010 for water. The theory that liquids contain points of abnormal coordination (holes) within their structure is receiving continued support and many calculations are being made on the activation energy required for movement of molecules from position to position (flow). Studying thermal conductivity of liquids, PALMER (1948) finds that in associated liquids H-bonds assist in the collisional transfer of heat. This is brought about by (1) causing orientation of the molecules in the direction of flow, and (2) assisting transfer by rupture of bonds at the high-temperature end and reforming them at the low-temperature end. If the entropy of vaporization can be considered a measure of H-bonding, then in water 80 per cent of heat transfer is by this mechanism.

As the picture of water structure becomes clearer, many of the anomalous properties of solutions are being elucidated. Swinging from early assumptions, based on studies of dilute solutions, that all solutions are perfect and that apparent deviations result from association or compound formation, physical chemists went to the other extreme and proposed that all solutes are completely ionized with abnormal behavior resulting from the interaction of force fields (DEBYE and HÜCKEL). Now a middle course wherein ionic and molecular interaction as well as chemical bonds are given due consideration seems best. With the introduction of spectrum analysis distinctions can be made and the type of bonding identified. Gradually the relations between the thermodynamic properties and the molecular structure of solutions are being studied, and concentrated as well as dilute solutions are being given consideration (REDLICH, 1949). The literature on the properties of solutions is too large to consider here and the reader is referred to the Journal of Chemical Physics, the Journal of Physical Chemistry and Chemical Reviews as fertile sources.

Coordination of water is reflected in the high internal pressure or cohesional force which this compound exhibits. TEMPERLEY (1947) has shown that liquid water can support tensions up to 60 atmospheres in glass tubes. Using air-free water in Berthelot tubes SCOTT et al.(1948) could develop a tension of only 32 atm. Though these values differ appreciably, the latter is sufficient to explain the flow of sap to the tops of the tallest trees. Hydration phenomena have also received attention. For example, SIMHA and ROWEN (1948) conclude that, in systems containing moist cellulose, silk, and wool, behavior at low moisture levels can be explained in terms of adsorption theory; at high moisture levels the systems can be analysed in terms of a theory of polymer-liquid mixtures; in between the two extremes a transition occurs.

Although osmotic pressure measurements continue to serve in the determination of the molecular weight of large molecules, little change has occurred in the theoretical aspects. BURSTRÖM (1948) has attempted an evaluation of the significance of turgor of the living cell. Departing from the classical definition "turgor is the pressure acting from inside the cell on the cell wall" (p. 58, last line), BURSTRÖM by devious analysis arrives at the expression $T = O - E$ where $T =$ turgor pressure; $O =$ osmotic value of the cell sap; and $E =$ osmotic value of the external medium. To us this T is simply a net or corrected osmotic pressure. It is shown as such in BURSTRÖM's Fig. 2 (page 61). It could equal our turgor pressure only when the cell is in equilibrium with the external solution of concentration E. As in several previous cases (CRAFTS, 1943), we feel that this redefinition of terms is not justified. It leads to such confused statements as—"T increases as the cell loses water—" (page 62, lines 1 and 2), "turgor—expresses a pressure realized in the cell—," "This deduction of turgor pressure—exactly shows the pressure actually exerted from within the cell on the cell wall" (p. 63), and "The turgor pressure must decrease when a cell absorbs water and the wall pressure increases" (p. 64).

This dilemma seems to arise from a failure to appreciate that (in our symbols) when $OP = DPD$, $T = 0$, when $OP = TP$, $DPD = 0$, and at all other states $OP = DPD + TP$. While these relations are most easily examined at equilibrium, a state of flux does not invalidate them. And the definitions which they imply are simple, clear, and in accord with classical considerations of osmotic pressure.

In the field of cell water relations a number of valuable contributions have appeared. In a general discussion of swelling and shrinking (Trans. Faraday Soc., 1946) water-holding forces in biological systems received critical consideration. The nature of vacuolation of protoplasm following certain types of swelling is made more clear by FAURÉ-FRÉMIET. SEIFRIZ presents convincing arguments for a distinction between osmotic pressure and imbibition, and discusses swelling and shrinking phenomena in the light of known protoplasmic structure.

In a subsequent general discussion on interaction of water and porous materials (Faraday Soc. Discussion, 1948), BENNET-CLARK restates his belief that water secretion from the cytoplasm into the vacuole of the plant cell actually occurs. In considering LEVITT's (1947) claim that secretion values reported are thermodynamically unsound, BENNET-CLARK casts doubt on the validity of the value used by LEVITT to represent water permeability in calculation of water velocity.

LUNDEGÅRDH further identifies an active water mechanism in roots with the absorption of salts from the culture medium. As in previous work, he assumes that "anion respiration" provides the energy.

Recent findings have added to our understanding of auxin-induced water uptake by cells. In an important paper LEVITT (1948) offers convincing evidence that auxin-enhanced water absorption by potato discs is not active water uptake, as suggested by several investigators, but rather a result of altered plasticity of the cell wall. The manner in which auxin may increase wall plasticity is not understood but KELLY (1947) has shown that it is an aerobic process in *Avena* coleoptile segments. AUDUS has critically reviewed the problem of cell elongation (Biol. Rev., 1949).

Studies on water secretion and transport by *Nitella* cells have been extended by OSTERHOUT (1949). That the pumping mechanism demonstrated in *Nitella* under somewhat arbitrary conditions could operate in certain kinds of cells seems validated by a theoretical consideration by FRANCK and MAYER (1947) of an osmotic diffusion pump.

The absorption of water by root systems is being given detailed consideration by KRAMER, whose book on the subject is in press. FREY-WYSSLING (1941) has demonstrated guttation under conditions of high water absorption and low transpiration in several woody species, and DANIEL (1949) observed xylem exudation from excised roots of several coniferous species. Studies on the effect of certain salts on increasing root pressure and tissue resistance to infiltration in sunflower, tomato, and dahlia were made by VOLK (1944).

HAGAN (1949), by measuring water intake by excised root systems of sunflowers growing in moisture-deficient soil, has verified the autonomic diurnal cycle of root activity studied by GROSSENBACHER (1938). The diurnal cycles continued for about 6 days but were terminated if the roots were aerated with N_2 or CO_2. Similar cycles observed in roots washed free of soil indicate that the activity is a function of the root and not of its environment. Such roots in water exuded water during the day and withdrew it during the night. HAGAN attributes this activity to changing hydration of the cytoplasm.

MITSCHERLICH (1947) has pointed out that water requirements of plants follow the law of plant growth. Water requirements are high for plants having short vegetative periods and they decrease with increasing nutrient supply. More specific data on the effects of potassium and calcium on the water relations of plants were given by WOESTMANN (1942). Potassium induced water storage, water uptake, and transpiration, probably through its effect of promoting hydration of the protoplasm. Calcium diminished protoplasmic hydration and consequently lowered protoplasmic permeability and hence water absorption. Water storage and transpiration were reduced. Plants deficient in nitrogen showed decreased transpiration, a failure of guard cells to function normally, and an increase in cold resistance and protoplasmic viscosity (GESSNER and SCHUMANN, 1948).

WADLEIGH (1945) has made a new approach to the problem of plant-soil water relations. He devised a method for integrating the variables that account for the total soil-moisture stress against which the plant absorbs water. When leaf elongation of cotton plants was expressed empirically as a second degree function of soil-moisture stress, values close to 15 atmospheres for the stress inhibiting leaf growth were calculated (WADLEIGH and GAUCH, 1948). Additional data indicating that under good conditions of soil aeration and fertility the rate of vegetative growth increases with increasing soil moisture within the range from near the permanent wilting percentage to near soil saturation have been presented by HAYNES (1948). He concludes that corn plants subjected to daily periods of temporary wilting produce small vegetative growth when under humid conditions. On the other hand, WILSON (1948b) has shown that tomato stem tips can maintain their highly hydrated state at the expense of older mature tissues. Thus they can increase steadily in length throughout the day and night even when the plant as a whole passes through a diurnal cycle with the water balance on the negative side during the day.

MORTON and WATSON (1948) conclude that the rate of leaf production by apical meristem is unaffected by water supply. The number and size of cells per leaf increased with increasing water supply. Net assimilation was greatly reduced by water deficit.

Reviewing plant-water relations, TAGEEVA (1946) found that wheat plants have reduced water content as they mature; upper leaves dehydrate more than lower ones. Nevertheless, the upper leaves have a greater rate of photosynthesis than lower ones. Low water supply results in an increase in soluble carbohydrates leading to decrease in photosynthesis. EATON and ERGLE (1948) find that in certain plants such as cotton, water deficit may depress carbohydrate utilization to a greater extent than it does photosynthesis leading to an increased sugar content.

In the discussion mentioned above (Faraday Soc. Discussion, 1948) papers by VAN DEN HONERT, LEWIS, FOGG, and CRAFTS deal with water and food movement in plants and the relations of leaf cell walls and leaf surfaces. VAN DEN HONERT, considering the role of living root cells, xylem conductors, living leaf cells and the "gaseous part" (intercellular spaces, stomata, and air layer around the leaf) concludes that the greatest resistance to water movement is the "gaseous part." He agrees with GRADMANN's (1928) views that this phase may exert limiting influence on water transport.

LEWIS presents further data on the hydrophobic nature of the outer walls of leaf mesophyll, while FOGG pictures the effects of varying water conditions of underlying tissues on the nature of the leaf surface.

CRAFTS, in an analysis of the physical nature of sieve-tube protoplasm, and sieve tube walls, concludes that the mature, functioning sieve tube is a highly specialized structure. The optical nature of the walls and their high water content suggest that they have a loose open structure. The degradation of the sieve-tube cytoplasm attending maturation of these elements results in a loss of their semipermeability. It is concluded that this also denotes an open mesh structure. It is suggested that the open structure of sieve-tube walls and cytoplasm constitute specialization favoring a mass flow of the assimilate stream. WENT and HULL (1949) present evidence for a temperature coefficient of less than 1 for both rate and intensity of sugar transport in the tomato plant.

The perplexing problem of stomatal behavior was reviewed critically by WILSON (1948a). Theories proposing that stomatal action can be accounted for by changes in permeability, changes in enzyme activity, or variation in colloidal hydration were not considered adequate as an explanation for the observed effects of light, temperature, and humidity on stomatal aperture.

Literature cited:— AUDUS, L. J. 1949: Biol. Rev. 24: 51-93. — BURSTRÖM, H. 1948: Physiol. Plant. 1: 57-64. — CRAFTS, A. S. 1943: Chronica Bot. 7: 386-8. — DANIEL, T. W. 1949: Plant Physiol. 24: 327-30. — EATON, F. M., and D. R. ERGLE 1948: Plant Physiol. 23: 169-87. — Faraday Soc. Discussions No. 3, 1948: 1-293. — Faraday Soc. Trans. 1946, 42B: 1-304. — FRANCK, J., and J. E. MAYER 1947: Archives of Biochem. 14: 293-313. — FREY-WYSSLING, A. 1941: Ber. Schweiz. bot. Ges. 51: 321. — GESSNER, F., and M. SCHUMANN 1948: Z. Naturforsch. 3b: 36-41. — GRADMANN, H. 1928: Jahrb. wiss. Bot. 69: 1-100. — GROSSENBACHER, K. A. 1938: Plant Physiol. 13: 669-76. — HAGAN, R. M. 1949: Plant Physiol. 24: 441-454. — HAYNES, J. L. 1948: Jour. Amer. Soc. Agron. 40: 385-95. — KELLY, S. 1947: Amer. Jour. Bot. 34: 521-6. — LEVITT, J. 1947: Plant Physiol. 22: 514-25. — LEVITT, J. 1948: Plant Physiol. 23: 505-15. — MITSCHERLICH, E. A. 1947: Z. Pflanzenernähr., Düngung u. Bodenk. 38: 202-15. — MORTON, A. G., and D. J. WATSON 1948: Ann. Bot. 12: 281-310. — OSTERHOUT, W. J. V. 1949: Jour. Gen. Physiol. 32: 553-66. — PALMER, G. 1948: Ind. Eng. Chem. 40: 89-92. — PARSHAD, R. 1947: Jour. Phys. Chem. 15: 761-2. — REDLICH, O. 1949: Chem. Rev. 44: 1-5. — SCOTT, A. F., D. P. SHOEMAKER, K. N. TANNER, and J. G. WENDEL 1948: Jour. Chem. Phys. 16: 495-502. — SEARCY, A. W. 1949: Jour. Chem. Phys. 17: 210-11. — SIMHA, R., and J. W. ROWEN 1948: Jour. Amer. Chem. Soc. 70: 1663-5. — TAFT, R. W. and H. H. SISLER 1947: Jour. Chem. Educ. 24: 175-81. — TAGEEVA, S. V. 1946: Trudy Inst. Fiziol. Rastenii un K. A. Timiryazeva 4, No. 1: 161-75 and 176-92. — TEMPERLEY, H. N. V. 1947: Proc. Phys. Soc. (London) 59: 199-208. — VOLK, A. 1944: Bodenk. u. Pflanzenernähr. 34: 190-204. — WADLEIGH, C. H. 1945: Soil Sci. 61: 225-38. — WADLEIGH, C. H., and H. G. GAUCH 1948: Plant Physiol. 23: 485-95. — WEISSLER, A. 1947: Jour. Chem. Phys. 15: 210-11. — WENT, F. W., and H. M. HULL 1949: Plant Physiol. 24: 505-26. — WILSON, C. C. 1948a: Plant Physiol. 23: 5-37. — WILSON, C. C. 1948b: Plant Physiol. 23: 156-7. — WOESTMANN, E. 1942: Jahrb. wiss. Bot. 90: 335-81.

July 1949   THE AUTHORS

ACKNOWLEDGEMENTS

Grateful acknowledgement is made for permission to reproduce certain copyrighted materials. Our Table 12 comes from HALDANE's paper in the Biochemical Journal; Figure 41 and Table 3 and a part of Table 4 are from HÖBER, Physical Chemistry of Cells and Tissues, courtesy of the Blakiston Co., Philadelphia; Figures 22-27 are from STRUGGER's Praktikum der Zell- und Gewebephysiologie, Gebrüder Borntraeger, Berlin. The latter also permitted reproduction of (our) Figures 33 and 36, and Tables 21, 22 and 24, appearing in the periodicals Jahrb. f. wiss. Bot. and Protoplasma. The Canadian Journal of Research has permitted reproduction of our Figure 10 from a paper by BABBITT. Our Table 17 is taken from a paper by MORSE, published by the Carnegie Institution of Washington; to the Faraday Society we are indebted for Table 10 and a portion of Table 4, from papers in the Transactions by LONDON and PORTER respectively; Tables 8, 11, and 13 are reproduced from a paper by FRAZER and MYRICK, courtesy The Journal of the American Chemical Society. By permission of the Macmillan Co., New York and London, we have copied (our) Figure 50 from FOGG's paper in the periodical Nature, and Table 36 from DIXON's monograph, Transpiration and the Ascent of Sap in Plants. The New Phytologist and Dr. T. A. BENNET-CLARK have allowed reproduction of Fig. 42 and Tables 30 and 34. Figure 12 comes from HILDEBRAND's Solubility, Reinhold Publishing Co., New York; Figure 40 from a paper by OSTERHOUT and MURRAY, by permission of the Rockefeller Institute for Medical Research, New York; Tables 14, 15, and 16 from BERKELEY, HARTLEY and BURTON in the Transactions of the Royal Society; Table 45 after LEICK in ABDERHALDEN's series on biological methods, published by Urban and Schwarzenberg, Berlin. Figures 11, 19, and 49 are copied from MEYER and ANDERSON's Plant Physiology, copyright Van Nostrand Co., Inc., New York.

Thanks are also due the following for authorization to quote from original publications: Dr. MATILDA M. BROOKS; The Faraday Society (Transactions); Journal of Experimental Biology; Longmans, Green and Co., Inc., New York (FINDLEY, Osmotic Pressure); Reinhold Publishing Co., New York (HILDEBRAND, Solubility of Non-Electrolytes); The Ronald Press Co., New York (ADOLPH, Physiological Regulations); John Wiley & Sons, Inc., New York (GORTNER, Outlines of Biochemistry, 2nd Ed.; BULL, Physical Biochemistry; HEUSER, Cellulose Chemistry); Williams and Wilkins Co., Baltimore (Chemical Reviews).

Where other materials not listed above are used in the text, the source is indicated. Unfortunately the authors were unable to contact a few authors and publishers. To all whose published data were found useful the writers wish to express their gratitude.

CONTENTS

Chapter I

INTRODUCTION 1

Chapter II

STRUCTURE OF WATER: — INTRODUCTION — STRUCTURE — EARLY THEORIES — THE HYDROLS — THE FARADAY SYMPOSIUM — LATER WORK ON THE HYDROL THEORY — "NORMAL" AND "POLAR" LIQUIDS — MOLECULAR CONCENTRATION — MODERN STUDIES — X-RAY ANALYSIS — THE SECOND FARADAY SYMPOSIUM — CURRENT RESEARCH — SUMMARY OF WATER STRUCTURE 3

Chapter III

PROPERTIES OF SOLUTIONS: — INTRODUCTION — THE IN-TERRELATION OF THE PROPERTIES OF SOLUTIONS — THE FORCES BETWEEN ATOMS AND MOLECULES — MOLECULAR INTERACTION AND WATER BIND-ING — HYDRATION — MOBILITY OF IONS — SUMMARY 18

Chapter IV

OSMOSIS AND OSMOTIC PRESSURE: — INTRODUCTION — REFINEMENT OF THE OSMOTIC PRESSURE LAW — CAUSES FOR NON-IDEAL BEHAVIOR OF SOLUTIONS — SUMMARY 32

Chapter V

THE MECHANISM OF OSMOSIS: — INTRODUCTION (Osmosis — Osmotic pressure — Diffusion — Diffusion pressure — Diffusion pressure deficit — Turgor — Turgor pressure) — THE KINETIC BASIS OF OSMOSIS — OSMOSIS IN LIQUID SYSTEMS — THE MECHANICS OF OSMOSIS — THE "SOLVENT" AND "SOLUTE" PRESSURE THEORIES — CALCULATION BY INDIRECT METHODS — EVALUATION OF DIFFUSION PRESSURE — THE DIFFUSION PRESSURE OF THE SOLVENT — SUMMARY 43

Chapter X

WATER LOSS AND WATER RETENTION: — Introduction — Laws of Evaporation — Evaporation from a Free Water Surface — Evaporation from Tubes — Factors Affecting Evaporation from Free Water Surfaces of Uniform Shape and Area (Solutes — Temperature — Dryness of the air — Atmospheric pressure — Wind velocity) — Transpiration — Methods of Measuring Transpiration — Expression of Results — Cuticular Transpiration — Fluctuations in the Rate of Transpiration — Internal Factors Affecting Transpiration — Wall Structure — Physical Resistance to Water Movement — Osmotic Properties — Internal Surface — Stomatal Number and Distribution — Methods of Measuring Stomatal Openings — Genetic Factors — Stomatal Regulation of Transpiration — Effect of Mineral Nutrients on Transpiration — Influence of Disease, Sprays, Dusts, and Waxes on Transpiration Rate — Physiological Effects of Water Deficits — Subaqueous Transpiration — Conclusions — Summary 179

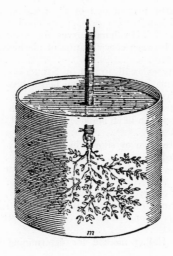

LIST OF TEXT ILLUSTRATIONS

LIST OF TABLES

Pl. 1.

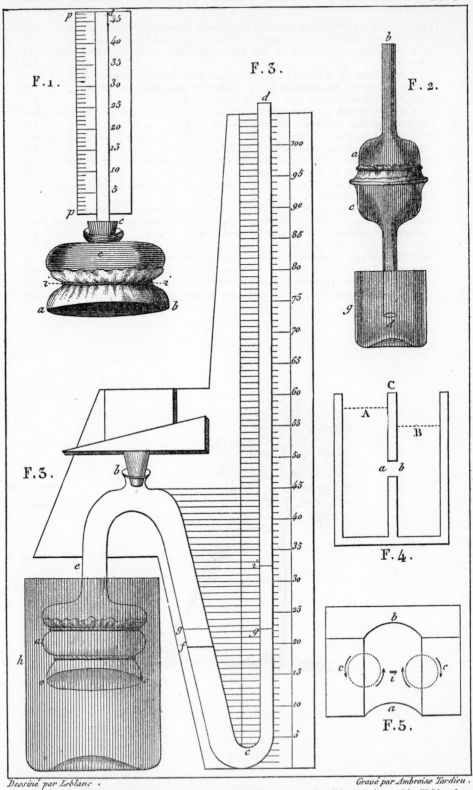

Dessiné par Leblanc.   Gravé par Ambroise Tardieu.

Dutrochet's apparatus "pour mesurer la force de l'endosmose."— Plate 1 *from his* "Mémoires pour servir à l'Histoire Anatomique et Physiologique des Végétaux et des Animaux" (1837).

Chapter I

INTRODUCTION

The relation of water to plant cells is at the same time one of the oldest and one of the most modern of physiological problems. MALPIGHI, HALES, KNIGHT, and a host of early plant scientists recognized this important field of study. Survey of modern literature proves that water relations still claim the attention of leading plant physiologists. Viewpoints change; methods improve; still the underlying principles of water absorption and utilization challenge the researcher. Almost all plant functions involve water relations in some form or other; provision of adequate water for maximum growth of plants is the basis of successful agriculture in many parts of the world.

Writing a concise monograph on water relations is a difficult task for it involves selecting from an immense literature material relevant to modern concepts and problems. To be of value, furthermore, such a monograph should contain original work by the authors or it should involve synthesis of new concepts from previous publications. Availability of modern abstracting and reviewing agencies renders almost useless a mere compilation or uncritical review of published articles.

This volume aims to attain both of the above objectives; it also attempts to aid students in becoming familiar with contemporary literature in the field. A balanced treatment of the subject involves a description of the structure of water and aqueous solutions, a review of the concepts of the mechanism of osmosis, consideration of the water relations of individual cells, and finally, analysis of the functions of absorption, movement, retention, and loss of water by organized plants. It is obvious that space cannot be devoted to a detailed historical review. Mainly as an aid to students, the following introduction to source materials is included.

Works of MALPIGHI (1675), HALES (1738), and KNIGHT (1801) are of historical interest only. Ideas in their time were confused by failure to clearly distinguish between the water relations of plants and animals.

Discovery of the microscope stimulated interest in plant structure. The earlier works on conducting systems are thoroughly covered by STRASBURGER (1891) and HABERLANDT (1914). Meanwhile DUTROCHET (1827), PFEFFER (1877), VAN'T HOFF (1887 and 1888), and DE VRIES (1918) laid the foundations for a physical analysis of cell water relations through their studies on osmosis and osmotic pressure. Work by BERKELEY and HARTLEY (1906), MORSE (1914), FRAZER and MYRICK (1916), and BERKELEY, HARTLEY, and BURTON (1919) provides a quantitative basis for such analysis.

Theoretical treatment of osmotic systems by LEWIS (1908), HALDANE (1918), BANCROFT and DAVIS (1928), and others has materially broadened our concepts while reviews by FINDLAY (1919), MEYER (1938), and URSPRUNG (1938) have marked progress in this field. Of treatments in physico-chemical texts, those of WASHBURN (1921), LEWIS and RANDALL (1923), GLASSTONE (1940), and GETMAN and DANIELS (1943) are noteworthy.

Application of physical principles to the problems of water conduction in trees led to the cohesion theories of DIXON (1914) and RENNER (1915). Measurements by MacDOUGAL (1926) have largely substantiated the theoretical considerations involved as have biophysical studies by BODE (1923).

The general field of plant water relations has been covered by the works of LIVINGSTON (1903), MAXIMOV (1929a), and WALTER (1931b). URSPRUNG (1938) has presented a detailed review of most of the early work including his own and that of his collaborators. Ecological aspects of water relations are stressed by MAXIMOV (1929a), WALTER (1931b), and MONTEMARTINI (1943). Applications of the principles of soil physics and plant physiology to problems of water utilization by plants have been made by BRIGGS and SHANTZ (1912) and MAXIMOV (1929a) ; and more recently by VEIHMEYER and HENDRICKSON and their associates (see papers from 1927 to 1946). The relations of soil salinity to plant growth have been investigated at the U.S.D.A. Salinity Laboratory. This and other works on soil salinity have been reviewed by MAGISTAD (1945).

Thermodynamic treatments of plant and soil water relations are given by EDLEFSEN and ANDERSON (1943) and BROYER (1946), and also by STERN (1933).

Specialized aspects of water relations involve the binding of water by cellular constituents including cellulose, proteins, and the living protoplasm. Hydration of cellulose is treated by STAMM (1936), HEUSER (1944), and WISE (1944). Protein hydration is discussed by GORTNER (1938), SCHMIDT (1938), and SPONSLER, BATH, and ELLIS (1940). SPONSLER (1940) and FREY-WYSSLING (1938) have studied hydration phenomena of the living protoplasm.

Problems of permeability are reviewed periodically in the Annual Review of Physiology. In 1945 this topic was covered by S. C. BROOKS. Work on the uptake and exchange of solutes is described by HOAGLAND (1944) and KROGH (1946). Theories of membrane permeability are extensively treated in the works of BROOKS and BROOKS (1941), DAVSON and DANIELLI (1943), and HÖBER (1945).

Osmotic quantities of cells and their interrelations have received detailed attention by THODAY (1918), HÖFLER (1920), BECK (1928), and MEYER (1938, 1945). Cryoscopic determination of osmotic pressure values has been stressed by WALTER (1931a) and his associates. URSPRUNG (1938) has compiled much of the work on the plasmolytic method. HARRIS (1934) has accumulated an abundance of data on freezing point lowering of plant saps, particularly as related to distribution of the plants.

BENNET-CLARK, GREENWOOD, and BARKER (1936) have renewed the interest in active cell water relations. Papers by BENNET-CLARK and BEXON (1940, 1943, 1946), MASON and PHILLIS (1939), VAN OVERBEEK (1942, 1944), and LYON (1942) treat various aspects of the same subject.

Water relations are intimately involved in frost and drought resistance. Reviews by LEVITT (1941) and SCARTH (1944) report work on frost resistance. MAXIMOV (1929a, 1929b, 1941), TUMANOV (1929), VASSILIEV and VASSILIEV (1936), MARTIN (1930), and AAMODT and JOHNSTON (1936) have covered drought resistance.

The role of water in the physiology of plant cells has been studied in detail in recent years. KÜSTER (1935), URSPRUNG (1938), and GUILLIERMOND (1941) have provided monographs covering this subject, while BRAUNER (1932) and STRUGGER (1935) describe methods for studying the physiology of cells. The AAAS' monograph "The Cell and Protoplasm" (1940) covers many aspects of cell physiology as does also the monograph of the American Society of Plant Physiologists, "The Structure of Protoplasm" edited by SEIFRIZ (1942).

Finally, REED (1942) gives a historical view of plant water relations with additional reference material ; two recent books covering the field of physical biochemistry by BULL (1943) and HÖBER (1945) provide a wealth of information for the student of cell physiology.

Chapter II

STRUCTURE OF WATER

Introduction:— Most cells originate in a highly aqueous medium; they use water in growth and other vital processes; in most instances, they consist largely of water throughout their life span. Logically there should be an intimate relation between the functions of cells and the properties of water and dilute aqueous solutions. A study of plant water relations impresses one that this is true.

Water enters into the composition of carbohydrates, proteins, and other compounds making up the walls and protoplasts of plant cells; it is combined with various colloidal constituents of cells as water of hydration; it is involved in many metabolic processes in the plant; and it exists as a liquid in the solutions occupying the vacuoles of living cells and the lumina of conducting elements. Due to the many forces tending to reduce the activity of water molecules, it may be difficult to distinguish between the various states in which water exists within the plant.

Combining the elements hydrogen and oxygen, water in its simplest form corresponds to the formula H_2O. Many more complicated forms have been proposed to explain its various properties. Most of these involve association or polymerization.

Water boils at 100° C. and freezes at 0° C. when under one atmosphere pressure; it is liquid throughout the temperature range at which plants thrive. Many plants can survive freezing temperatures; certain spores can stand boiling; photosynthesis and transpiration may take place through a range from near freezing to the thermal death temperature around 40° to 50° C. Many plant functions, however, find their optimum within the range from approximately 20° to 30° C. The occurrence over a large portion of the earth's surface of temperatures within these narrow limits depends, among other things, upon the large latent heats of vaporization and freezing of water, and upon its heat capacity and conductivity. HENDERSON (1924), discussing the fitness of the environment, points out the many unusual properties of water, most of which apparently contribute in some way to the well-being of plants. It is interesting to note the exceedingly narrow range of temperature and moisture within which our important economic plants thrive, and to point out the role played by water in maintaining these conditions.

Structure:— Water has long been recognized as a compound of unusual character. TABLES 1 and 2 list some of the physical properties of common elements and liquids. Water stands out, having a very high heat of vaporization and a fairly high heat of fusion. (For further data of this type, *see* BERNAL and FOWLER, 1933, Table III). Of the compounds listed, water has the greatest surface tension, internal pressure, and dielectric constant. These latter properties indicate the interatomic forces present in the molecule.

Formed from hydrogen which boils at —253° C. under atmospheric pressure, and oxygen which boils at —180° C., water boils at 100° C. If normal in its properties water should boil at a very low temperature variously estimated at from —65° C. to —100° C. Its freezing point should

TABLE 1. — *Some thermal properties of water and several elements and compounds:* —

SUBSTANCES	HEAT CAPACITY PER GRAM FORMULA WEIGHT		HEAT OF FUSION CALORIES PER GRAM		HEAT OF VAPORIZATION CALORIES PER GRAM	
	Calories	Temp. ° C.	Calories	Temp. ° C.	Calories	Temp. ° C.
Hydrogen	3.4	0	15.0	....	108.0	—252.8
Oxygen	3.5	0	3.3	—219.0	50.9	—182.9
Nitrogen	3.5	0	6.1	—210.0	47.6	—195.5
Sulfur	5.3	0	10.4	119.0	66.3	444.6
Water, liquid	18.1	0	....	....	539.0	100.0
Water, solid	9.1	0	80.0	0	....	....
Carbon dioxide	8.7	0	45.4	— 56.2	87.0	— 60.0
Ammonia	8.8	0	108.0	— 75.0	327.0	— 33.4
Hydrogen sulfide	4.6	10	....	....	132.0	— 61.4
Sulfur dioxide	15.4	10	....	....	95.0	— 10.0

TABLE 2. — *Physical properties of water and some other common liquids:* —

SUBSTANCES	SURFACE TENSION		INTERNAL PRESSURE	DIELECTRIC CONSTANT	
	Dynes/cm.	Temp.	Atmospheres	E	Temp. ° C.
Water	75.6	0	16,400	81.000	17
Mercury	47.6	20	13,050	....	....
Carbon disulfide	35.3	0	5,400	2.600	0
Benzene	31.6	0	4,050	1.002	100
Carbon tetrachloride	29.0	0	3,640	1.003	110
Hexane	20.5	0	2,020	1.874	20
Ethyl alcohol	24.0	0	7,200	1.006	100

be around —100° C. to —150° C. In comparison H_2S, containing sulfur that boils at 444° C., is a gas boiling around —61° C.

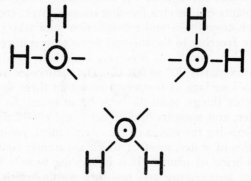

FIG. 1.—Trihydrol molecule as pictured by SUTH-ERLAND (1900).

Other anomalous properties of water include its minimum specific heat at 37.5° C., its maximum density at 4.0° C., and its great expansion upon solidification. This latter property has played an important part in all attempted explanations of the structure of water.

Early Theories:— The earliest concepts of the liquid structure of water pictured it as composed of spheroid molecules, heterogeneously arranged, and having the unordered motion of a very dense gas. As early as 1884, however, WHITING visualized liquid water as a solution of ice particles and RAOULT (1885) pictured association of water molecules into groups of four. VERNON (1891) explained the maximum density of water by association of the molecules from $(H_2O)_2$ above 4° C. to $(H_2O)_4$ below that temperature. In 1892 RÖNTGEN independently proposed that liquid water is made up of a saturated solution of ice in some other form of water. He pictured ice molecules as complex, but less dense than water; when ice melts the volume is decreased.

As water is warmed, however, thermal expansion increases the volume. RÖNTGEN explained the maximum density as a combination of these two effects.

The compressibility of a normal liquid decreases with temperature. RÖNTGEN from the association theory suggested that pressure would decrease the number of ice molecules; hence there should be a point of minimum compressibility of water. Such a point occurs at about 50° C. He explained the increase of the thermal coefficient of expansion at pressures around 3,000 atmospheres by the effect of pressure in breaking up ice molecules. He suggested that the point of maximum density would occur at lower temperatures under pressure and that the freezing point would also be lowered. This has proved true. The anomalous decrease in viscosity with increasing pressure he explained on the assumption that the simpler water molecules had a lower viscosity than ice molecules.

The Hydrols:— In 1900 SUTHERLAND proposed that water vapor is H_2O (hydrol), ice pure $(H_2O)_3$ (trihydrol), and liquid water a mixture of $(H_2O)_2$ (dihydrol) and $(H_2O)_3$ in proportions dependent upon the temperature. FIGURE 1 shows the latter molecules as pictured by SUTHERLAND. At 0° C. the fraction of $(H_2O)_3$ in water was calculated to be 0.375; at 20° C., 0.321; at 40° C., 0.284; at 60° C., 0.255; at 80° C., 0.234; and at 100° C., 0.203. At the critical temperature water was supposed to be composed of nearly pure hydrol. At 4° C. SUTHERLAND supposed it to be approximately $\frac{1}{3}$ $(H_2O)_3$ and $\frac{2}{3}$ $(H_2O)_2$.

SUTHERLAND concluded that the latent heat of fusion of ice is mostly a latent heat of dissociation of trihydrol into dihydrol, partly masked by heat of solution of trihydrol in dihydrol; and that the latent heat of vaporization also includes the heat of dissociation of the dihydrol and trihydrol of water into the hydrol of steam. The specific heat of water is not an ordinary specific heat but includes heat of dissociation. Pressure dissociates trihydrol; at temperatures between 0° and 100° C. trihydrol is completely dissociated at pressures about 2300 atmospheres. Since pressure causes dissociation, tension should bring about association; at temperatures below 40° the surface layer of water he thought to be largely trihydrol.

SUTHERLAND explains the polymerization of hydrol on a tetrad oxygen valence, the assumption being that three H_2O molecules of trihydrol are bound into a triangular grouping by the extra oxygen bonds. The sharp melting point of ice depends upon molecular resonance resulting in the breaking of these bonds.

ARMSTRONG, et al. (1908) proposed the possible existence of water isomers of different structure, the hydrones. Active water molecules, hydrone (HOH) or hydronol ($H_2O{<}^{H}_{OH}$), take part in chemical reactions whereas inactive molecules formed by association are closed and hence chemically inert. Such molecules he diagrammed thus:

Dihydrone	Trihydrone	Tetrahydrone
$H_2O = OH_2$	$H_2O - OH_2$	$H_2O - OH_2$
	$\diagdown \diagup$	$\vert \quad \vert$
	O	$H_2O - OH_2$
	H_2	

Dissociation takes place constantly and is conditioned by temperature and the presence of solutes. $(H_2O)n \rightleftarrows n\ H_2O$.

Solution of HCl would produce the following molecules:

$$H_2O{<}^{H}_{Cl} \qquad HCL{<}^{H}_{OH} \qquad H_2O:ClH$$

The first two he considered active, the third inert so long as it remained closed. Dilution should bring about increase in the active forms.

The Faraday Symposium:— The constitution of water engaged the attention of the Faraday Society in their symposium of 1910. The association theory predominated and most papers concerned estimation or measurement of the degree of association under different conditions. GUYE (1910) calculated the association factor assuming that association occurs in both the vapor and liquid states. His values were 80° C., 1.90; 100° C., 1.86; 120° C., 1.82. These compared well with values derived from surface tension measurements. Much of the interest in association grew out of work on molecular weight determination by physical measurements such as surface tension, cohesion, etc. GUYE, however, emphasized the chemical nature of association and used the term polymerization more often than association.

BOUSFIELD and LOWRY (1910) from studies on solution volume proposed that liquid water is a ternary mixture of hydrol, dihydrol, and trihydrol. Cooling water results in production of polymerized ice molecules; heating causes dissociation yielding more steam molecules (hydrol). Each change results in increase in volume, this increase being superposed upon the expansion or contraction caused by change in temperature. They showed that the solution volume (change in volume upon addition of a solute) goes through a maximum between 0° and 100° C. when salts having a strong affinity for water are dissolved.

According to BOUSFIELD and LOWRY, this phenomenon depends upon the presence of steam molecules at temperatures above the maximum, and ice molecules at temperatures below, both of which are destroyed by the addition of the hydrate-forming solute. The regions of minimum volume at temperatures below and above this point of maximum solution volume represent points of maximum density for the combined water (water of hydration) and a density value of 1.24 for the water of crystallization of the sulfates of certain divalent metals is quoted as an example of the contraction due to intermolecular forces. Such reasoning brings the solution-volume phenomenon into agreement with the theory used to explain the maximum density of water at 4° C.

Concerning the valence forces of trihydrol, SUTHERLAND (1910) diagrammed to scale the structure of the molecule and calculated from atomic diameters its dimensions. He arrived at a density value of 0.986 whereas that of ice at 0° C. is 0.917. Since the discrepancy is only about 8 per cent, the method suggests that some such grouping may be involved in the formation of ice crystals. SUTHERLAND maintained that water is a binary system, hydrol, as such, being present in water in quantities too small to detect. Water of crystallization, he suggested, was solid hydrol having a mean density of 1.31.

In a discussion of ionization, SUTHERLAND (1910) stated "ionization of all electrolytic solutions at all strengths is complete" and explained the apparent lack of ionization of so-called weak electrolytes on the basis of mobility of ions. He pointed out the remarkable change in volume occurring when metals of the lithium family combine with halogens, but did not agree with either the theory of partial ionization or the hydration theory to explain the retention of this altered volume by the ions in solution. The mutual energy of the ion and solvent, representing both attractive and repulsive forces, are concerned; ionic mobility is dependent upon dielectric capacity; undoubtedly forces between solute and solvent are involved.

SUTHERLAND attempted an explanation of the unusually high mobilities of hydrogen and hydroxyl ions; he calculated the heat of fusion of water of crystallization to be 1.8 K. cal. per mol; the heat of vaporization is 5.0 K. cal. This totals 6.8 K. cal. for the change from hydrol of vapor to the solid hydrol of crystallization, evidence of a profound change in the internal electrical energy of the hydrol brought about by the proximity of the electrical fields around the molecules of salt. NERNST (1910) showed that the differences in the specific heats of steam, water, and ice could be explained by the relation

$$2H_2O = (H_2O)_2 + 2.5 \text{ K. cal.} \tag{1}$$

Professor WALKER (1910) summarized the principal conclusions of the symposium with the statement "I should think, as a result of this discussion, one will soon find, even in the textbooks, that whilst ice is trihydrol, and steam monohydrol, liquid water is mostly dihydrol with some trihydrol in it near the freezing point, and a little monohydrol near the boiling point."

Later Work on the Hydrol Theory:— BOUSFIELD (1914) has proposed that the vapor pressure of water has an intimate connection with the proportion of steam molecules present, and that the addition of solutes reduces the numbers of both ice and steam molecules in water. This explains the reduction of vapor pressure by solutes. In 1917 he attempted to reconcile the osmotic properties of solutions with the structure of water. He attributed osmotic pressure to the thermal agitation of the water vapor molecules, and explained the depression of the vapor pressure and of the freezing point as resulting from a shift in the equilibrium conditions of the liquid water. This contrasts with the view of VAN'T HOFF, ARRHENIUS, and many subsequent workers on the osmotic relations of solutions.

Cryoscopic measurements, used primarily to determine molecular weights, indicated that water in solutions was associated. Studies on specific heats of crystalline hydrates also confirmed this view. Studies on the structure of ice have given association factors of from 3 to 23 while data from vapor density are controversial, some indicating association, others none. A compilation of estimates of water association is given by BARNES and JAHN (1934, Table A).

Studies on solution volume, viscosity, surface tension, compressibility, and other properties of solutions have yielded a variety of evidence on the structure of water. RICHARDS and PALITZSCH (1919) interpret their results as indicating that trihydrol is bulky tending to dissociate under the influence of solutes. PAGLIANI (1920), RABINO-VICH (1922) and RICHARDS and CHADWELL (1925) consider polymerization as one factor in explaining viscosity and volume changes upon compression of solutions. BANCROFT and GOULD (1934) studying the effect of the Hofmeister series on boiling points, adsorption by gelatin, electromotive forces of cells, solubility of gases, and heats of neutralization of acids, conclude that the two factors determining the order of the series are 1) displacement of the water equilibrium and 2) selective adsorption. With gelatin displacement of the water equilibrium is the more important; with al-bumin selective adsorption predominates. They conclude that, under ordinary condi-tions, liquid water is a mixture of trihydrol, dihydrol, and monohydrol coexisting in reversible equilibrium.

According to this interpretation, chloride, bromide, thiocyanate, and iodide ions tend to change dihydrol into monohydrol, and have no specific effect on trihydrol be-yond that caused by the above mentioned shift in equilibrium. They concluded that nitrate ion tends to convert trihydrol into monohydrol; that the sulfate ion tends to convert trihydrol and monohydrol into dihydrol; that the electrolytic solution pressure of hydrogen is greater in dihydrol than in monohydrol; that of oxygen is less. Sulfur dioxide tends to depolymerize water. Trihydrol tends to promote fluorescence, mono-hydrol to check it. Changes in viscosity of water and salt solutions with changing pressure fit the concept of displacement of the water equilibrium by pressure and by salts. Since the Debye-Hückel theory postulates interaction of the ions as the only disturbing factor in the behavior of solutions, BANCROFT and GOULD consider that it must break down at all concentrations at which displacement of the water equilibrium is a disturbing factor.

RAO (1934), from Raman spectrum studies concluded that water vapor consists of single H_2O molecules, water is predominately dihydrol and ice trihydrol. Though ice contains no monohydrol, liquid water at 0° C. to 98° C. contains varying propor-tions of all three molecular types. The shifting values that he presents fit well into the picture of shifting coordination with temperature presented by more modern studies.

"Normal" and "Polar" Liquids:— Starting with the properties of pure water, and proceeding to studies on aqueous solutions, the investiga-tions of physical chemists on the structure of water have thus led many to the belief that the anomalous behavior of water and solutions can largely be explained on the basis of association. On the other hand, studies involv-ing many other liquids and proceeding from a consideration of the prop-erties of ideal solutions as described by the laws of VAN'T HOFF, RAOULT, and HENRY, give a different view. Though often attributing anomalous behavior to association of liquids, this latter type of study emphasizes intermolecular forces, stressing the properties of both solute and solvent as they relate to the behavior of the solvent. As noted by HILDEBRAND (1924, pp. 84-85) objections to assuming association as explaining devia-tions from Raoult's law apply not so much to the concept as to the arbi-trary choice of definite polymers. Chemists have long distinguished two classes of liquids: one, the "normal liquids" having low dielectric constants, surface tensions, heats of vaporization, etc.; the other "polar liquids" hav-ing high values for these constants. Normal liquids are poor solvents for electrolytes, polar liquids good solvents. The former include paraffins, benzene, carbon tetrachloride, bromine, and carbon disulfide; the latter water, alcohol, ammonia, sulfuric acid, and acetone. Salts melt to form polar liquids.

The fundamental distinction between the normal and the polar or asso-ciated liquids lies in the greater symmetry of the fields of force surround-ing the molecules of the former, the field surrounding a polar molecule being unsymmetrical. The polar molecules have great mutual attractions resulting in greater cohesions, internal pressures, surface tensions, and heats of vaporization. They tend to "squeeze out" non-polar or slightly polar molecules resulting in strong deviations from Raoult's law and low solvent power.

This concept differs from that of the previous group in that it postulates not definite polymers (dihydrol, trihydrol, etc.) but a liquid mass that tends, by intermolecular attractive forces, to become one large "group" molecule, as LANGMUIR has termed it. Such a mass resembles in a way the crystal of sodium chloride in which the identity of any single molecule of NaCl has completely disappeared.

If the forces between molecules of one type are great, these molecules will tend to associate, and solubility of compounds of the other type will be low. This is illustrated by the low solubility of paraffins, benzene, etc., in water. If the attractive forces between polar and non-polar molecules are great, negative deviations from Raoult's law will occur and the molecules will tend to unite to form compounds.

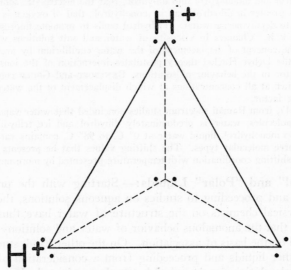

FIG. 2.—The tetrahedral water molecule of PENNYCUICK (1928). The oxygen nucleus with its two helium electrons is omitted.

This concept eliminates the distinction between chemical and physical attractive forces. All intermolecular forces are electric in nature, as conceived by SUTHERLAND as early as 1902.

Molecular Concentration:— In 1929, LONGINESCU attempted to reconcile the complexities of liquid association under the concept of molecular concentration. Associated liquids differ from normal ones in the degree of accumulation or crowding of the molecules into a given volume. The molecular concentration C_m equals 1000 times the density divided by the molecular weight. Thus the molar concentration of ether is 9.6; of CCl_4, 10.4; of toluene, 9.4; of benzene, 11.2; of water, the largest of all, 55.5.

For 350 compounds molar concentration values lie between 55.5 for water and 0.09 for tristearin. All organic liquids that are considered associated have values near 10. In 16 cases cited by LONGINESCU the association factors determined by various workers are compared with the value $\frac{C_m}{10}$ and the agreement is very close.

By this concept there is no molecular complexity; only the number of simple molecules in the unit volume varies; when this number exceeds a certain value, experimentally determined by the formula $\frac{100d}{m}$, where d = density, and m = molecular weight, the state of molecular accumulation occurs. As van der Waals explained the difference in compressibility of gases by molecular attraction, Longinescu explains molecular association in liquids by the internal compression of molecules. Thus he restates Avogadro's law, "Equal volumes of fluids, and possibly solids, at the same temperature and under the same external pressure, contain numbers of simple molecules proportional to the internal pressure." Since Avogadro's law expresses the molecular weight in the gaseous state by the equation 28.9d = m, Longinescu's expression for molecular weight in the liquid state would be 100d = m. This would give liquid water a molecular weight of 100 and a degree of molecular concentration of 5.5. Though this concept is useful in consideration of molecular weight, Longinescu made no attempt to explain such anomalies as the maximum density, minimum specific heat, and expansion upon freezing of water.

Modern Studies:— In 1928 Pennycuick, pointing out that oxygen may display a valence of four and hydrogen of two, attributed many of the anomalous properties of water to the activity of these auxiliary valence forces. Assuming a tetrahedral structure for the water molecule as shown in Figure 2, Pennycuick stated that water can attach itself to other molecules either through its own negative electron pairs or through its positive hydrogen nuclei.

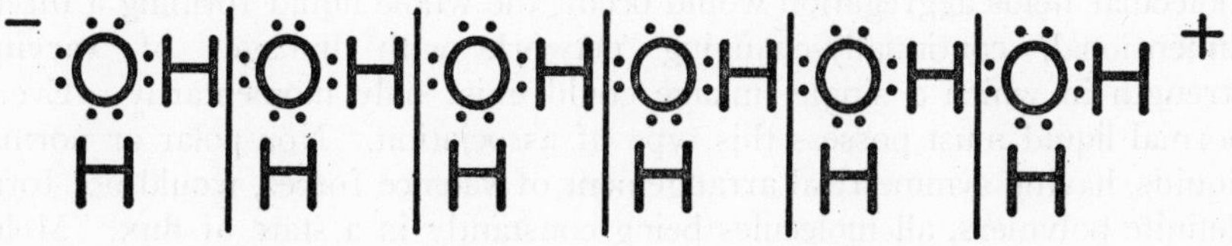

Fig. 3.—The polar water chain. (From Pennycuick, 1928).

The molecule being small (*cf.* Longinescu above) with 4 active auxiliary points of attack, its great activity is not surprising.

To satisfy the auxiliary valences of oxygen and hydrogen, and to explain association Pennycuick proposed that polar chains may be formed as in Figure 3.

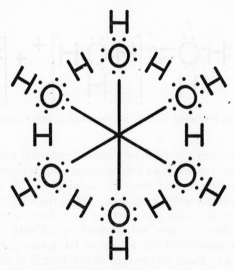

Fig. 4.—The hexagonal ring structure of water, comparable with the crystal structure of ice. (From Pennycuick, 1928).

Furthermore these may close to form hexagonal rings as in Figure 4.

This structure supports the view, obtained from x-ray analysis of ice, that each oxygen atom is surrounded by four atoms of hydrogen and that each hydrogen atom lies symmetrically between two atoms of oxygen. A clear picture of such structure can only be obtained from a three dimensional view of the crystal lattice model. Such a view shows that the term ice molecule has no meaning, the atom being the only real unit of structure. PENNYCUICK pictures the hexagonal units in ice fabricated into a continuous lattice structure; the primary and secondary valences are of equal strength, making the whole structure symmetrical.

In liquid water HOH chains would be irregular and distorted because of tetrahedral structure; if the ends of a chain combine and neutralize each other, the resulting ring would be relatively inactive (*cf*. FIGURE 4). Such rings should play important parts in the structure of water and ice, and the tetrahedral form of the water molecule led PENNYCUICK to conclude that such rings in water must contain six oxygen nuclei.

In contrast with the crystal lattice structure of the solid, with zero resultant field around each atom, in the liquid the molecule preserves its individuality and the system lacks stable structure. With definite resultant molecular fields aggregation would occur, the whole liquid forming a three-dimensional, continually-changing network with linkages of varying strength in which a single linkage could exist only momentarily. Every normal liquid must possess this type of association. Non-polar or normal liquids, having symmetrical arrangement of valence forces, would not form definite polymers, all molecules being constantly in a state of flux. Molecules of polar or associated liquids, having asymmetric fields, would tend to combine to form stable groups, and these (*i.e.*, FIGURE 4) would behave like solute molecules moving as independent units through the remainder of the liquid which is normal in its behavior. This view of PENNYCUICK differs from the older one that water is a mixture of mono-, di-, and tri-hydrol, each having a statistically average existence expressible as a constant value.

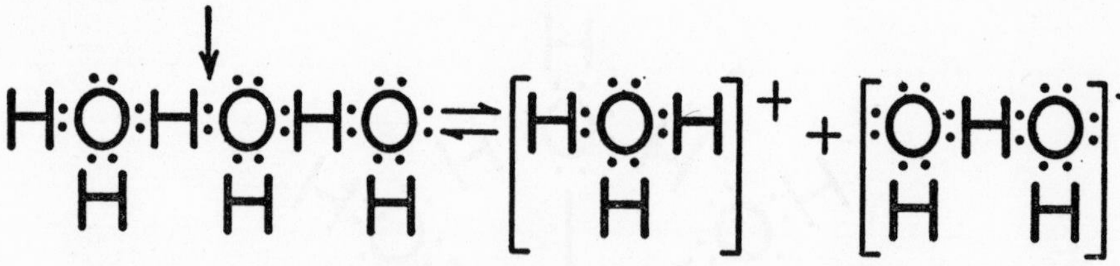

$$\downarrow$$
$$H:\overset{..}{\underset{..}{O}}:H:\overset{..}{\underset{..}{O}}:H:\overset{..}{\underset{..}{O}}: \rightleftharpoons \left[H:\overset{..}{\underset{..}{O}}:H\right]^{+} + \left[:\overset{..}{\underset{..}{O}}:H:\overset{..}{\underset{..}{O}}:\right]^{-}$$
$$\quad H \qquad H \qquad H \qquad\qquad H \qquad\quad H \qquad H$$

FIG. 5.—Diagram indicating the self-ionization of a water chain. (From PENNY-CUICK, 1928).

If water is a mixture of relatively stable hexagonal molecules in a normal solvent, it may represent an intermediate step between vapor and the hexagonal crystal structure of ice. The auxiliary fields of the molecules are presumably strong enough to build as far as the $(HOH)_6$ ring but the molecular energies are sufficiently strong to prevent coordination into a lattice. The fraction of water polymerized would vary with temperature and PENNYCUICK considered the values of RICHARDS and his co-workers as most probable, *i.e.*, about 28 per cent as polyhydrol at 20° C.

In terms of the above suggestions, PENNYCUICK proposed that when ice melts there is a loosening of the structure and a breaking of the rings, resulting in a contraction of volume or an increase in the density of the liquid. On the other hand, the increase of molecular energy with rise in temperature brings about wider spacing of the attractive centers. The minimum volume shown at 4° C. results from alternate predominance of these effects. The latent heat of fusion is not unexpectedly high; it represents only the separation and not the destruction of ring structure. Evaporation breaks all the intermolecular bonds; as high as three-fifths of the latent heat of vaporization has been ascribed to the dissociation of the complex molecules. Water is unusual in its solvent power because the solute is held in solution by its auxiliary valence forces that the solvent is able to neutralize. Since a solute will first be attacked by the more active unassociated molecules, the effect of solution is to reduce the number of such molecules with a corresponding shift in equilibrium and a decrease in association. The lowering of the temperature of the maximum density of water and the decrease in compressibility upon addition of a solute may be explained on this basis. The predominance of compounds containing six and twelve molecules of water of crystallization results from incorporation of hexahydrol in crystals. The self-ionization of water is explained by occasional breaks as indicated in Figure 5.

The high dielectric constant of water is pictured as resulting from the short-time displacement of a hydrogen nucleus under the influence of the field due to a lone oxygen electron pair as rupture of a polar chain occurs. The abnormal velocities of hydrogen and hydroxyl ions are related to the possible addition of water at the active end and loss at the inactive end of each ion under the influence of an applied E.M.F. Thus by applying the principles of molecular structure and crystal structure to water, many of the abnormal or anomalous properties may be explained. He fails to explain the reason for polymers that would act as solute molecules. The formation of such stable groups in contrast to the tendency toward lattice formation is difficult to visualize.

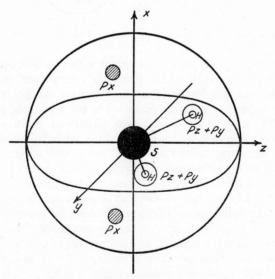

Fig. 6.—Electronic distribution in the simple water molecule. (From Bernal and Fowler, 1933).

X-Ray Analysis:— Analysis by x-rays has become an invaluable tool in the hands of the scientist. It has been used in the attack on the structure of water. Chadwell (1927) points out the discrepancies in the earlier interpretations of such studies. Ice apparently has lattice structure but workers disagree on the details. PENNYCUICK accepts the interpretation of BRAGG that each oxygen atom is surrounded by four atoms of hydrogen and that each hydrogen atom lies symmetrically between two oxygen atoms. Assuming a tetrahedral structure for the water molecule and a hexagonal ring structure for association of water molecules, a lattice structure may be visualized.

BERNAL and FOWLER (1933) discuss in detail the structure of ice and water from the standpoint of infra-red and Raman absorption spectra and x-ray diffraction. They see no reason to assume that the molecules of liquid water differ from those of steam except for small mutual deformations. They picture the electronic distribution in the simple water molecule as shown in FIGURE 6.

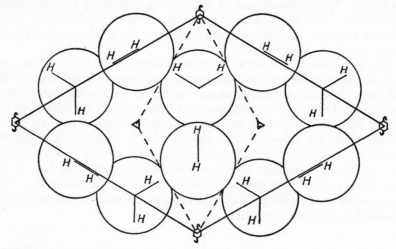

FIG. 7.—The crystal lattice of ice as pictured by BERNAL and FOWLER (1933).

This shows the oxygen atom at the center with two hydrogens in a horizontal plane with the HOH angle 103°-106°, very near the tetrahedral angle. The two charges Px represent the negative charges in the vertical plane at right angles to the HOH plane. The net electronic density distribution resembles a tetrahedron with two corners of positive and two of negative charge. The radius of the molecule is taken to be 1.4Å.

Analysing the x-ray scattering curve for liquid water, BERNAL and FOWLER arrive at a fundamental grouping of five molecules, one in the center surrounded by four others to form a tetrahedron. This structure, however, is not flexible enough to cover all requirements imposed by experimental results. Studying the distribution functions for the neighbors around a water molecule they conclude that water may have three chief forms of arrangement: *water I*, tridymite, ice-like, present to a degree below 4° C.; *water II*, quartz-like, predominating at ordinary temperatures; *water III*, close packed, ideal liquid, ammonia-like, predominating at high temperatures below the critical point at 374° C. Close packed in the above sense refers to a uniformity of distribution in which deviations from the average spacing are at a minimum. These forms pass continuously into each other with change in temperature. The liquid is homogeneous at all temperatures but the average mutual arrangements of the molecules resemble *water I, II,* and *III* in more or less degree.

The immediate effect of breaking down the relatively empty ice-like structure of *water I* would be a decrease in volume to *water II* (maximum density) followed by an increase of a more normal type to *water III* where the increase in spacing due to thermal agitation would more than compensate for the change from the quartz-like to the close-packed structure. The fact that several forms of ice occur under different pressures and that these vary in density confirms the x-ray evidence that the structure of water is not a close-packed one. Trihydrol, dihydrol, and hydrol, as visualized by the earlier workers have no direct structural analogy with *water I, II, and III*. BERNAL and FOWLER explain, by means of geometrical internal structure of the liquid, physical properties which the hydrol theory attempted to explain in terms of hypothetical molecules. Ice, they conclude, has a crystalline structure in which the H nuclei and hence the orientation of the molecules are fixed. Every molecule is surrounded by four others in a tetrahedron with the H nuclei opposite two of the neighbors and one of the H nuclei of each of the remaining neighbors lying opposite a negative corner of the original molecule. This forms the simplest possible regular physical structure. It is illustrated in FIGURE 7.

PAULING (1939) differs from BERNAL and FOWLER stating that if the water molecules in ice are oriented in a definite way so that a unique configuration could be assigned to the crystal there should be no entropy. The fact that ice retains appreciable entropy even at very low temperature indicates that the molecules retain some freedom for motion and that the crystals can exist in a number of configurations. This is further borne out by the fact that above about 200° K. the dielectric constant of ice is of the same order of magnitude as that of water.

BERNAL and FOWLER conclude that the magnitudes of the dielectric constants of water and ice can be explained by molecular rotation, but only if the majority of the water molecules are not entirely free to respond by orientation to the electric field. They propose that its unique properties are due not only to its dipole character, but even more to the geometrical structure which is the simplest that can form extended four-coordinated networks. Studying ionic solutions they postulate that the strongly polarizing ions H^+, Li^+, Na^+, all divalent and trivalent positive ions, and OH^- and F^- are hydrated; whereas NH_4^+, Rb^+, Cs^+, and most negative ions are not. The degree of ionic hydration, they conclude, depends mainly on the ionic radius, and is the same in solutions as in crystals. In view of their dipole character it seems to us that all ions should be hydrated, the effects of NH_4^+, Rb^+, Cs^+, and most negative ions upon the activity of water being relatively less than the effects of those listed above as being strongly hydrated.

Concerning the high mobility of hydrogen and hydroxyl ions, BERNAL and FOWLER arrive at a new theory. Assuming H^+ to exist in solutions as $(OH_3)^+$, they suggest that a proton may jump from one water molecule to another along the coordinated network when favorable configurations occur. Similarly for OH^- a proton under the influence of an electric field may pass from H_2O to the $(OH)^-$ and the systems can separate again with the ion and neutral system interchanged. Thus with models built almost entirely from absorption and diffraction data, BERNAL and FOWLER have postulated a structure for water that accounts for many of its unusual properties. They picture water as an organized system of irregular, four-coordinated molecular groups exhibiting three different intermolecular arrangements in the liquid form. Properties are explained on the basis mainly of internal geometrical structure.

KATZOFF (1934) made x-ray studies on water and arrived at a molecule having essentially the same electron distribution as postulated by BERNAL and FOWLER (FIGURE 5). He also agreed on the arrangement of molecules in the liquid where each molecule has four others around it. He found no evidence for the quartz-like structure (*water II*) nor for the degree of close packing described by BERNAL and FOWLER in water at high temperatures. If in ice each oxygen is tetrahedrally surrounded by four others with the hydrogens on or near the center lines between adjacent oxygens, then water appears to have a broken down ice structure with less regularity of arrangement but still maintaining the tetrahedral order characteristic of ice. Hot water also maintains the fundamental four-coordination but has more randomness of arrangement than that of cold.

The Second Faraday Symposium:— A symposium of the Faraday Society on the structure and molecular forces in pure liquids and solutions, in 1936, brought together many workers in this field and accumulated in one publication (Trans. Faraday Soc. Vol. 33) the current views. KENDALL (1937) commented on the changing opinion regarding the nature of liquids. The hard and fast distinction between the solid, liquid, and gaseous states has largely disappeared. Differences do exist; the close packing of molecules in the liquid state renders intermolecular forces much greater than those between gaseous molecules. In contrast to the older belief that such forces were essentially similar in nature (ordinary van der Waals attractions or valence forces) the modern view involves the stresses caused by dipole structure, the coulomb forces in electrolytes, and the metallic cohesive forces in metals. Association into definite groups (polyhydrol concept) has been largely abandoned, most scientists subscribing to the view of LANGMUIR that a liquid consists of one loose molecule.

If the solute in a solution were in the gaseous state the heat of solution of a gas would be zero, those for a liquid and solid respectively should approximate the heats of vaporization and sublimation. This is not the case. In the ideal case, the heat of solution of a gas is equal to its heat of condensation, the heat of solution of a liquid is zero, and the heat of solution of a solid is equal to its heat of fusion. In other words, any substance dissolved in a liquid, itself assumes the liquid state.

Ideal solutions are rare; solutions deviating from Raoult's law have been studied in detail and their behavior explained on the basis of the magnitude of forces between solute and solvent molecules. Whereas most positive deviations were at one time explained in terms of association of the solvent, they are now considered to result from differences in internal pressure. Negative deviations which LONGINESCU (1929) states have been "timidly assumed" to be non-electrolytic dissociation, KENDALL explains as resulting from molecular attractions that, in the extreme case, result in compound formation. This is in agreement with HILDEBRAND (1924).

The simple concept of intermolecular forces exemplified by van der Waals force was expanded by LONDON (1937) to account for orientation, induction, and dispersion effects and MACLEOD (1937) proposed a compressional effect to cover the forces of molecules under high pressure.

BERNAL (1937) postulated points of abnormal coordination in liquids to explain their properties. His theory pictures the liquid as like an ordered solid containing a number of holes. Water, he concluded, is a liquid whose molecules, though tetrahedral in structure, behave as spheres with directed intermolecular forces. The low (fourfold) coordination results from hydrogen bonds that affect both viscosity and thermal properties.

HILDEBRAND (1937) stated that the term "association" under which all departures from normal behavior of liquids have been lumped must now be subdivided into association arising from the interaction of dipoles, and that due to the formation of definite chemical bonds. To hydrogen bonds he assigned great importance. Substances containing hydroxyl, carboxyl, or amino groups show a type of association markedly different from that of most other dipoles. These bonds are of particular interest to biochemists because of their existence in proteins.

Current Research:— MORGAN and WARREN (1938) by carefully conducted x-ray diffraction analysis of water showed that, whereas water in the neighborhood of freezing temperature has open tetrahedral structure as in ice, at higher temperatures the tetrahedral bonding becomes less sharply defined. In ice the intermolecular separation of neighboring molecules is 2.76Å; of next nearest neighbors it is 4.5Å. In liquid water this distance for nearest neighbors is 2.90Å; for next nearest neighbors it is 4.5Å or slightly more. Because the density of water at 0° C. is greater than that of ice, MORGAN and WARREN believe that the increased density is due, not to a crowding in of next nearest neighbors, but to a filling in between the first and second neighbors, in other words a loss of the highly regular pattern of the ice lattice and substitution of a closer packed structure. They picture this as a shift from the hexagonal lattice of ice to a quadrangular pattern having a density 27 per cent greater as indicated in FIGURE 8. The line indicating the next nearest neighbor distance of

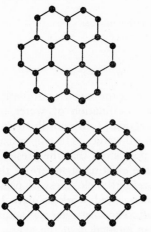

FIG. 8. — Diagrammatic illustration of the shift from the hexagonal lattice of ice to a closer packed structure for water. Redrawn from MORGAN and WARREN (1938).

4.5Å is strong in their diffraction picture at 1.5° C.; it is less distinct at 13° C., and still less at 30° C., and disappears at 62° C. This adds weight to their conclusion that the structure of water changes with rise in temperature through this range. Although the average number of molecules per unit space (density) is greater, the coordination may decrease; from an average value of 4 at 0° C. the coordination number decreases approaching a value of zero in the vapor.

The concept expressed by BERNAL (1937) that a liquid possesses points of abnormal coordination that act as "holes" into which neighboring molecules may "flow" has been elaborated by later workers on liquids (ALTAR 1937). In their theory of liquid structure HIRSCHFELDER, STEVENSON, and EYRING (1937) picture a mechanism of viscous flow involving the formation of double molecules that rotate into new positions and then separate. The ability of such double molecules to rotate depends upon empty spaces or holes into which the molecules pass during rotation and the activation energy of viscous flow they consider to be needed for the formation of these holes. Since the activation energy of normal liquids is around $\frac{1}{3}$ to $\frac{1}{4}$ the heat of vaporization they assume the required hole to be $\frac{1}{3}$ to

¼ the space occupied by the molecule since it requires the same energy to make a hole of molecular size against the forces of cohesion as to vaporize a molecule. A property peculiar to liquids is that such holes are shared communally by all molecules. For a thermodynamic consideration of viscous flow of electrolytic solutions *see* HARNED and OWEN (1943, p. 67).

In their theory of the viscosity of liquids as a function of temperature and pressure, EWELL and EYRING (1937) state that the unusually high viscosity of water is brought about by the hydrogen bond structure. When a molecule in such a liquid flows, it must not only break van der Waals and dipole forces, but hydrogen bonds as well. As water is warmed the number of these hydrogen bonds that must be broken decreases rapidly and this is reflected in a decreasing coordination number. Assuming that the activation energy for cavity formation in the liquid is ⅙ the molecular vaporization energy, they calculate the following coordination numbers for water:

Temperature °C.	Coordination number
0	2.68
50	1.44
100	1.04
150	0.60

STEWART (1939), on the other hand, considering the mean coordination of large numbers of molecules, finds that the coordination of water increases with the shift of structure from the hexagonal, four coordinate lattice of ice to the more closely packed structure of water. He emphasizes the extremely labile character of the liquid and points out that the presence of ions or rising temperature does not contract the existing structure of the fluid but tends to shift the coordination and increase the closeness of packing. The views of STEWART and the previously cited workers may be brought into agreement if one considers the difference between the actual coordination of a single molecule at a particular moment and the average coordination of a large group over an indefinite time. With increasing temperature the number of actual bonds per molecule at a given time will decrease; on the other hand, because of the increasing thermal agitation the possibilities for contacts between different molecules increase immensely and the tendency toward bonding is greater. This is particularly true during the shift from the stable structure of ice to the labile structure of liquid water; the increased closeness of packing still furthers this tendency. In a later paper, STEWART (1943) states that increase in temperature (0° to 4° C.) breaks hydrogen bonds and alters the structure of water, decreasing its molal volume. Ions in aqueous solution break hydrogen bonds and alter water structure, decreasing its molal volume; they consequently increase the pure temperature expansion of the solvent. He uses the phrase "smeared out" to describe the relation of liquid to crystal structure of water (1944). He concludes that water should be visualized as having open tetrahedral structure and that the true aqueous solution develops a new liquid structure in which both solvent and solute participate. FINBAK and VIERVOLL (1943) picture the structure of water as a three-dimensional network of pliable branched chains of tetrahedrons with the corners linked together in such a way that rotations about the lines between centers of neighboring tetrahedrons may occur.

ELEY (1944) points out that for water the energy required to produce a cavity is small at low temperature and increases until it reaches 80° C., at which point it equals the energy of solution of a gas. This explains the decrease in solubility of gas in water with increasing temperature. ELEY relates this effect to the polarization of the water molecules around the cavity. Since the energy required to make a cavity of molecular size equals the internal energy of evaporation, for one mol at room temperature it would be about 10 K cal. The energy of polarization for a molecule the size of water is shown to be about 9 K cal. per mol. The difference, 1 K cal. per mol, represents the net energy required to form cavities within the liquid equivalent to one mole volume.

Since the polarization of molecules around a cavity would disorganize the open tetrahedral structure of water, the formation of cavities would contribute to a close-packed structure. With increasing temperature, however, the energy supplied by polarization would decrease due to the increasing rotational freedom from normal thermal effects. Consequently, the net energy required to produce cavities would increase. It seems possible also that increased energy might be needed to form holes in the close packed structure of liquid water. This would agree with the conclusion of MORGAN and WARREN (1938) concerning the shift in structure between 1.5° C. and 83° C.

ELEY postulates further that of all the cavities in water only certain ones are available to neutral molecules, whereas ions and water molecules are interchangeable in the lattice structure. Polarization of water about a cavity occupied by an inert gas is limited to the immediate neighborhood; about an ion the force field extends through several molecular shells tending to increase the regularity of molecular configuration. For compilation of the physical and chemical properties of the water see the monograph by DORSEY (1940). Detailed reviews of the structure of water as it relates to biological problems are given by BARNES and JAHN (1934) and BLANCHARD (1940).

Summary of Water Structure:— This review of work on the structure of water indicates that, far from being a simple mass of spherical molecules, randomly arranged, and independently agitated by thermal energy, water is composed of polar molecules coordinately arranged in some sort of lattice-like network and bound by a number of intermolecular forces such as dipole attractions, London forces, and hydrogen bonds. As ice, water apparently assumes a normal four-coordinated hexagonal structure with 12 H_2O molecules per unit cell. Although variously assumed to have three-fold association, hexagonal ring structure, and a four-coordinated hexagonal lattice (the latter seems best substantiated by modern methods of analysis), the important point is that a regularity of structure compatible with geometrical arrangement of molecules and intermolecular forces predominates in water in the solid form.

As liquid, water apparently has abnormal coordination and several forms may occur. These forms apparently coexist and the shift from one to another depends largely upon temperature and the presence of solutes. Though liquid water forms a continuum with sufficient order to give an x-ray diffraction pattern, the existence of any one molecular configuration is only of statistical significance, the total structure being in continual flux.

Recent theories of liquid structure postulate points of abnormal coordination that act as cavities or holes. Such holes are shared communally by all molecules of the liquid, and viscous flow involves formation of double molecules that rotate into new positions within the holes. With rise in temperature a shift in structure from the hexagonal ring lattice to a closer-packed quadrilateral structure apparently occurs but coordination of the individual molecules decreases.

The dipole character of water molecules and their tendency toward hydrogen bonding are important in their role as solvent. In the formation of solutions the participation of both solute and solvent in the structure should be considered.

As water passes into the vapor state, intermolecular distances increase immensely, forces between molecules diminish, and, it seems agreed, coordinate structure gives way to the chaos of the typical gaseous state.

Chapter III

PROPERTIES OF SOLUTIONS

Introduction:— Studies on the structure of water have tended to single out the water molecule as being most influential in molding the molecular architecture of aqueous solutions; where solutes have been considered, the primary emphasis has been on the effects of solute molecules upon the arrangement and properties of water molecules.

The Interrelation of the Properties of Solutions:— Studies on solutions have tended to center about the effects of solute molecules upon such properties of the solution as osmotic pressure, thermal properties, vapor pressure, and the like. Most of the calculations have involved an equation of state, that is, an equation expressing the relations between pressure, volume, concentration, temperature, and similar physical characteristics. Starting from the concept of an ideal solution, they have attempted to reconcile deviations from ideality with known or predicted properties of the solute and solvent.

The first comprehensive theory of dilute solutions was founded by VAN'T HOFF (1887, 1888). Acquainted by the Dutch botanist DE VRIES with the osmotic experiments of PFEFFER, he formulated an equation relating osmotic pressure with the concentration of a solution. The expression is

$$P_o V = nRT \tag{1}$$

where P_o = osmotic pressure of the solution,
V = volume of the solution,
n = number of mols of solute,
R = the molar gas constant, and
T = absolute temperature.

Proving that for dilute solutions the value of the constant R was identical with that of the gas equation, VAN'T HOFF arrived at the important generalization that the osmotic pressure of a dilute solution is equal to the pressure that the molecules of the solute would exercise if they existed in a gaseous state in the volume occupied by the solution. As pointed out by FINDLAY (1919), the unique value of this finding lies in the fact that the concept of osmotic pressure and the use of semi-permeable membranes allows the properties of solutions to be treated like those of gases, particularly the quantitative relation between colligative properties and concentration.

Though his law has been misused, VAN'T HOFF realized that it applied only to very dilute solutions. This is apparent from the expression given because, in it, osmotic pressure varies as the ratio of mols of solute per volume of solution, whereas in an exact law it should depend upon the ratio of solute to solvent molecules and the forces between them. The above law provides no correction for the effect of the solute molecules upon the properties of the solvent or vice versa.

The ideal equation for one mol of gas is usually given in the form

$$P_g V = RT \qquad (2)$$

where P_g = the pressure of the gas against the walls of the container,
  V = the volume of the gas,
  R = a proportionality constant commonly termed the molar gas constant, and
  T = absolute temperature.

Though useful for gases at high temperature and low pressure this law, because it neglects attractive forces between molecules and provides no correction for the space occupied by the gas molecules, is invalid for gases at low temperatures and high pressures. Thermodynamically it is based on the assumption that gas molecules are elastic spheres having no attractive forces and occupying no space.

To correct the weaknesses of this law VAN DER WAALS derived the equation

$$\left(P_g + \frac{a}{V^2}\right)(V - b) = RT \qquad (3)$$

in which

$\frac{a}{V^2}$ is a measure of the attractive forces of the gas molecules or the cohesive forces as applied to liquids. V-b is the free space unoccupied by molecules. The VAN DER WAALS constants a and b have been widely used in dealing with the properties of non-ideal gases and liquids.

Many other refinements to the gas laws have been offered. Emphasis here is on the fact that just as the ideal gas law finds an analogy in van't Hoff's law of osmotic pressure, the van der Waals equation, and subsequent improved equations have been applied to the relations of solutions.

Meanwhile RAOULT had proposed a law relating the vapor pressure of a solution to the mol fraction of the solvent or solute in it.

$$p = p° x_1 = p° (1 - x_2) \qquad (4)$$

where p = the vapor pressure of the solution,
  $p°$ = the vapor pressure of the pure solvent,
  x_1 = the mol fraction of the solvent, and
  x_2 = the mol fraction of the solute.

LEWIS (1908) recognized the validity of Raoult's law as applied to both dilute and concentrated solutions and HILDEBRAND (1924) has pointed out its wide applicability to studies on solutions. Ideal solutions may be defined as those that obey Raoult's law at all temperatures and pressures. Only liquids having equal changes in pressure with temperature at constant volume will obey Raoult's law. Such liquids mix without heat of dilution or change in volume.

From the above considerations it is possible to formulate a thermodynamic equation of state to cover all liquids.

$$\left(\frac{\partial E}{\partial V}\right)_T = T\left(\frac{\partial P}{\partial T}\right)_V - P \qquad (5)$$

where P = pressure on the liquid,
  E = total energy of the liquid,
  V = volume of the liquid, and
  T = absolute temperature.

HILDEBRAND (1936) gives the following empirical expression for the members of this equation:

$$\left(\frac{\partial E}{\partial V}\right)_T = \frac{-a}{V^2} + \frac{c}{V^{10}} = T\left(\frac{\partial P}{\partial T}\right)_V - P \qquad (6)$$

Internal   Attractive   Repulsive   Thermal   External
Pressure   Pressure   Pressure   Pressure   Pressure

a = the constant of the VAN DER WAALS equation,
V = the molal volume of the liquid,
c = a constant, and
$\frac{a}{V^2}$ measures an intermolecular force of attraction between the molecules of a liquid.

The difficulty often experienced in using such an equation is in evaluating the energy factor E from data on osmotic pressure, or thermal properties. HILDEBRAND and others have determined values for the internal pressure of liquids by measuring changes of pressure with temperature at constant volume $\left(\frac{\partial P}{\partial T}\right)_V$ and substituting these in equation (5).

The Forces Between Atoms and Molecules:— The properties of solutions depend ultimately upon the molecules and the electric forces within and between them. The ideal gas law assumed that there was no attraction between molecules but experiment proved that at low temperatures and high pressures attractive forces existed.

Deviations from ideality in solutions are even greater than in gases. Much of the modern theory of solutions deals with analysis of the forces between atoms and molecules.

The electrons within a molecule are in constant motion. The average positions can be so designated that the potential at a distance from a molecule due to its charge can be calculated. If e represents charge and r distance, the field strength of a charge varies as $\frac{e}{r^2}$ according to Coulomb's law. This field strength is zero for a neutral atom. Atomic ions such as Na⁺ or Cl⁻ will have fields varying as $\frac{1}{r}$. More complex neutral molecules or ions in general have potentials varying as $\frac{1}{r^2}, \frac{1}{r^3}$, etc. The term $\frac{1}{r^2}$ represents the field strength of a dipole. The term $\frac{1}{r^3}$ represents a quadrupole moment, important when the effective dipole is small.

By similar treatment it is possible to calculate the force upon a second particle located at a distance from the first. An ion in a field of the type mentioned above experiences a force of translation; a neutral molecule with an electrical moment does so only if the field is non-uniform. Characteristics of the above forces of interaction are summarized in TABLE 3, numbers 1, 2, and 3.

TABLE 3. — *Characteristics of molecular interaction*
(*from* BATEMAN, *in* HÖBER, 1945) : —

TYPE NUMBER	INTERACTING PARTICLES	ATTRACTIVE FORCE PROPORTIONAL TO
1	Ion—Ion	$e_1 e'_1 \cdot r^{-2}$
2	Ion—Permanent dipole	$\mp u' e_1 \cdot r^{-3}$
3a	Permanent dipoles coaxial	$u u' \cdot r^{-4}$
3b	Permanent dipoles at right angles	o
4	Ion—Induced dipole	$a e_1^2 \cdot r^{-5}$
5	Permanent dipole—Induced dipole	$a u^2 \cdot r^{-7}$
6	Transient dipole—Transient induced dipole	$a^2 \cdot r^{-7}$

e_1, e'_1 denote ionic charge.   a denotes polarizability.
u, u' denote dipole moment.   r denotes distance between centers.

In addition to the forces described above, dipoles and higher poles experience a torque making certain orientations more stabile than others. For this reason the electric axis in the field of an ion tends to orient toward the ion. In the field of a second dipole the axes tend to become parallel. These forces are disturbed by thermal agitation so that complete orientation is prevented under most conditions but the tendency toward alignment is reflected in an attractive force termed the orientation effect.

When two molecules approach each other until their electronic charges encounter the fields of their nuclei there are strong attractive forces between them. As they come even closer together their electronic clouds no longer screen their nuclear charges; the nuclei repel each other by the electrostatic Coulomb forces. The strength of primary chemical bonds cannot be accounted for by the attractive forces mentioned above at the equilibrium point but the polarization effect does explain some types of residual force.

Even spherically symmetrical molecules are polarized in an external field and the forces between the inducing particle and the induced dipole are shown in numbers *4* and *5* of TABLE 3. Spherically symmetrical molecules with a zero average field may show temporary asymmetry and hence give rise to a fluctuating field. These transient fields induce transient electric moments producing the dispersion forces listed in number *6* of TABLE 3.

TABLE 4. — *Contributions of the three constituents of the van der Waals forces to intermolecular forces of the liquid state (selected data from* HÖBER *(1945) and* LONDON *(1937) : —*

COMPOUND	MOLECULAR VOLUME	$a \times 10^{-12}$ EXPERIMENTAL	b	DIPOLE MOMENT $\mu \times 10^{18}$	POLARIZABILITY $\alpha \times 10^{24}$	ENERGY $h\nu_0$ (VOLTS)	ORIENTATION $\frac{2}{3} \frac{\mu^4}{\kappa 293°} \cdot 10^{60}$ [ERG CM.^{6}]	INDUCTION $2\,\mu^2\,\alpha \cdot 10^{60}$ [ERG CM.^{6}]	DISPERSION $\frac{3}{4}\,\alpha^2 h\nu_0 \cdot 10^{60}$ [ERG CM.^{6}]
CO	32.7	1.50	39.7	0.12	1.99	14.3	0.0034	0.057	67.5
HI	...	...	...	0.38	5.40	12.0	0.35	1.68	382.0
HBr	37.5	4.51	44.1	0.78	3.58	13.3	6.2	4.05	176.0
HCl	30.8	3.72	40.7	1.03	2.63	13.7	18.6	5.40	105.0
NH$_3$	24.5	4.22	36.9	1.50	2.21	16.0	84.0	10.00	93.0
H$_2$O	18.0	5.53	30.4	1.84	1.48	18.0	190.0	10.00	47.0

TABLE 4 presents values for the contributions of the orientation, induction, and dispersion effects to the van der Waals forces between molecules for six well known compounds. Common values for the van der Waals constants a and b are also included.

Although the details of atomic interaction cannot be treated here it seems well established that under certain conditions, as atoms or molecules come together there is a tendency toward an equilibrium distribution of outer shell electrons in the internuclear region that constitutes the "electron sharing" postulated by electronic theories of valence. These forces are responsible for all attractions between non-ionic particles exemplified by numbers *3, 5,* and *6* of TABLE 3.

A detailed analysis of the general theory of molecular forces is given by LONDON (1937). The above treatment follows closely that of BATEMAN in HÖBER (1945).

The development of the modern views of intermolecular forces has come through many stages. Early chemists speaking in terms of chemical affinity drew a sharp distinction between primary and secondary or residual affinities. They failed to realize that chemical affinity has dimensions of both quantity and intensity. Organic chemists recognized coordination groups or spheres within which valence forces became identical and they recognized conjugation as a means of satisfying unsaturated valence force. It was not however until the discovery of the electron and the demonstration of its relation to valence that a clear picture of chemical affinity became available. In 1916 LEWIS presented his electronic theory of valence postulating complete transfer of electrons to explain the formation of ionic, or valence bonds, and mutual sharing of electrons to explain covalence.

Examples of these types of bonding are given in the following reactions.

Ionic:　　　　$:\overset{..}{\underset{..}{Na}}: \cdot + \cdot \overset{..}{\underset{..}{Cl}}: \rightarrow :\overset{..}{\underset{..}{Na}}: :\overset{..}{\underset{..}{Cl}}:$　　　　　　　　　　　　(7)

Covalent:　　　　　$4\,H \cdot + \cdot \overset{.}{\underset{.}{C}} \cdot \rightarrow H : \overset{\overset{\displaystyle H}{..}}{\underset{\underset{\displaystyle H}{..}}{C}} : H$　　　　　　　　(8)

Covalences may be of two types, normal and coordinated. In the normal type (equation 8), both of the reacting atoms contribute an electron to complete the octet and thus form a stable bond; in the coordinate type both of the electrons are supplied by one of the atoms, which results in a somewhat weaker bond. These two types of covalent linkage may be generalized in the following way:

Normal covalent:　　　　$A \cdot + \cdot B \rightarrow A : B$　　　　　　(9)

Coordinate covalent:　　　$A : + B \rightarrow A : B$　　　　　　(10)

The hydrogen bond, a somewhat different type of linkage, which is partly ionic and partly covalent in character, is of great significance in biology. This is found only between atoms of high electronegativity (*i.e.,* F, O, N, and Cl) and the strength of the bond is determined by the degree of electronegativity and the ionic radii of the groups joined. Hydrogen bonds are involved in many biological systems. As explained they are responsible for coordination of water in the liquid and solid states. They are responsibe for formation of chelate rings as in the following dimer of formic acid vapor.

$$H - C \overset{\displaystyle O \cdots H\text{———}O}{\underset{\displaystyle O\text{———}H \cdots O}{\Big\langle\qquad\qquad\Big\rangle}} C - H \qquad\qquad (11)$$

They account for the hydration of colloids such as cellulose and proteins. And they form the bridges responsible for the 3-dimensional architecture of many bio-colloids, possibly of the living protoplasm. For a detailed treatment of chemical affinity *see* REMICK (1943).

In aqueous solutions in which the biologist is interested practically every form of bond known to the chemist may be involved. The nature of the forces of coordination between water molecules has been pointed out in Chapter II. The values of 1.04 at 100° C. and 0.60 at 150° C. (page 16) given by EWELL and EYRING indicate the coordination of water vapor. At 0° C. the number is variously estimated from 2.68 (page 16) to 4.

Water molecules are pictured as small spheres having two positive and two negative residual valence charges. The separation of these charges gives the molecule dipole character and water has a dipole moment of 1.85.

The force of attraction between water molecules is equal to the product of their dipole moments divided by the fourth power of the distance between centers. This is great enough to bring about a quasi-crystal lattice as mentioned in the previous chapter. The energy of the O-H-O bond of water is assigned a value of 4.5 K cal. Electronic theories of valence have indicated that all types of bonds result from mutual potential energies of atomic nuclei and their associated electrons.

BATEMAN also considers van der Waals forces as active in the determination of the molecular volume of liquids. They are brought into calculations to explain the discrepancies between the observed and calculated values of the osmotic pressures of concentrated solutions, possibly because, here too, they affect the partial molal volume of the solvent. LONDON (1942) has treated systems containing long-range van der Waals forces that may be of biological significance. Such long-range forces acting in conjugated chains may account for the elasticity of rubber. In hydrophilic systems these forces may even be visualized as affecting the properties

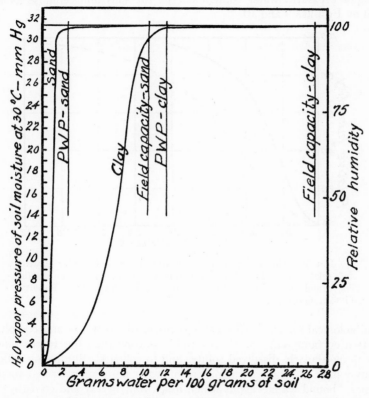

FIG. 9.—Typical vapor pressure-water content curves for sand and clay showing the values of the permanent wilting percentage (PWP) and field capacity for each. (From VEIHMEYER and EDLEFSEN, 1936).

of whole molecules and molecular aggregates. ELEY (1944) discusses the effects of ions upon the heat capacity of water from the standpoint of hydration shells and long-range structure. Thus we perceive how, starting with nuclear atoms, and utilizing the directive forces of electrons, it is possible to build a picture of morphological organization conditioned largely by the geometry of molecules and restriction of their random motion by bonding forces. And dominating this picture, as it applies to biological systems, are those influences that determine the behavior of molecules in the liquid state.

Molecular Interaction and Water Binding:— From the foregoing discussion it seems evident that the nature of aqueous solutions is definitely conditioned by the forces exerted by water molecules among themselves and upon molecules of the solute. In simple one salt solutions the force relations may be analysed without too much difficulty but as the solutions become complex a satisfactory analysis is impossible. The problem is made difficult not alone by the complexity of the relations between solvent molecules and between solvent and solute molecules but by interactions between solute and solute both as these relate to the solvent and to the state of aggregation of the solute. Although a number of types of forces are exerted between the molecules of a solution as illustrated by TABLE 3, these forces are all electrical in nature and are so integrated that within a single system they form a smooth series. This is reflected in the form of the vapor pressure: water content curves for soils and cellulose as illustrated by FIGURES 9 and 10.

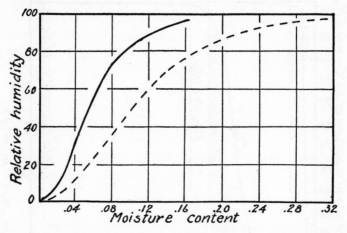

FIG. 10.—Curves showing the relation between moisture content and relative humidity of the atmosphere surrounding cotton (solid line), and spruce wood (broken line). Redrawn from BABBITT (1942), figure 3.

In biological systems molecular structures of great size and complexity are often encountered. Much research has concerned the forces binding water to molecularly dissolved solutes and to colloids. Studies on colloidal hydration have given rise to a concept of water adsorption termed for convenience, "bound water" about which much controversy and confusion has centered. The many definitions given including "water—in living tissues in a state different from that of water as we know it in bulk" (GORTNER, 1938), "adsorbed water," "oriented water molecules," "non-solvent water," "non-freezable water," and the like, all indicate that water in the bound state deviates in physical or chemical properties from water in an ideal solution. GORTNER states, "Heats of hydration, dielectric constant measurements, and the contraction of the system colloid-water—all indicate that the H_2O molecules in bound water are more closely packed and are probably specifically oriented in relationship to each other possibly in a more or less true crystal lattice which is more densely packed than the crystal lattice of ice." Out of these definitions has grown the idea that in colloidal systems water may exist in two different states, bound water and free water.

Modern studies have changed this concept. Just as the idea of definite water polymers has been displaced by the newer picture of coordinated water molecules making up a continuum of quasi-lattice properties, so has the concept of bound water been gradually broadened to the extent that all inter- or intra-molecular forces affecting the activity of water molecules are given consideration. For this broader concept the term hydration is commonly used. From one viewpoint it seems that there is no such thing as free water; all water molecules in the liquid state have restricted motion because of their own intermolecular bonding. The restrictions and the forces causing them may vary in intensity because of the variety of possible types of hydration complexes; the water molecule, however, does not lose its chemical identity by reason of the forces with which it is held. Although BERNAL and FOWLER postulate three types of water, they state that they pass continuously into each other with change in temperature. To deny the binding of water molecules would require a complete neglect of those secondary valence forces that, through hydrogen bonding, account for so many of the unusual properties of water. To adhere to the sharp distinction between bound and free water, on the other hand, would necessitate drawing a clear line between the behavior of such valence forces toward crystalloidal, and colloidal substances, a line that is not indicated in physico-chemical studies of solutions. That GORTNER was fully aware of the nature of these forces is evidenced by his statement, "We may conclude therefore that the forces which bind water on the surface of the lyophilic colloids are of the same nature as the forces which cause the association of water in bulk and which immobilize water molecules in the ice crystal lattice. However, there is evidence that these forces on a surface or at an interface may be of greater magnitude than the forces of association of water molecule for water molecule or the forces which tend to arrange water molecules in the ordinary ice crystal lattice. Therefore at least a part of the molecules of the bound water film may be expected to have an activity which is less than the activity of the H_2O molecule in the ordinary ice lattice" (1938, p. 304).

It should be pointed out here that these forces show no unique response to colloids; they are the forces that cause hydration of ions and molecules as well as micelles and hence cause the major deviations from ideality of aqueous solutions.

It is often implied that bound water bears a numerical relationship to the colloid (*i.e.*, so many grams of water per gram of colloid) and that this relationship is constant at different concentrations of the solution. If we can believe the vapor pressure: water content curves this is not the case. These curves show that as the water content of a solution decreases the intensity of the binding force per water molecule increases. Therefore, if equilibrium exists between the solute and the solvent, it seems evident that the amount of water bonded to the colloid shifts continuously with water content, there being much loosely held water at high water contents. As the water content decreases, the remaining water is more tightly held.

For example, in the hydration of cellulose it has been postulated that, between the dry and saturated conditions, three different mechanisms are responsible for holding water. At low water contents the water molecules are pictured as being held as monomolecular layers, probably by hydrogen bonds. At intermediate contents the layers become polymolecular with a diminished intensity of bonding force per molecule of water. As the water content approaches saturation capillary condensation is suggested to account for the loosely held water. However, these three mechanisms are so closely integrated that the vapor pressure : water content curves are smooth. BABBITT (1942) shows such a curve in his FIGURE 3. The relation of binding energy to vapor pressure in terms of relative humidity is shown in his FIGURE 7.

GORTNER (1938) has reviewed the literature on bound water and has described thirteen methods for measuring it. Though results vary, all methods show appreciable quantities of water that fail to obey the laws of dilute solutions. Deviations from laws of concentrated solutions are not always so great.

Any molecular species which dissolves in water, when added to a water mass, tends by means of its own valence forces to satisfy those of the water. When added, not only the water molecules in the immediate vicinity but statistically all water molecules in the system are affected, as evidenced by a change in vapor pressure and a corresponding lowering of activity. With continued addition of solute there results a smooth and progressive reduction in activity of the water. Provided there is no change in state, the initial addition of solute to the solvent results in reduced activity also of the solute. The case of a single undissociated solute is relatively simple to analyse. With dissociation of the solute molecules three activities are involved, and with the addition of two or more solutes a high degree of complexity occurs with the possibility pointed out by CHANDLER (1941), that sufficient decrease in two or more activities may actually allow increase in a third without disturbing the thermodynamic balance. This phenomenon may possibly explain negative values for bound water that are found occasionally.

As one deals with more complex situations involving both colloidal and crystalloidal solutes, accurate determination of the activities of all constituents becomes impossible. Hence many of the measurements on so-called "bound" water do not necessarly prove its existence but simply reflect complex intermolecular reactions that are incapable of analysis. On the other hand, there are many examples of the hydration of colloids in which small but measurable amounts of water are held by intense binding forces. The use of the term "bound" to describe such water is very convenient.

Hydration:— The relations of the solvent to the solute in aqueous solutions has received much study and theories of hydration enter into most considerations of the properties of solutions. In ARMSTRONG'S (1908) theory of the polymeric isomerism of water the presence of solutes is supposed to affect materially the dissociative change

$$(H_2O)n \rightleftarrows n H_2O \qquad (12)$$

When a compound such as HCl dissolves, complexes are assumed to be formed as follows:

$$H_2O\diagupstart{H}\diagdownstart{Cl} \quad,\quad HCl\diagupstart{H}\diagdownstart{OH} \quad,\quad \text{and } H_2O:ClH$$

The first two are active, the last inactive so long as it remains closed.

Dissolved molecules may be converted into inactive closed groups:

$$RX \overset{H}{\underset{OH}{\diagup}} + \overset{H}{\underset{HO}{\diagdown}} XR \leftrightarrows RXXR + 2H_2O \qquad (13)$$

Dilution would increase the number of active molecules of the type $HCl \overset{OH}{\underset{H}{\diagup}}$, whereas in concentrated solutions the hydrolyzed solute $H_2O \overset{H}{\underset{Cl}{\diagup}}$ would increase.

Most of the earlier workers on osmotic properties of solutions postulated hydration of the sucrose molecules to explain the fact that observed values of osmotic pressure were higher than calculated values. Calculations were based on the assumption that a hexahydrate existed in solution (FINDLAY, 1919); HALDANE (1918) postulated a pentahydrate; for the highest concentrations lower hydration values were used (FINDLAY, Tables XXV and XXXI).

PENNYCUICK (1928) pictures the reaction between H_2O and HCl as follows:

$$HCl + H_2O \rightleftarrows H^+ : \overset{..}{\underset{..}{Cl}} : \quad \Big| \quad H : \overset{..}{\underset{H}{O}} :^- \qquad (14)$$

This compound would react with ammonia in this manner

$$NH_3 + HCl \cdot H_2O \rightleftarrows H : \overset{H}{\underset{..}{\underset{H}{N}}} : \quad \Big| \quad H : \overset{..}{\underset{..}{Cl}} : \quad \Big| \quad H : \overset{..}{\underset{H}{O}} : \qquad (15)$$

which in turn would break down thus

$$H : \overset{H}{\underset{..}{\underset{H}{N}}} : H : \overset{..}{\underset{..}{Cl}} : \quad \Big| \quad H : \overset{..}{\underset{H}{O}} : \leftrightarrows NH_4Cl + H_2O \qquad (16)$$

Because the water molecule has both the plus charges of the hydrogen nuclei and the negative charges of the lone oxygen electron pairs it will hydrate any substance having a force field.

BERNAL and FOWLER (1933) conclude that all strongly polarized ions, all divalent and trivalent positive ions, and the negative ions OH^- and F^- are hydrated (*see,* however, page 7). The effect of hydration of ions is to lower the refractive index of water by the coordination of water molecules around these ions. This would tend toward an increase in the regularity of arrangement (*i.e.,* a shift in the direction *Water III* → *Water II* → *Water I*). (*See* page 12).

In the past there has been a tendency to draw a distinction between hydration and imbibition, the former term being applied to the association of water with ions and molecules, the latter to colloidal materials. Modern views would favor the definition of hydration as the resultant of any interaction between solute and water molecules tending to reduce the activity of the latter. Such a definition erases any line that has been arbitrarily drawn between imbibition and hydration. Though the extreme examples of crystalloidal and colloidal hydration may be readily distinguished the fundamental nature of the process is the same in both cases, namely, a satisfaction of electrical forces of attraction between molecules.

Some have pointed out the close connection between imbibition and osmotic pressure. HEUSER states (1944, p. 62), that thermodynamically swelling (or imbibition) pressure appears to be identical with osmotic pressure, and quotes STEINBERGER to the effect that "osmotic pressure is nothing but swelling pressure, made evident by the external device of a semipermeable membrane."

BROOKS and BROOKS (1941) similarly point out the lack of a clear distinction between the two phenomena: "Imbibition is simply absorption of water by a system which is in effect an exceedingly concentrated solution, and can often be shown to obey the laws of ideal concentrated solutions. . . ." And "Imbibition, in any fundamentally sound sense, is not a property of colloidal systems alone, but may be exhibited by homogeneous solutions of crystalloids, among which are such diverse substances as gases, molecules of solid or liquid non-electrolytes, and ions of electrolytes." This constitutes a redefinition of imbibition. We favor the use of hydration in the sense that BROOKS and BROOKS define imbibition.

BULL (1943) uses an equation to calculate swelling pressures of a gel that is identical with the vapor pressure equation for osmotic pressure (equation 2, Chapter IV). This equation is:

$$P_h \overline{V} = RT \ln \frac{p_o}{p} \tag{17}$$

Where P_h is the swelling pressure and $\overline{V}$ is the partial molal volume of the liquid. Since he found that the swelling of a gel can be evaluated in terms of vapor pressure lowering of the solvent, regardless of the factors responsible, its close similarity to osmotic pressure is evident. Because such vapor-pressure lowering creates an energy gradient, it accounts for water absorption by vacuolated cells and colloidal imbibants whenever water at higher diffusion pressures is available.

At their extremes, osmotic and imbibition pressures are clearly different. For instance, the retention of imbibitional water by cellulose fibers involves little or no osmotic effect, and the reduction of the diffusion pressure of water by the presence of ions or small molecules (*i.e.*, in a solution of NaCl) entails no imbibitional effect. However, when one considers larger and larger molecules or molecular aggregates in solution, he encounters a marginal region where the two effects are not distinct. Just as it is impossible to differentiate sharply between the crystalloidal and colloidal states, so it is difficult to draw a line between osmotic and imbibitional forces. In the crystalloidal solution, all of the molecules are relatively mobile and if a differentially permeable membrane is used, the solute and solvent may be separated. In the colloidal solution, on the other hand, some of the water of imbibition may be held so firmly that it is removable from the colloid only by vaporization. Because of the localization of imbibed water on the surface of the colloid, its solvent powers for crystalloidal molecules may not be uniform throughout a given system. Hence, where both crystalloids and hydrophyllic colloids are involved in cells, although an equilibrium of forces exists, measurable in terms of the osmotic concentration of the cell sap, some water may be held by imbibitional forces, and such water must be accounted for in any attempt to evaluate the water status of the cell. In this connection, it should be emphasized that the effects of both osmotic and imbibitional forces are similar in that they bring about a reduction in the total volume of the system (solute, or imbibant, plus solvent). This indicates an ordering of molecules and an evolution of energy and invariably results in a reduction in diffusion pressure. Thus water of imbibition includes "bound water" as described by GORTNER in the quotation on page 24. Though hydration has been defined to include both osmotic and imbibitional phenomena, it may be very convenient to make a qualitative distinction between them.

According to modern views on the structure of water, as explained in Chapter II, forces of coordination resulting from hydrogen bonds tend to hold water in a quasi-crystalline lattice and solutes capable of satisfying these forces may enter into this structure. Numerical relations of coordination are of statistical significance only as the molecules are in a continuous state of flux, coordination becoming less and less definite with increasing temperature. The firmness of binding is a matter of the nature and intensity of the bonds involved. Hydrogen bonds are relatively weak, covalent bonds stronger, and ionic bonds of great strength. When water of hydration or imbibition near the saturation point is removed, little energy is required; as more and more water is removed greater force is necessary. For most colloids, however, water has little or no stoichiometric relation to the hydrated or imbibing compounds. Probably both hydrogen and covalent bonds account for its binding. With water of crystallization, definite numerical relations exist and much energy is required to remove such water from the crystal; it is largely held by covalent bonds. Undoubtedly all possible types of bonds are involved in the hydration of cell walls, protoplasm, and vacuole.

The effects of force fields upon the packing of water molecules have been discussed by BERNAL and FOWLER (1933), MORGAN and WARREN (1938), and others. Though the arrangement of molecules may differ with the resulting variation shown by the properties of liquid water, water of crystallization, and ice, the state of aggregation does not change excessively as shown by the limited variation in coordination throughout the range from water at 100° C. to ice. ELEY (1944) points out that the molal heat capacity of hydrate water approximates the value -9 cal. deg^{-1} mol^{-1}, the value for ice. For further consideration of the effect of binding forces upon the density of water as shown by adsorption on cellulose *see* BABBITT (1942). HEUSER (1944) devotes a complete chapter to the reactions of cellulose with water.

In contrast to the solvent, the state of aggregation of the solute molecules may vary widely and the definition of hydration involves solutes that form ions, that dissolve as undissociated molecules, or that form molecular aggregates of great magnitude. Though the forces causing hydration obey a hyperbolic law and hence at certain proportions of solute to solvent may exhibit a high rate of change, this region of high curvature of the free energy: water content curve does not represent a break. FIGURE 9 shows two such curves for soils (VEIHMEYER and EDLEFSEN, 1936). Others are presented by BRIGGS (1932, Figures 1 and 2) and EDLEFSEN and ANDERSON (1943, Figure 1). GREENBERG (*in* SCHMIDT, 1938, page 472) presents a similar curve for swelling pressure.

There is considerable literature to indicate that a water content of 0.3 to 0.5 grams per gram of colloid may be a critical region for gelatin, casein, acacia, fibrin, agar, and many other biocolloids (GORTNER, 1938). Possibly this water content may fall within the region of maximum curvature of the free energy: water content curve and hence separate a region where energy change with change of moisture is low from one where energy change is high. The changes through these regions however are smooth and continuous; they are quantitative rather than qualitative. Evidences for breaks or plateaus on such curves usually involve changes of state (sol $\rightleftarrows$ gel etc.) or very low water contents.

Early attempts to explain deviation of observed osmotic pressure measurements from ideality involved association of the solvent and hydration of the solute. The graph for observed osmotic pressure curved rapidly upward at high sugar concentrations whereas the law of ideal solutions followed a straight line. Differences between the curves represent losses of water activity that could as well have been attributed to water binding. These losses result from intermolecular forces characteristic of the solute and solvent. Of the various methods for measuring hydration the vapor pressure method should excel for it integrates these forces and gives a true picture of water activity in the system; it also avoids pitfalls such as super-cooling in the freezing methods and molecular interaction where a reference solute is used. CHANDLER (1941) has obtained accurate results by this method.

GREENBERG (*in* SCHMIDT, 1938) states "—hydration does not appear to be an important factor in determining the properties of protein solutions." BULL (1943), on the other hand says "bound water may or may not contribute greatly to the understanding of physiology and pathology, but its importance for the understanding of protein reactions is extreme." GREENBERG along with many others has pointed out the shortcomings of the various methods for determining bound water. If these methods are inadequate for measuring the amount of bound water in a protein how much less adequate are they for indicating its importance.

In conclusion it should be emphasized that the differences in degree of hydration that have been measured and that surely exist between different biological systems reflect differences in the intensity of binding forces and in the packing and configuration of the molecules of solvent and solute that these forces control. The nature of the forces and of the water molecules doesn't vary; the differences in state between the substrates however are real and important. They typify the differences that exist between water in the beaker, solutions as they occur in cells, and protoplasm, seat of the complex and baffling activities of the living organism.

Mobility of Ions:— The migration of ions and molecules in aqueous solution is of great importance to biology. Much research has been directed toward problems of permeability and solute uptake by living organisms.

A perplexing problem in ion mobility is the high migration velocity of hydrogen and hydroxyl ions. Velocities of K^+ and NH_4^+ are quoted as 6.7×10^{-4} F cm. per sec. where F = the potential gradient in volts per cm. Those of H^+ and OH^- are 32.5×10^{-4} F cm. per sec. and 17.8×10^{-4} F cm. per sec. respectively. BERNAL and FOWLER explain these high velocities by a mechanism involving a proton jump from one water molecule to another when favorable configurations are presented. Such a mechanism presupposed an appreciable degree of organization of the structure of water. Much of modern physical chemistry involves the types and strengths of chemical bonds. The structure of water as related to such bonds, and the forces between ions and water are all concerned in ion mobility. Also involved are the membranes encountered and the interfaces between them. It is evident from this discussion that the problems of the mobility and uptake of solutes by plants are exceedingly complex when viewed from the standpoint of molecular kinetics as exemplified by the process of diffusion. When one adds the metabolic activities of the growing cell to this picture it is easy to understand the difficulties encountered in the study of plant nutrition. The material presented in this chapter indicates the progress that is being made in the study of solutions. It is not the purpose of the present publication to go further into this subject. Interested readers are referred to the books of REMICK (1943) and HÖBER (1945) which have been drawn on freely for the contents of this chapter. Further source material on the dielectric properties of matter appears in Chemical Reviews of 1936. Articles by DEBYE, SIDGWICK, WYMAN, COHN, KIRKWOOD, and SCATCHARD in this review should all prove of interest to biologists. A symposium on structure and molecular forces in pure liquids and solutions held in 1936 in Edinburgh is reported in volume 33 of the Transactions of the Faraday Society. Further detailed work on solutions is reviewed by KINCAID, EYRING, and STEARN (1941), and by SCATCHARD and EPSTEIN (1942). The thermodynamics of electrolytic solutions have received excellent treatment in a recent monograph by HARNED and OWEN (1943).

Summary:— Two viewpoints are expressed in explaining the properties of aqueous solutions. One emphasizes the importance of the molecular constitution of water relating the discrepancies from ideal behavior to polymerization, hydration, and complex formation involving water molecules. The other stresses the effects of intermolecular forces between solute and solvent and their effect upon colligative properties.

Molecular interactions involve electrical forces resulting from the charges on electrons and atomic nuclei. They are comprised of ion to ion attractions, ion : dipole forces, and interaction between various types of polar molecules. They result in the numerous types of valence forces known to exist between molecules; ionic bonds, covalent bonds, and hydrogen bonds. The latter are of great interest in biology as they account for the coordination of water, the hydration of crystalloids and colloids, and the formation of bridges responsible for the three dimensional archiecture of bio-colloids.

Studies on the hydration of biological materials has given rise to the concept of "bound water." Well deserved criticism has been directed toward certain of the methods used to determine this water. While some would deny its existence entirely, a more plausible view is that a small amount of water can be bonded to colloidal surfaces by intense forces. Such bound water must differ from free water in some of its physical and chemical properties; its molecular constitution, however, remains unchanged. No sharp line can be drawn between bound and free water, there being a smooth deviation in the average intensity of the binding forces as water is added to or withdrawn from the system.

Hydration is defined as the resultant of any interaction between solute and water tending to reduce the activity of the latter. Water does not vary greatly in closeness of packing but the state of aggregation of solutes may vary from ions to colloidal micelles. The forces causing hydration obey a hyperbolic law and the curve relating free energy to water content is smooth and continuous. Breaks in such curves involve changes of state or very low water contents.

The vapor pressure method should be best for measuring hydration because it integrates all factors causing deviations from ideality. It avoids supercooling and the use of reference solutes.

High ion mobilities of H^+ and OH^- are explained in the basis of a proton jump along coordinated chains of water molecules when favorable configurations occur.

Chapter IV

OSMOSIS AND OSMOTIC PRESSURE

Introduction:— The Abbé Nollet (1748) is credited with performing the first recorded experiments on the phenomenon of osmosis. Using an animal bladder, he found that water would pass through but that alcohol would not. Traube (1867) discovered the copper ferrocyanide membrane, and Pfeffer (1877), by precipitating such a membrane in a porous pot, was able to measure osmotic pressures up to several atmospheres. Examples of Pfeffer's results are given in Tables 5 and 6.

Table 5. — *Osmotic pressures of sucrose solutions at constant temperature:* —

Concentration (c) g. per 100 g. H_2O	Osmotic pressure (P_o) mm. of mercury	$\dfrac{P_o}{c}$
1	535	535
2	1016	508
2.74	1518	554
4	2082	521
6	3075	513

Table 6. — *Influence of temperature on osmotic pressure:* —

Temperature °C.	Temperature absolute (T)	Osmotic pressure (P_o) mm. of mercury	$\dfrac{P_o}{T}$
6.8	279.8	505	1.80
13.7	286.7	525	1.83
22.0	295.0	548	1.85
32.0	305.0	544	1.79
36.0	309.0	567	1.83

Because the concentration of a solution in mols per liter equals the reciprocal of the volume V in which one mol of solute is dissolved, it follows from Table 5 that $P_o V$ = a constant. This is analogous to Boyle's law for gases. The proportionality shown in Table 6 between osmotic pressure and absolute temperature shows that a relation analogous to Gay Lussac's law for gases also applies to solutions; that is $\dfrac{P_o}{T}$ = a constant.

By combining these equations one obtains the relation $P_o V$ = RT where R is a proportionality constant. For dilute solutions van't Hoff gave the equation

$$P_o V = nRT \qquad (1)$$

where n = the mols of solute in V liters of solution.

By a comparison of the osmotic pressure of a cane sugar solution with gas pressure exerted by hydrogen gas at the same temperature and concentration van't Hoff showed that the constant R in the equation above had the same value as the gas constant.

Table 7 from van't Hoff (1888) shows the results of such a comparison. The data are osmotic pressures of a sucrose solution containing 1 gram in 100.6 cc. of solution compared with pressures of an ideal gas at the same concentration.

TABLE 7. — *Comparison of osmotic and gas pressures:* —

TEMPERATURE °C.	OSMOTIC PRESSURE atmospheres	IDEAL GAS PRESSURE atmospheres
6.8	0.664	0.665
13.7	0.691	0.681
14.2	0.671	0.682
15.5	0.684	0.686
22.0	0.721	0.701
32.0	0.716	0.725
36.0	0.746	0.735

Though the parallelism is not perfect, these results show that, within the limits of the methods available at the time, the osmotic pressure of a cane sugar solution is equal to the pressure of a gas at the same temperature and containing the same number of molecules as there are solute molecules in unit volume.

Starting with cane sugar, VAN'T HOFF showed that approximately the same relation could be calculated for other dissolved substances such as invert sugar, malic acid, tartaric acid, citric acid, magnesium malate and citrate, all of which DE VRIES had shown to be isotonic in equimolecular concentrations. This offered confirmation for Avagadro's law as applied to dilute solutions.

From the above work VAN'T HOFF made the important deduction that the osmotic pressure of a solution is equal to the pressure which the dissolved molecules would produce if they existed as a gas in the volume occupied by the solution. This kinetic view of osmotic pressure has been termed the *bombardment theory* (GLASSTONE, 1940) or the *solute pressure theory* (MEYER and ANDERSON, 1939) of osmotic pressure. Obviously, as VAN'T HOFF pointed out, his deduction applies only to very dilute solutions; theoretically, it would apply only to solutes that obey Henry's law and to solvents whose vapors are perfect gases; practically, as expressed in van't Hoff's equation, it holds fairly well for aqueous solutions of non-electrolytes below 0.1 M in concentration.

Refinement of the Osmotic Pressure Law:— In addition to the solute pressure theory some advocate a *solvent pressure theory* (MEYER and ANDERSON, 1939), whereas others advance the *vapor pressure theory* (CALLANDER, 1908). To one familiar with modern views of molecular kinetics, it should be clear that the diffusion pressure of solute and solvent molecules in a solution as well as their vapor pressures should all be interrelated. And, theoretically at least, changes in concentration should alter pressures not in proportion to the ratio of solute molecules to a fixed volume of solvent as is implied by van't Hoff's law, but in relation to the mol fraction of solute in the solution (LEWIS, 1908).

Assuming that the vapor of the solvent obeys the gas laws, the relation between the osmotic pressure of a solution and the vapor pressure is as follows:

$$P_o \overline{V} = RT \ln \frac{p_o}{p} \qquad (2)$$

where

P_o = osmotic pressure of the solution,

$\overline{V}$ = the partial molecular volume of the solvent under standard pressure,

p = vapor pressure of the solvent above the solution,

p_o = vapor pressure of the pure solvent.

BANCROFT and DAVIS (1928) and LEWIS (1908) have derived similar equations.

By Raoult's law if $\dfrac{p}{p_0} = x_1 = 1 - x_2$, where $x_1 = $ mol fraction of the solvent and x_2 the mol fraction of the solute, the osmotic pressure equation becomes

$$P_0 \overline{V} = -RT \ln (1 - x_2) \tag{3}$$

for an osmotic system in which the vapor of the solvent obeys the gas law. This gives the osmotic pressure law in terms of the mol fraction of solvent in the solution. If one expands the term $[-\ln(1 - x_2)]$ he obtains

$$P_0 \overline{V} = RT \ (x_2 + \tfrac{1}{2} x_2^2 + \tfrac{1}{3} x_2^3 \ . \ . \ .) \tag{4}$$

For dilute solutions the higher powers can be neglected and the equation becomes

$$P_0 \overline{V} = RT \ x_2 \tag{5}$$

Likewise, for very dilute solutions if $n_1 = $ number of mols of solvent in the solution and $n_2 = $ number of mols of solute, then

$$x_2 = \frac{n_2}{n^1} \text{ and } P_0 \overline{V} = RT \ \frac{n_2}{n^1} \tag{6}$$

Again for dilute solutions $n_1 \ \overline{V}$ may be replaced by V_1, the volume of solvent associated with n_2 mols of solute in the solution, and

$$P_0 V_1 = n_2 RT \tag{7}$$

This is the equation used by MORSE (1914). It gives the relation of osmotic pressure to concentration of the solution in weight molality and is accurate to a concentration of about 1 molal.

By one more assumption, namely that volume and weight molar solutions of a solute do not differ (valid only for very dilute solutions) one can substitute V, the volume of the solution, for V_1, the volume of solvent, and obtain $PV = nRT$ where $n = $ the number of mols of solute in the solution. This is the van't Hoff law; as he emphasized, it applies only to very dilute solutions. Its principal value is to show the analogy between the gas law and the osmotic pressure law.

To indicate the type of results to be obtained by use of these equations, TABLE 8 reports values obtained by FRAZER and MYRICK (1916) and pressures calculated by several formulae.

TABLE 8. — *Observed and calculated osmotic pressure values for sucrose solutions at 30° C.* (R = .08206, $\overline{V}$ = 18.052, V_1 = 1001.9, T = 303°) : —

CONCENTRATION, mols per 1000 g. of water	Observed (FRAZER and MYRICK)	Calculated VAN'T HOFF equation 1	Calculated RAOULT law equation 3*	Calculated MORSE equation 7
	atm.	atm.	atm.	atm.
1.0	27.22	20.4	25.0	24.82
2.0	58.37	34.8	49.0	49.64
3.0	95.16	45.3	72.1	74.46
4.0	138.96	53.4	97.0	98.28
5.0	187.30	59.8	119.3	124.10
6.0	232.30	64.0	142.0	148.92

* These values were not corrected for the change in $\overline{V}$ with concentration.

From these results it is shown that van't Hoff's equation falls far short of providing agreement with the observed values; Raoult's law is somewhat closer; Morse's equation is even nearer. This is to be expected because van't Hoff's law was proposed to apply only to very dilute solutions; equation (3) is calculated from the mol fraction of solvent but does not take into account the departure from ideal behavior of the solvent water; Morse's equation is based on weight normal solutions but does not include a correction for hydration. LEWIS shows that Morse's equation fails at high concentrations of solute because upon expansion it gives, in contrast to equation (4), the relation

$$P_o \overline{V} = RT \ (x_2 + x_2^2 + x_2^3 + \ .\ .\ .\ .) \tag{8}$$

Whereas the higher powers of x_2 may be neglected at low concentrations, at higher ones the differences between equations (4) and (8) become great and Morse's equation gives excessive values. For examples, *see* LEWIS, Tables V and VI.

Further refinements of the osmotic pressure laws involved corrections for hydration, association of the solvent, the volume occupied by the solute molecules, and for the mutual attraction between solute and solvent molecules as in the van der Waals equation for gases. An equation involving a correction of the latter type is that of PORTER (1917)

$$P_o \ (V\text{-}b) = RT \tag{9}$$

where b represents the space occupied by solute molecules with a consequent reduction in free space. Values for the osmotic pressure of cane sugar solutions calculated according to VAN'T HOFF (equation 1), MORSE (equation 7), FINDLAY (1919) (equation 3), and PORTER (equation 9) are presented in TABLE 9.

TABLE 9. — *Osmotic pressure of cane sugar solutions at 20° C.; observed and calculated values:* —

WEIGHT NORMAL CONCENTRATION	OSMOTIC PRESSURE OBSERVED MORSE	Osmotic pressure calculated according to			
		VAN'T HOFF	MORSE	FINDLAY	PORTER
	atm.	atm.	atm.	atm.	atm.
0.1	2.59	2.34	2.39	2.38	2.43
0.2	5.06	4.59	4.78	4.76	4.91
0.3	7.61	6.74	7.17	7.14	7.43
0.4	10.14	8.82	9.56	9.51	10.02
0.5	12.75	10.81	11.95	11.87	12.64
0.6	15.39	12.72	14.34	14.24	15.35
0.7	18.13	14.58	16.73	16.59	18.09
0.8	20.91	16.36	19.12	18.94	20.87
0.9	23.72	18.08	21.51	21.29	23.74
1.0	26.64	19.73	23.90	23.64	26.64

The values presented by PORTER show almost perfect agreement but this does not represent a fundamental improvement in the osmotic pressure formula for PORTER selected by trial and error a value for b to bring about such agreement. The value proved to be 0.310 liters per mol. The actual volume of cane sugar is 0.214 liters per mol at 20° C. The difference between these, 0.096 liters per mol, PORTER assumed to represent water of hydration corresponding to $\frac{96}{18}$ or 5.3 molecules of water per molecule of sucrose.

Assuming that sugar solutions are hydrated throughout the range of temperatures from 0° C. to 60° C. and the range of concentration from 0.1 to 1.0 weight normal, PORTER calculated a series of hydration numbers from MORSE's data that give an idea of the corrections required to fit formula (7) to observed values. TABLE 10 presents these values.

TABLE 10. — *Calculated hydration numbers for sucrose solutions at various temperatures and concentrations:* —

WEIGHT CONCENTRATION	0° C.	10° C.	20° C.	30° C.	40° C.	50° C.	60° C.
0.1	53.0	43.0	45.0	3.0	6.9	8.8	11.5
0.2	15.8	16.0	16.0	7.0	5.5	4.5	5.8
0.3	10.3	10.3	11.2	6.7	6.0	4.1	3.5
0.4	7.7	8.0	8.3	6.3	6.4	4.3	2.8
0.5	6.9	6.8	7.2	6.0	6.0	4.3	3.0
0.6	6.4	6.3	6.5	5.7	5.7	4.3	3.2
0.7	5.9	6.0	6.3	5.6	5.2	4.3	3.2
0.8	5.7	5.7	6.5	5.6	5.0	4.2	3.3
0.9	5.5	5.5	5.8	5.4	5.0	4.4	3.3
1.0	5.5	5.5	5.8	5.4	4.9	4.5	3.6

Assuming again that hydration is a factor in determining the value of b, hydration numbers have been calculated by FINDLAY (1919, Table 26) for a set of determinations carried out by BERKELEY and HARTLEY at 0° C.

Since all of these hydration numbers were calculated in order to make equation (9) fit the observed values, they simply indicate the correction in volume required to account for the departure from ideal behavior of these sucrose solutions. Since the attractive forces between adjacent molecules have not been considered in these calculations, the whole deviation has been thrown into the hydration number.

The degree of hydration has not been established experimentally; the above calculations are highly empirical.

Equation (4) can be expressed in the form

$$P_o = \frac{RT}{V_o} \, x(1 + \tfrac{1}{2}x + \tfrac{1}{3}x^2 \ldots) \quad \text{(FINDLAY, p. 61)} \qquad (10)$$

If the concentration of the solution is expressed in terms of c gram-molecules of solute in 1000 grams of water, x can be put equal to $\dfrac{c}{55.5 + c}$ where 55.5 represents the number of gram molecules in 1000 grams of water. Since the molecular volume of water at 20° C. is $\dfrac{1001.8}{55.5}$, equation (10) may be written

$$P_o = \frac{(81.6)\,(293)\,(55.5)}{1001.8} \cdot \frac{c}{55.5 + c} \cdot \left[1 + \tfrac{1}{2}\left(\frac{c}{55.5 + c}\right) \ldots\right] \qquad (11)$$

It has been assumed for years that water is associated. In order to correct for association the term $\dfrac{1001.8}{55.5}$ in equation (11) has been altered to $\dfrac{1001.8}{55.5 \div a}$ where a is the association factor. Using van Laar's value 1.65 at 20° C. for a, $V_o = \dfrac{1001.8}{34}$ and if the osmotic pressure of weight normal sucrose is calculated by equation (11) the value of 23.50 is found for P_o in place of 23.64 (*see* TABLE 9). Since the observed value was 26.64, this correction is of doubtful use. Evidently association is not important at this concentration and at higher concentrations it should be lower according to common opinion as to the effect of solutes on association at 20° C.

Correcting further by including a factor β for degree of hydration, the term for the mol fraction takes the form $\dfrac{c'}{55.5 + c' - \beta c'}$, where c' is the concentration of the hydrated molecules. Assuming a hydration number of 5, the value of P_o for weight normal sucrose at 20° C. becomes 25.96 and including the association factor of 1.65 the value becomes 27.50.

FRAZER and MYRICK (1916) have used the same formula to calculate osmotic pressure values for cane sugar solutions at 30° C. TABLE 11 gives their data.

TABLE 11. — *Osmotic pressure of solutions of cane sugar at 30° C.:* —

WEIGHT MOLAR CONCENTRATION ($H = 1$)	OSMOTIC PRESSURE OBSERVED	OSMOTIC PRESSURE CALCULATED ACCORDING TO MORSE	OSMOTIC PRESSURE CALCULATED ACCORDING TO EQUATION (10)				
			$a = 1$ $\beta = 0$	$a = 1$ $\beta = 6$	$a = 2$ $\beta = 6$	$a = 2$ $\beta = 5$	$a = 2$ $\beta = 4$
	atm.	atm.	atm.	atm.	atm.	atm.	atm.
1	27.22	24.72	24.4	27.28	26.99	26.45	25.98
2	58.37	49.43	48.32	61.19	59.89	57.41	55.1
3	95.16	74.15	71.85	104.65	100.95	94.03	88.0
4	138.96	98.86	94.80	162.25	153.7	138.2	125.5
5	187.3	123.58	117.7	242.6	224.2	192.5	168.8
6	232.3	148.3	140.1	361.7	323.9	261.4	219.3
6.5	252.8	173.0	151.2	446.9	391.75	303.4	247.9

From these values it is apparent that no one hydration number or association factor will account for the deviations at these high concentrations. Up to two molar, the osmotic pressures agree well with values calculated on the assumption of the existence of hexahydrate, but at higher concentrations the best correspondence occurs where association is assumed and hydration decreases as concentration increases. All of these assumptions are empirical however and when considered along with the hydration numbers calculated by PORTER (TABLE 10) they suggest a smooth and continuous change of hydration and association with concentration such as would occur if the increase in solute shifted the intermolecular force fields and hence the coordination of the molecules of both solvent and solute.

HALDANE (1918) has recalculated data of BERKELEY and HARTLEY according to the formula

$$P_o = \frac{n}{N_1 - n} \, 0.082 \, NT \qquad (12)$$

where n, N, and N_1 = the gram molecules of solute, pure solvent, and solution per liter. This is identical with the formula of MORSE. HALDANE, in assuming sucrose to exist as a pentahydrate, corrected for the space occupied by the water of hydration. TABLE 12 gives HALDANE's values.

TABLE 12. — *Osmotic pressure of sucrose solutions at 0° C.* (*data of* BERKELEY *and* HARTLEY, *calculations by* HALDANE) : —

CONCENTRATION OF SUCROSE				OSMOTIC PRESSURE IN ATMOSPHERES			
Volume molar	Weight molar	Grams sucrose per 100 g. water	Grams sucrose pentahydrate per 100 g. free water	Observed by BERKELEY and HARTLEY	Calculated as per VAN'T HOFF	Calculated as per MORSE	Calculated as per HALDANE
				atm.	atm.	atm.	atm.
0.097	0.0992	3.393	4.33	2.23	2.17	2.22	2.24
0.281	0.2978	10.180	13.21	6.85	6.29	6.66	6.85
0.533	0.6001	20.525	27.39	14.21	11.95	13.44	14.77
0.754	0.894	30.610	42.04	21.87	16.90	20.04	21.80
0.822	0.992	33.945	47.07	24.55	18.41	22.22	24.40
1.585	2.37	81.26	130.54	67.74	35.48	53.19	67.66
1.933	3.26	111.73	199.70	100.13	42.20	73.14	103.50
2.201	4.12	141.11	282.97	134.84	49.31	92.37	146.66

These values of HALDANE follow the observed values to a concentration about 2 molal and then depart, becoming higher than the observed values. This probably results from use of the ratio of solute to solvent molecules in place of the logarithm of the mol fraction of solvent as pointed out by LEWIS (1908) and explained on page 33.

All of the calculations so far presented have been based upon the concentration of solute in the solution. By shifting the basis for calculating concentration and by assuming association of the solvent and hydration of the solute fair approximations of the observed values have been obtained.

Another method of arriving at the osmotic pressures of solutions is to use a different basis for starting calculations; one that is more reliable than concentration in reflecting the properties of the solution. One such basis is vapor pressure. The vapor pressure of the solvent vapor above a solution is an index of the escaping tendency of its molecules; such forces as association and hydration, in other words, the intermolecular forces determining coordination of solvent and solute molecules are integrated into the vapor pressure value. Though it tells nothing concerning mechanism, it does reflect the true activity of the solvent in the solution and it is the difference between this activity and the activity of pure solvent molecules that determines the true osmotic pressure of the solution (LEWIS, 1908).

TABLE 13 presents values for the osmotic pressure of sucrose at 30° C. observed by FRAZER and MYRICK and values calculated from the vapor pressure of solvent molecules above the solutions.

TABLE 13. — *Observed and calculated osmotic pressure values for sucrose solutions at 30° C.: —*

CONCENTRATION, mols per 1000 g. of water	Observed (FRAZER and MYRICK)	Calculated from vapor pressure (equation 2)
1.0	27.22	27.0
2.0	58.37	58.0
3.0	95.16	96.2
4.0	138.96	138.5
5.0	187.30	183.0
6.0	232.30	230.9

TABLES 14, 15, and 16 present osmotic pressure values of cane sugar at 30° C. and 0° C., methyl glucoside at 30° C. and 0° C., and calcium ferrocyanide at 0° C. calculated from vapor pressure data compared with directly observed values. These are from BERKELEY, HARTLEY, and BURTON (1919) and the formula used for calculating the osmotic pressures

TABLE 14. — *Observed and calculated values of the osmotic pressure of sucrose solutions: —*

WEIGHT CONCENTRATION g. per 100 g. H2O	At 30° C.			At 0° C.			
	$\log_e p_o/p$	$\overline{S}$	Calculated osmotic pressure	$\log_e p_o/p$	$\overline{S}$	Calculated osmotic pressure	Direct osmotic pressure
			atm.			atm.	atm.
34.00	0.0195	1.0029	26.82	.....	.....	.....	.....
56.50	0.0343	1.0010	47.25	0.0352	0.9951	43.91	43.84
81.20	0.0526	0.9987	72.59	0.0538	0.9916	67.43	67.68
112.00	0.0776	0.9955	107.55	0.0798	0.9869	100.53	100.43
141.00	0.1030	0.9918	143.33	0.1067	0.9832	134.86	134.71
183.00	0.1423	0.9865	198.98	0.1471	0.9784	186.86	.....
217.50	0.1759	0.9736	249.16	0.1808	0.9740	230.70	.....
243.00	.....	.....	.....	0.2067	0.9712	264.46	.....

contained values of the partial specific volume of water $\overline{S}$ derived from its compressibility instead of the usual mol volume $\overline{V}$. The vapor pressures were very carefully measured and the values were corrected for known sources of error.

TABLE 15. — *Observed and calculated values of the osmotic pressure of α-methyl glucoside solutions:* —

WEIGHT CON-CENTRATION g. per 100 g. H$_2$O	At 30° C.				At 0° C.			
	$\log_e p_o/p$	$\overline{S}$	Calculated osmotic pressure	$\log_e p_o/p$		$\overline{S}$	Calculated osmotic pressure	Direct osmotic pressure
			atm.				atm.	atm.
35.00	0.0359	1.0026	49.42	0.0383		0.9981	48.29	48.11
45.00	0.0473	1.0019	65.14	0.0515		0.9971	64.22	63.96
55.00	0.0593	1.0009	81.73	0.0645		0.9960	80.50	81.00
64.00	0.0701	0.9996	96.75	0.0770		0.9949	96.17	96.24
75.00	0.0835	0.9988	115.34	0.0925		0.9935	115.74	115.92
90.00	0.1024	0.9972	141.66	0.1137		0.9917	142.46	.....
105.00	0.1214	0.9951	168.34	0.1355		0.9897	170.18	.....

TABLE 16. — *Observed and calculated values of the osmotic pressure of calcium ferrocyanide solutions at 0° C.:* —

WEIGHT CONCENTRATION g. per 100 g. H$_2$O	CALCULATED OSMOTIC PRESSURE	DIRECT OSMOTIC PRESSURE
	atm.	atm.
31.389	41.10	41.22
39.504	70.59	70.84
42.889	86.62	87.09
47.219	112.97	112.84
49.857	131.33	131.00

Calculations by the vapor-pressure formula (equation 2) follow the observed values to a high concentration as shown in TABLES 13-16. Where vapor pressure values are available, this basis for calculation is more reliable because it does not throw the correction upon a postulated mechanism (hydration, association, etc.) but deals with values that integrate these physical properties of the solution in a reliable manner. Freezing point values may be used in a similar way, as pointed out by LEWIS.

The examples given are a sample of the calculations that bear a certain resemblance to the gas laws. Many more such values have been calculated. Over fifty modifications of the van der Waals equation alone have been used to calculate osmotic pressure values. These different laws of solutions deduced thermodynamically on various bases are in reality independent of the phenomenon of osmosis; they all entail a central concept, namely, that there is a difference between the free energy of the solvent in the solution and in the free state, and that a pressure imposed upon the solution that is sufficient to equalize these free energies will vary with concentration of the solute in the same general way as does the partial pressure of a gas under analogous conditions.

There is an obvious and fundamental weakness in this whole concept; whereas the gas laws apply to a single component, in solutions there are two components to deal with. Because of the philosophy behind van't Hoff's law of osmotic pressure there has been a tendency to treat the solution as a one component system in which the solvent simply provides space for dispersion of the solute molecules. The corrections for space occupied by the molecules of the system and the forces between them as provided in the van der Waals equation were applied only to the solute molecules and neglected the solvent. And where corrections did consider the solvent they were formulated in terms of stereotyped and arbitrary behavior as in the corrections for association and hydration in the case of water. HILDEBRAND (1936) states, "Moreover, the concept of osmotic pressure as an effect primarily of the solute, with the solvent simply furnishing space, has obscured the effects of intermolecular forces and the interchangeability of solute and solvent. . . ."

Using the modified van der Waals formula

$$(P + \frac{a}{V^2}) \cdot (V - b) = RT \tag{13}$$

where P is the osmotic pressure and V is the volume of solution containing one gram molecular weight of the solute, BANCROFT and DAVIS (1928) have calculated osmotic pressures for mixtures of benzene and toluene in which the two materials are considered as interchangeable.

Although their V values at the high concentrations are smaller than the possible volume into which the liquid solute could be compressed and consequently improper for calculating R values, the latter values between mol fraction values of 0.9 and 0.1 are fairly close to the true ones. By adding two more constants to the equation BANCROFT and DAVIS were able to calculate R values from mol fractions of 0.99 to 0.01 that agreed very closely with theory. For similar calculations involving ethylene chloride and bromide in benzene, see LEWIS (1908), Tables V and VI.

Fundamentally there is no difference between solute and solvent in a solution. In an osmotic system the permeability of the membrane to one constituent designates that constituent as the solvent. However, substitution of a different membrane may reverse the designation.

Practically, the physical state of the pure constituents at the operating temperature and pressure may determine the more convenient designation; if one constituent is a solid or a gas it is most conveniently considered as the solute. If both are liquids solubility relations may determine the designation, the least soluble being designated the solute. However, since in liquid solution all constituents assume the liquid state, there is no unique basis for naming the solute and solvent; in osmotic systems the permeability of the membrane constitutes the only true basis for designation. In biological systems water is usually the solvent; in some situations, however, permeability of membranes to gases in solution may complicate analysis of the osmotic system involved.

In the example illustrated by BANCROFT and DAVIS, benzene and toluene were selected because they form an ideal solution at the temperature used. In most osmotic systems the solutions are not ideal; because of the anomalous properties of water, all aqueous solutions are non-ideal. Gases themselves, with a few exceptions, are not ideal in their behavior and the corrections developed to take care of departures from ideality of gases do not apply to two-component systems. While the use of the van der Waals corrections for space occupied by solute molecules and intermolecular forces between them may give fair agreement between calculated and observed values of osmotic pressure for aqueous sugar solutions (TABLE 9), the agreement is largely coincidental. True correction for non-ideality of such solutions should establish a proper balance between factors of the van der Waals type and adjustments for the polarity of water molecules and their high cohesional interaction forces.

Causes for Non-Ideal Behavior of Solutions:— Two general explanations may be given for departure of a solution from ideal behavior: *1*) the two components may be so dissimilar in properties that they are incapable of forming an ideal system and so the escaping tendency of each component is affected by the other; *2*) the two components may have such great attractive forces for each other that they form compounds (*i.e.,* hydrates) or one component may associate or polymerize reducing the total number of molecules present.

The internal pressure (cohesion) of a liquid is a measure of the attractive forces between the molecules of that liquid, and differences in internal pressure between solute and solvent determine, at least roughly, deviation from ideal behavior of the solution. Deviations caused by differences in internal pressure, and hence escaping tendencies greater than ideal, result in positive departures from Raoult's law. If one component is highly polar and the other less so, a positive deviation from ideality will result.

On the other hand, attractive forces great enough to cause association or compound formation alter the properties of solutions by reducing the number of active molecules, and bring about negative deviations from Raoult's law. Association of either solute or solvent leads to increase in vapor pressure of the solution and positive deviations from Raoult's law (GLASSTONE, 1942). Generally speaking, positive deviations from Raoult's law result in osmotic pressures less than those calculated from concentration and negative deviations result in higher values. All of the deviations mentioned are appreciable only as the concentration of the solute becomes appreciable.

Thermodynamically, it is possible to derive equations for non-ideal solutions that are independent of the factors causing departures. Though such treatment gives no hint as to the mechanism of the behavior of the solution, it does give a convenient method for calculating values for various functions of the solution. Because vapor pressure seems most accurately to mirror the true escaping tendency of solvent molecules, be their behavior ideal or non-ideal, vapor pressure measurements of the solvent above a solution are made; their departures from ideality are determined by calculation from concentrations on the basis of Raoult's law; the departure times the mol fraction is termed the activity and the corrected vapor pressure is named the fugacity. Because activity is measured in terms of concentration, it may be expressed in units of mol fraction, concentration, or molality. It is more accurate as an expression of the physical properties of a solution than is osmotic pressure, in the same degree as vapor pressure exceeds concentration in accuracy as an index of escaping tendency.

Due to the untiring efforts of BERKELEY and HARTLEY (1906), MORSE (1914), FRAZER and MYRICK (1916), BERKELEY, HARTLEY, and BURTON (1919), and others, accurate measurements have been made on the osmotic pressure, not alone of dilute solutions but, in the case of sucrose, of solutions almost saturated. Values from these studies have been cited in tables in this chapter.

Physical chemists, realizing the difficulties in osmotic pressure measurement, have been interested in the properties of solutions from a broader viewpoint and have devised many methods for studying them. Because the surface layer of a solution, in contact either with the vapor or the solid solvent, acts like a semi-permeable membrane with respect to the escaping tendency of the solvent molecules, measurements of vapor pressure, freezing point, and boiling point of solutions may be used to calculate the activities of solutions. Such measurements may be used directly to indicate concentrations, conductivities, or activities, or they may be converted to osmotic pressures by appropriate formulae. Because such methods may be more accurate or convenient than direct osmotic pressure measurements, they have been widely used.

. There remains one field of physico-chemical study in which osmotic pressure measurements are of value, that is, in determining the molecular weight of large molecules. Substances such as dextrin, albumin, and many others that form colloidal solutions cannot be studied by the indirect methods mentioned above because the low molecular concentrations render the readings so small, and minute traces of impurities may overshadow the true determinations. Membranes impermeable to such large molecules yet unaffected by the impurities may be readily prepared; they are sufficiently rigid to withstand the small pressures involved. Many descriptions of such osmotic pressure measurements may be found in the current chemical literature. Although they constitute an appreciable portion of current research, they in no way reflect the immense importance of osmosis and osmotic pressure in biology. In the latter field the study of the mechanism of osmosis as it relates to turgor of cells, translocation of solutes, absorption of water, and the more complex functions of growth and movement seems highly important.

Summary:— The Abbé NOLLET performed the first recorded experiments on osmotic pressure. TRAUBE discovered the copper ferrocyanide membrane, and PFEFFER using such a membrane precipitated in a porous pot made the first reliable quantitative measurements. VAN'T HOFF, realizing the significance of PFEFFER's measurements, derived the simple relation $PV = n\,RT$ relating the osmotic pressure of a solution containing n mols of solute in V liters of solution at the absolute temperature T to the constant R. He showed this R to be identical to the gas constant. van't Hoff's law, as given above, applied only to *very* dilute solutions.

Many refinements of the osmotic pressure law have been made. Corrections have been made to put the concentration on a weight molar basis, to correct for the forces of attraction between solute molecules and for the space they occupy, for hydration of the solute and association of the solvent and for other factors. The most satisfactory measurements for determining the osmotic pressure of an unknown solution, in addition to direct measurement, which is difficult, are vapor pressure lowering, boiling point raising, and freezing point lowering. The latter three types of determination may be used in some form to determine the physical properties of almost any type of solution and by proper formulae the osmotic pressure may be calculated.

A fundamental weakness in most considerations of osmotic pressure has been a neglect of the role of the solvent. Molecules of solute and solvent are equally important in determining the osmotic properties of a solution.

Many gases are non-ideal in their behavior; most solutions are non-ideal; all aqueous solutions are non-ideal because water is highly irregular in its role of solvent.

Solutions may be non-ideal 1) because the two components are so dissimilar that they are incapable of forming an ideal system; the escaping tendency of each component is affected by the other; 2) because the two components have such attraction that they tend to form compounds (*i.e.*, hydrates). Dissimilarity of components results in positive deviations from Raoult's law and osmotic pressures are found that are less than those calculated. Excessive attraction of components results in negative deviations from Raoult's law and observed values of osmotic pressure are higher than calculated.

Most osmotic pressure determinations are made by indirect methods; the freezing point method is probably most useful. Direct determinations have been made on sucrose solutions and a few other solutes at ordinary concentrations. Such determinations are laborious. Direct determination is used now only to determine molecular weights of large molecules. Continued study of the mechanism of osmosis seems justified in the field of biology, particularly in the field of cell water relations.

Chapter V

THE MECHANISM OF OSMOSIS

Introduction:— In an accurate description of a physical mechanism, critical definitions of the processes involved are necessary.

A large number of plant physiologists are agreed on the terminology of the Physical Methods Committee of the American Society of Plant Physiologists as presented by MEYER (1945). This terminology is used here and the following definitions are given for use in the discussion that follows:

Osmosis "may be conveniently, but not rigidly, defined as the diffusion of a solvent across a differentially permeable membrane" (MEYER, 1945). It is a result of the kinetic energy of the molecules.

Osmotic pressure. — "Historically . . . . osmotic pressure has been used to designate the maximum pressure which develops within a solution under ideal conditions . . . . the solution must be confined within a membrane permeable only to the solvent, ... the membrane [must] be immersed in the pure solvent, ... and the construction of the osmometer and attached pressure measuring apparatus [must] be such as to permit the development of a pressure equilibrium without any appreciable dilution of the solution. This concept of osmotic pressure is not a very useful one. . . ."

"The term 'osmotic pressure' can be more usefully employed as an index of certain physical properties of a solution. Osmotic pressure is an evaluation of the *potential* maximum turgor pressure which will develop in a solution if it is permitted to come to equilibrium with pure water in an ideal osmotic system. . . ."

"Osmotic pressure is an index indicating quantitatively the amount by which the diffusion pressure of the water in the solution is less than that of pure water at the same temperature and under atmospheric pressure" (MEYER, 1945).

Diffusion is the net movement of the molecules in one direction resulting from their inherent thermal or kinetic energy and a difference in activities. The direction of diffusion is from a region of greater partial pressure to a region of lesser partial pressure.

Diffusion pressure. — MEYER defines diffusion pressure as "that physical property of a substance which is responsible for its diffusion whenever other prevailing conditions permit the occurrence of this process." He gives an extended discussion of the relation of diffusion pressure to diffusion, osmosis, and the development of osmotic pressure.

We offer the following definition. Diffusion pressure is a function of the free energy of a substance. The term may be applied to both solute and solvent of a solution. Ideally, the diffusion pressure of the solute is an expression of the driving force with which its molecules will diffuse into the pure solvent. Diffusion pressure of the solvent in pure solvent or in a solution is a measure of the driving force with which its molecules will diffuse into pure solute.

For example, if pure water were separated from pure glycerine by a membrane permeable only to water, the diffusion pressure of the water would be a measure of the tendency of water to cross the membrane into the glycerine. Thus the diffusion pressure of pure solute or pure solvent may be pictured as the driving force with which each would diffuse into the other in pure phase and would be equal and opposite to the force that would have to be applied on either pure phase to prevent entry of the other. This latter force on a unit area basis is equal to the osmotic pressure of the solution as its composition approaches pure solute.

From the formula

$$P\overline{V} = RT \ln \frac{p_o}{p} \tag{1}$$

it is obvious that the osmotic pressure of a solution approaches infinity as the concentration approaches 100 per cent solute. The same is true for the substance designated as the solvent if the differential permeability of the membrane be reversed. It seems therefore that the diffusion pressure of pure solute or pure solvent approximates infinity.

Ordinarily, diffusion pressures are not measured; only differences are of value in consideration of osmotic systems. Thus diffusion pressure requires mathematical treatment in a manner similar to that of free energy where only differences are measured. Furthermore, like free energy, diffusion pressure may be influenced by any force tending to restrict the activity of the molecules. Among such influences are osmotic pressure, hydrostatic pressure, and the action of adsorptive and electrostatic force fields. In a simple osmometer, osmotic pressure is the predominating force in determining the diffusion pressure differences of solvent and solute in the system. Cells in plants may also be under the influence of hydrostatic pressure other than atmospheric (usually subatmospheric) and adsorptive forces of colloidal hydration may also be involved.

EYSTER (1940) would identify osmotic pressure with the diffusion pressure of the solvent in an osmotic system. The distinction which must be made between these terms for a clear analysis of the subject should be apparent from the discussion that follows. We are in agreement with the definitions of HALL (1940) but would prefer the term "diffusion pressure" to "escaping tendency," which he favors.

The term diffusion pressure has been used for many years in publications on osmosis and diffusion. VAN LAAR used it in his contribution to the Faraday Society symposium (1917); HALDANE used it in his paper (1918); MEYER and ANDERSON use it in their Textbook of Plant Physiology (1939), to mention only a few.

"The *diffusion pressure deficit* of water [in a solution] . . . . is the amount by which its diffusion pressure is less than that of pure water at the same temperature and under atmospheric pressure" (MEYER, 1945).

This definition is adequate for the simple osmometer in contact with pure water at atmospheric pressure. For cells in plants where the diffusion pressure of water external to the cells may be above or below that of water at atmospheric pressure the DPD of water in a cell due to solute should be defined as the amount by which its diffusion pressure is less than that of pure water under the same external pressure (stage A of FIGURE 15). This DPD may not correspond to the DPD of water in the cell referred to pure water at atmospheric pressure. For example, the DP of water in the xylem conductors of plants may be lowered much more by transpiration pull than by the solutes dissolved in it.

Turgor may be defined as the state of an osmotic system such as a cell, a tissue, an organ, or a whole plant, that relates to the hydrostatic pressure of the free solution or liquid contained in it. Because of the tensile strength and the elastic nature of plant cell walls, the plant cell usually exhibits a certain degree of turgor.

Turgor pressure at full turgor is the excess pressure exhibited by solution inside a turgid cell or osmometer above the external pressure. The equal and opposite pressure exerted by the walls upon the cell contents is termed wall pressure. For cells in contact with free water the external pressure is approximately one atmosphere. Cells within a plant must obtain their water from the xylem in which the diffusion pressure of water may vary between wide limits. Such cells are seldom at full turgor; at times the DPD of water in the xylem may equal or exceed the osmotic pressure of cells in surrounding tissues: such a condition brings on wilting.

The Kinetic Basis of Osmosis:— Although the kinetic view of osmotic pressure has been criticised from many angles, it seems inevitable that any true explanation of pressure must rest upon a kinetic foundation. Ultimately the manifestation of pressure must be a result of bombardment by the molecules of the substance exerting the pressure, be it gas, liquid, or solid.

The mechanics of the process of osmosis may be clarified by use of a model to illustrate the difference in the rates of diffusion of different gases and the effects upon pressure.

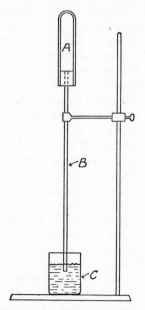

FIG. 11. — Apparatus for demonstrating differential diffusion of gases. A is a porous clay thimble, B a glass tube, and C a beaker of water. For explanation, see text. (Redrawn from MEYER and ANDERSON, 1939).

In FIGURE 11, A is a porous clay thimble closed at its lower end with a rubber stopper through which extends a glass tube B. The lower end of B is submersed in water in the beaker C. As the apparatus stands the thimble and tube are filled with air—mostly nitrogen and oxygen. If an inverted beaker filled with hydrogen is lowered very slowly over A nothing happens, but if it is lowered quickly bubbles of gas proceed from the lower end of B. If the beaker of hydrogen is kept over A bubbling proceeds for a time, slows down, stops, and then water enters B and is pulled up to a considerable height above the level in the beaker. If the hydrogen is removed from A quickly, bubbling ceases at once and the water rises in B. In each experiment water rises to a certain height in B and then slowly lowers again until it comes to the same level as it is in C.

The explanation of these phenomena is as follows. As the apparatus stands at rest, the thimble A and tube B are full of air and the molecules are diffusing in and out through the pores of the thimble at equal rates. When hydrogen surrounds A its molecules, having higher velocities and being smaller in size, diffuse inward more rapidly than air diffuses out; an increased pressure is built up in A and B and air bubbles from the tube. Rapidly, if the hydrogen is removed, or slowly, if it is allowed to dissipate, hydrogen concentration decreases around A and inward diffusion of molecules is lowered to the same rate as outward. Bubbling ceases. Then, if no more hydrogen is introduced, outward diffusion exceeds inward because, again, hydrogen moves through the porous thimble more rapidly than air. The pressure inside the apparatus becomes less than atmospheric and water rises in the tube. Finally, as hydrogen moves out and is slowly replaced by air again the apparatus attains its initial state. If hydrogen were maintained around A for a long time bubbling would continue as long as any air was left in the apparatus; when all air had left, either as bubbles from B or by diffusion outward through A, the water in B would return to the initial level in C and the apparatus would come to rest, being completely filled with hydrogen. Then if the hydrogen around A were removed the pressure would be reversed, as described above, the water in B rising, then lowering until it finally reached the initial state as all hydrogen was replaced by air in the thimble.

If, instead of a beaker of water, a water manometer is placed at the lower end of C, both positive pressure (corresponding to the bubbling) and negative pressure (as noted by the rise of water in B) could be registered. With a manometer in place, if a coarse-pored thimble is used, response to change of gas around A is more rapid but the maximum and minimum pressures measured in B would be less than with a fine-pored thimble. Finally, if a differentially permeable membrane (popularly termed semi-permeable) such as heated palladium or silica, which is permeable to hydrogen but not to oxygen or nitrogen, is used in place of a porous thimble at A, the pressure in B will rise to a high value, depending upon the partial pressure of hydrogen inside the apparatus and this pressure will remain at its maximum height so long as hydrogen is kept in contact with the differentially permeable membrane and no leaks develop.

Although the case of the porous membrane would be difficult to analyse because of the different velocities of the gases involved, that of the differentially permeable membrane seems clear. When the pressure within this gas osmometer reaches a maximum the partial pressure of hydrogen inside equals the pressure outside and movement of the molecules in the two directions is equal. The excess gas pressure within the apparatus must therefore be equal to the partial pressure of the molecules of air that are unable to penetrate the membrane when the system is placed under the total external applied pressure of the manometer.

Osmosis in Liquid Systems:— The problems of osmosis where a liquid solvent and liquid or solid solutes are involved differ from the above principally in the differences that exist between the gaseous state and the liquid state. With liquids the vapor pressure is a manifestation of the ability of the molecules to escape from the body of the liquid against attractive forces within the liquid and surface tension forces at the surface. It is the actual pressure (or partial pressure) of the vapor phase in equilibrium with the liquid and it reflects the kinetic energy of the molecules as influenced by temperature and, to a slight degree, total pressure. Diffusion pressure, on the other hand, is a measure of the average intrinsic energy of all the molecules and is a function of internal pressure, the force that renders all liquids relatively incompressible.

A gas under increasing pressure is readily compressed and eventually changes state to become a liquid under proper temperature conditions. A gas under reduced pressure will expand indefinitely. The repulsive forces between molecules are much greater than the attractive; both however are relatively small, and the latter almost disappear as a gas is rarified. A liquid represents a state of equilibrium between attractive forces and repulsive forces. As the molecules are forced closer together the repulsive forces increase very rapidly so that the pressure rises tremendously with small decrease in volume. Under reduced pressure a liquid expands very little and tensions of 72 atmospheres for ether and greater than 100 atmospheres for water have been attained before the forces of cohesion are overcome and a vapor phase appears. HILDEBRAND (1924, p. 102) has pictured the relation of internal pressure and cohesion in the following manner (FIGURE 12).

While the volume changes involved in the gas osmometer are different in magnitude than those of the liquid, the underlying kinetic principles are the same. As evidenced in Chapter IV, the improved formulae for calculating osmotic pressure from concentrations involve an expression of the relationship between the numbers of solute and solvent molecules present and corrections to account for the volumes occupied by the molecules and the attractive force between them. Though the formulae may not meet the requirements for solutions of all concentrations, it is not because of the failure of the basic principles upon which they are founded but because we do not yet know enough about the properties of liquids under all conditions of pressure and concentration to formulate a perfect equation.

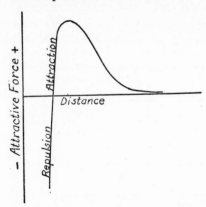

Fɪɢ. 12.—Diagram showing the relations between attractive and repulsive forces between molecules. (From Hɪʟᴅᴇʙʀᴀɴᴅ, 1924).

When a solute is dissolved in a liquid solvent its molecules disperse throughout the volume of solvent. The molecules of the solvent are now dispersed through somewhat more space than they were originally. And the solute molecules, depending upon the concentration, are dispersed through from somewhat more volume (for concentrated solutions) to very much more volume (for dilute solutions). The total volume of solute plus solvent, however, is usually somewhat reduced. Tᴀʙʟᴇ 17 shows the magnitude of this reduction for sucrose solutions (*cf.* also Bᴏᴜsғɪᴇʟᴅ and Lᴏᴡʀʏ, 1910). Because of the dispersion of the molecules and of the intermolecular forces of attraction between the molecules, the vapor pressure of both solute and solvent is reduced. The relation of these for an ideal solution is given by the diagram from Raoult's law shown in Fɪɢᴜʀᴇ 13.

Tᴀʙʟᴇ 17. — *Volume of weight-normal solutions of cane sugar at 0° C. (Sp. gr. cane sugar at 0° C. = 1.59231; from* Mᴏʀsᴇ, *1914*) :—

CONCENTRATION	VOLUME OF SOLVENT	VOLUME OF SOLUTE	SUM	VOLUME OF SOLUTION	DIFFER- ENCE	CON- TRACTION
	cc.	*cc.*	*cc.*	*cc.*	*cc.*	*p.ct.*
0.1	1000.13	21.328	1021.458	1020.73	0.728	0.07
0.2	1000.13	42.656	1042.786	1041.25	1.536	0.15
0.3	1000.13	63.984	1064.114	1061.80	2.314	0.22
0.4	1000.13	85.312	1085.442	1082.38	3.062	0.28
0.5	1000.13	106.640	1106.770	1103.01	3.760	0.34
0.6	1000.13	127.968	1128.098	1123.70	4.398	0.39
0.7	1000.13	149.296	1149.426	1144.39	5.036	0.44
0.8	1000.13	170.624	1170.754	1165.13	5.624	0.48
0.9	1000.13	191.952	1192.082	1185.91	6.172	0.52
1.0	1000.13	213.280	1213.410	1206.69	6.720	0.55

This diagram emphasizes that although the vapor pressure above the solution may be higher (in the case of a more volatile solute) or lower (in case of a less volatile solute) than that above the original solvent, the individual vapor pressures of the two components are both lowered.

In liquids, diffusion pressure is an expression of the balance between repulsive forces and attractive forces characteristic of the liquid state and is responsible for its low compressibility. In solids the forces of mutual attractions are so great and of repulsion so little that diffusion in the sense of molecular migration as it occurs in liquids is slow and almost escapes detection. The fact that the term diffusion pressure may be applied to the molecules of a solid solute depends upon the fact expressed by Professor Kᴇɴᴅᴀʟʟ (1937) that solids in solution are in the liquid state. That is, when solution takes place, the forces that serve to maintain the molecules of a solid in that state are overcome and the molecules in solution act under forces like those in the liquid.

Practically all liquids become solids below the critical temperature when pressure becomes sufficiently high, and so pass out of the liquid state where the laws of diffusion pressure apply. In the liquid state, however, the diffusion pressures of both solute and solvent are lowered as the solute dissolves, and it is this diffusion pressure lowering that becomes of paramount importance in the mechanism of osmosis.

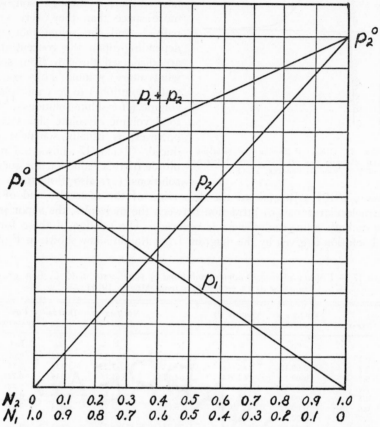

| N_2 | 0 | 0.1 | 0.2 | 0.3 | 0.4 | 0.5 | 0.6 | 0.7 | 0.8 | 0.9 | 1.0 |
| N_1 | 1.0 | 0.9 | 0.8 | 0.7 | 0.6 | 0.5 | 0.4 | 0.3 | 0.2 | 0.1 | 0 |

FIG. 13.—Diagram showing the relations of partial and total vapor pressures of solutions according to Raoult's Law. $p_1°$ is the vapor pressure of component 1 in the pure state; p_1 is its (partial) vapor pressure in the solution, and N_1 its mol fraction. $p_2°$, p_2, and N_2 are similar quantities for component 2.

The Mechanics of Osmosis:— The process of osmosis is independent of the pressure state under which the total osmotic system operates; the osmotic pressure and the turgor which the system is capable of developing are the same whether the system is atop a high mountain, at sea level, or within an evacuated chamber. This is true because turgor pressure is not an absolute pressure but an excess or differential pressure, and osmotic pressure is a physical property of the solution nearly independent of pressure. For convenience, it is usual to consider the system at atmospheric pressure and measure pressure differences from that base line setting the diffusion pressure of water under one atmosphere at zero. The principal difficulty that the plant physiologist encounters is in the treatment of problems in plants where the water is subject to tension and is not at atmospheric pressure.

In the following treatment the osmotic system will be considered as operating at atmospheric pressure. If a solution is placed in an osmometer surrounded by pure solvent an unbalance in forces is apparent. The diffusion pressure of the solvent on the outside is greater than that on the inside and solvent molecules diffuse inward. This is osmosis.

As osmosis continues and the mass of liquid inside the osmometer becomes greater, if the osmometer is closed and rigid, pressure is built up on the inside. This pressure, forcing all molecules of the solution closer together, increases the diffusion pressure of both solute and solvent in the osmometer. When the solvent molecules inside the osmometer have increased in diffusion pressure until they are in pressure equilibrium with those on the outside, the system is in osmotic equilibrium and *the difference in pressure between the liquid inside and the pure solvent outside is commonly termed the osmotic pressure of the solution.* Other terms that have been applied to this equilibrium pressure are hydrostatic pressure and turgor pressure. It should be noted that this is equal to the osmotic pressure of the solution as it exists at the equilibrium concentration, and not that of the original solution. To measure the osmotic pressure of the original solution it would be necessary to impose pressure upon it so that no solvent enters the osmometer.

Returning to the initial effect of adding a solute to a solvent, many writers have emphasized the resulting reduction in diffusion pressure of the solvent molecules. HALDANE (1918) by a rigorous mathematical analysis has shown that *the reduction in diffusion pressure of solvent molecules brought about by the addition of the solute is mathematically equal to the osmotic pressure of the solution* as defined above. Obviously osmotic pressure has been defined in two distinct ways. Can they be reconciled?

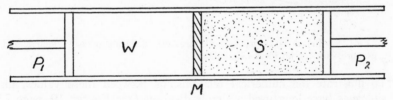

FIG. 14.—Apparatus useful in analysing problems of osmosis. M represents a differentially permeable membrane separating a cylinder into two chambers W and S containing pure water and sugar solution, respectively. P_1 and P_2 are frictionless pistons.

In FIGURE 14, M represents a differentially permeable membrane separating a cylinder into two cells W and S containing pure water and sugar solution respectively. If these two cells are closed by pistons P_1 and P_2, an osmotic system is provided that may be used in analysing the problem stated above. Starting with the fluids W and S both at atmospheric pressure and the same temperature, one can see that a difference in the diffusion pressure across the membrane M exists, water in the solution S having the lower diffusion pressure.

Obviously, too, the diffusion pressure of water across the membrane can be equalized in two ways:

1.) If pressure is applied to S by means of P_2, W remaining at atmospheric pressure, the diffusion pressure of the water molecules in S may be raised to equal that of W—namely, 1 atmosphere. And the hydrostatic pressure (above 1 atmosphere) in S at this state (water equilibrium) equals numerically the osmotic pressure of S. This is the pressure that the physicist has termed osmotic pressure and the physiologist has termed turgor pressure at full turgor.

2.) If pressure is lowered in W by moving P_1 to the left, S remaining at atmospheric pressure, the diffusion pressure of the water molecules in W may be lowered to equal that of the water in S. The hydrostatic pressure (subatmospheric) in W now equals the difference originally existing between the diffusion pressure of water molecules in W and those in the solution S—namely, the diffusion pressure deficit of the water in the system. As Haldane has shown, this diffusion pressure deficit of the water in the system numerically equals the osmotic pressure of the solution (turgor pressure at water equilibrium).

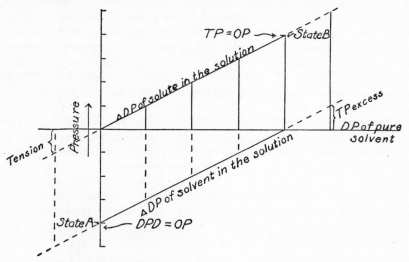

Fig. 15.—Relations among osmotic pressure, diffusion pressure deficit, and turgor pressure for an ideal osmometer.

To illustrate the numerical relationships between these values, plant physiologists have long used a simple diagram (*see* FIGURE 19, page 73). As presented by MEYER and ANDERSON (1939, p. 149), this diagram has a curved sloping line to designate osmotic pressure, a feature necessary to account for the changes in concentration resulting from increase in volume as the cell becomes more turgid. For years this diagram in varied forms has aided the student in understanding the osmotic relations of the vacuolated plant cell. It is introduced here in idealized form to aid in an understanding of the fundamental mechanics of osmosis and osmotic pressure as they occur in physical systems.

If we visualize an ideal osmometer having a perfect differentially permeable membrane and rigid enough to resist volume changes, FIGURE 15 illustrates the relations among osmotic pressure (OP), diffusion pressure deficit of water (DPD), and turgor pressure (TP) for the system. The expression diffusion pressure deficit has been given a number of names by physiologists including suction force, suction tension, suction pressure, turgor deficit, water-absorptive power, net osmotic pressure, osmotic diffusion pressure, and functional pressure. It is of great importance in plant physiology, as it is a measure of the force with which a cell may absorb water. For convenience it has been contracted to DPD.

FIGURE 15 reveals the following relationships existing among diffusion pressure deficit, turgor pressure, and osmotic pressure of an osmotic system:

$$OP = DPD + TP \qquad (2)$$
$$\text{When } TP = O, \; OP = DPD \; \text{(state A)} \qquad (3)$$
$$\text{And when } DPD = O, \; OP = TP \; \text{(state B)} \qquad (4)$$

At any point intermediate between the two limits indicated by equations (3) and (4) (state A and state B), the osmotic pressure is equalled only by a summation of two lesser pressures—namely, the DPD and the TP of the system at that particular state, as is indicated by equation (2).

That any of the states of FIGURE 15 may be set up as equilibrium states is illustrated by the following example. Referring to FIGURE 14 and assuming that solution S has an osmotic pressure of 10 atmospheres, state B may be accomplished by applying a positive pressure of 10 atmospheres, by means of piston P_2 leaving P_1 at atmospheric pressure as indicated under 1) on page 49. State A may be accomplished by lowering the pressure on W by means of P_1 to the extent of 10 atmospheres leaving S at atmospheric pressure (see 2, page 50). To visualize the intermediate states, if FIGURE 14 is turned so that M is horizontal with S on top and W below, (neglecting pressure due to gravitational force) by using a total weight of 10 atmospheres, if it be divided into two of 5 atmospheres each and one applied to P_2 and the other hung on P_1 then as equilibrium is attained the situation illustrated by the state $DPD = TP$ or the midpoint of FIGURE 15 is depicted. By dividing the total 10 atmosphere weight in other ways, any of the innumerable possible states of FIGURE 15 may be depicted.

Other methods more comparable to those used in plant physiology may be employed to bring about such equilibria. For instance, instead of hanging weights on P_1 it is possible to substitute solutions of equivalent DPD values in place of W; gases containing water vapor of equivalent DPD values could be used; colloids of like water deficiencies would serve.

In this analysis it should be emphasized that the concentration or osmotic pressure of the solution is the constant characteristic that is unique; it determines the distance between the parallel lines Δ DP of solvent and Δ DP of solute and so fixes the value of OP (or DPD + TP). The total pressure upon either or both phases at equilibrium as determined by the external pressure may vary either above or below the values of one atmosphere as indicated by the dotted extensions shown in FIGURE 15. In considering plant cell water relations, the concentration or the pressure of the external phase (comparable to W) may be of great importance as will become evident in subsequent chapters.

That the osmotic system of the plant may be described in terms of standard physical units is evident from the following analysis. If Δ f is defined as the partial specific free energy of the solvent in a solution, Δ f_H as the partial specific free energy of the solvent due to turgor pressure, and Δ f_o the partial specific free energy of the solvent due to osmotic pressure (presence of solute), then

$$\Delta f = \Delta f_H + \Delta f_o \qquad (5)$$

Transposing in (2) we have

$$-DPD = -OP + TP \qquad (6)$$
$$\Delta f = V \, (-DPD) \qquad (7)$$
$$\Delta f_o = V \, (-OP) \qquad (8)$$
$$\therefore \Delta f_H = \Delta f - \Delta f_o = V \, (-DPD + OP) = V \, (TP) \qquad (9)$$

Where V = specific volume.

Evidently the osmotic pressure of a solution can be equated to the sum of two definite measurable quantities, the diffusion pressure deficit and the turgor pressure of an osmotic system (equation 2). Osmotic pressure is equal to the DPD when turgor pressure equals zero (equation 3) or to the turgor pressure when DPD equals zero (equation 4). The conditions designated by equations (3) and (4), however, represent two different states of the osmotic system. And definitions of osmotic pressure based upon these two distinct states should recognize their mechanical differences.

The three terms *osmotic pressure, diffusion pressure deficit* (of water), and *turgor pressure* seem necessary in a consideration of an aqueous osmotic system. Each is a distinct property of the system. The identification of osmotic pressure with diffusion pressure deficit (*cf.* S. C. BROOKS, 1940; C. J. LYON, 1941) or with turgor pressure (*cf.* DUTROCHET as quoted by PALLADIN, 1923; and EYSTER, 1943) has undoubtedly caused the greatest confusion in discussions of osmotic systems. WANN's (1943) attempt to do away with the concept of osmotic pressure does not eliminate the difficulty.

Because of its relation to turgor in cells, the condition of osmotic equilibrium termed "state B" in FIGURE 15 is of much interest to the physiologist. In this state the turgor pressure in the solution is such that movement of water molecules through the membrane is equal in each direction. This is the pressure that is commonly termed the "osmotic pressure" of the cell. Since only at water equilibrium is this turgor pressure equal to the osmotic pressure of the cell, it seems best to term any hydrostatic pressure above the diffusion pressure of the pure solvent, as arbitrarily designated by the base line in FIGURE 15, the turgor pressure, for at all states but full turgor this is only one component of the value that equals osmotic pressure. The term could serve equally well in describing the properties of a purely physical osmotic system (*cf.* MEYER, 1945, page 154). The turgor pressure of an osmotic system varies through a range of pressure values which lies above the one atmosphere reference level numerically paralleled by those traversed by the diffusion pressure of the solvent in the region below one atmosphere./ And as diffusion pressure deficit of a solution is a measure of the excess diffusion pressure of the pure solvent over that of the solvent in the solution in "state A," turgor pressure measures the excess diffusion pressure of the solute in the osmometer in "state B" over the diffusion pressure of the solute in the solution at atmospheric pressure. In this way the activity of both solute and solvent are expressed in their logical relationship. To limit the term *diffusion pressure* to the solvent is arbitrary; the custom has resulted from the unbalanced view of osmosis that grew out of the van't Hoff relation, and from the fact that most membranes used in osmotic pressure studies have been permeable to water, so that osmotic adjustments occurred mainly through water diffusion.

The "Solvent" and "Solute" Pressure Theories:— Many have rejected the kinetic view of turgor pressure development in an osmotic system, chiefly on the basis that the pressure results from the entrance of the solvent into the solution through the semipermeable membrane. FINDLAY (1919) has pointed out that this criticism rests on a misunderstanding. (*See also* footnote f, p. 110, of PALLADIN, 1923).

When turgor pressure is at its maximum ("state B") and is therefore equal to the osmotic pressure, water is in equilibrium; hence turgor pressure at this stage cannot be explained on the basis of excess of entry over loss of water. And when the tendency for water to enter the osmometer (DPD) is at a maximum ("state A") and therefore numerically equal to osmotic pressure, there is no turgor pressure, and hence no excess pressure (above the diffusion pressure of pure solvent) resulting from the diffusion of solute molecules.

Some confusion results from the search for the source of energy responsible for the expression of turgor. When an osmotic system in the initial stage ("state A," FIGURE 15) is allowed to come to water equilibrium ("state B") by the absorption of water, the energy required to account for the osmotic work that the system can perform comes from the water molecules that enter. This does not prove that the turgor pressure against the membrane results solely from diffusion of water molecules. In the first place, the membrane is permeable to water and will not sustain a static pressure from water molecules. And, secondly, the diffusion pressure of water in the solution has arisen from an initially low value. With the absorption of water to attain water equilibrium, *all* molecules in the osmometer are raised in energy value. Water molecules in the solution attain a new energy level equal to those outside the membrane. The solute molecules pass through an equivalent increase in energy. Being the molecules that cannot pass through the membrane, these are responsible for a static pressure equal to the turgor pressure in the solution. Whether their increase in energy comes from the water molecules entering the osmometer, or from work done in compressing the solution by means of a piston, the end result is the same, namely, an increase in the diffusion pressure of the solute. This increase in the diffusion pressure of the solute equals the turgor pressure which in turn equals in value the diffusion pressure deficit of the water in the solution at the same concentration and under only atmospheric pressure.

Controversy still exists over the "solute pressure" and "solvent pressure" theories of osmotic pressure (BECK, 1928; MEYER and ANDERSON, 1939). Early physicists, following VAN'T HOFF defined osmotic pressure as the hydrostatic pressure in an ideal osmometer at water equilibrium. They attributed the pressure to bombardment by solute molecules. Opponents of this view define it in terms of the lowered vapor pressure, diffusion pressure, or activity of the solvent. This viewpoint was carried to the extreme by BOUSFIELD (1917) who stated, "It has also been shown that the osmotic phenomena may be interpreted as resulting from the activity of the steam (monohydrol) molecules in the molecular interspaces of the solution, which when subjected to external pressure approximately obey the gas law. This leaves us free to conclude that osmotic pressure has no real existence as an expansive force in the interior of a solution, attributable to the molecules of a solute behaving like an enclosed gas." In view of the permeability of the membrane to water this interpretation is difficult to understand.

Study of the literature indicates that the controversy has been based on confusion of the two definitions that have been discussed. Advocates of the "solute pressure" mechanism have pointed out that a static pressure such as those measured by MORSE, *et al.*, BERKELEY and HARTLEY, and others, could not be caused by bombardment of the membrane by water molecules because the membranes are permeable to water. Those supporting the "solvent pressure" hypothesis insist that it is the water entering the osmometer that brings about the pressure. Both groups have failed to appreciate the significance of the range of states through which the osmometer passes from "state A" to "state B." Both are right insofar as their definitions go but both definitions are deficient. The only complete definition involves the concept expressed by the relation

$$OP = DPD + TP \qquad (2)$$

In words, osmotic pressure is a physical property of a solution. For an osmotic system it measures the limiting value that the turgor pressure, or the diffusion pressure deficit, or their sum, may attain.

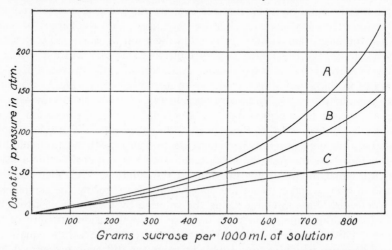

FIG. 16.—Calculated and observed values of osmotic pressures of cane sugar solutions. A, observed values of FRAZER and MYRICK. B, values calculated according to MORSE. C, ideal values from van 't Hoff's law.

The "solute pressure" theory attempts to explain turgor pressure at water equilibrium ("state B") whereas the "solvent pressure" hypothesis tries to rationalize osmotic pressure in terms of the diffusion pressure deficit of the water in the solution ("state A"). The force causing osmosis is obviously this excess diffusion pressure of the pure solvent. And *at the instant* the differentially permeable membrane comes in contact with pure solvent this force is numerically equal to the osmotic pressure of the solution. But it is directed inward and it is not the osmotic pressure of the system as commonly defined by physicists. Only *after* the solution is compressed until it is in water equilibrium across the membrane is osmotic pressure in the classical sense manifested and that pressure—the hydrostatic or turgor pressure of the system—is an outwardly directed force of the proper dimensions.

Calculation by Indirect Methods:— Many methods have been used to avoid the controversial aspects of osmosis. One has been to work in terms of vapor pressure. Because the reversible work done in a change of state does not depend upon the process, vapor pressure measurements may provide accurate data from which to calculate osmotic pressure values, as shown by TABLE 13. They are, however, of little aid in clarifying the mechanics of osmosis. CALLENDAR (1908) has gone so far as to propose that osmosis takes place as passage of water vapor through minute capillaries in the membrane. A vapor phase seems highly improbable as an essential feature of the artificial membranes used to measure osmotic pressure (copper ferrocyanide in colloidal form), and of plant membranes in view of their hydrophilic nature.

Another method is to calculate osmotic pressure values from indirect measurements upon thermodynamic principles avoiding the question of mechanism. Although such values may be very accurate, they do not give the answer that the biologist is seeking, namely, a picture of the underlying principles of osmosis upon which the mechanism is based.

Evaluation of Diffusion Pressure:— If, in considering an osmotic system, one attempts to assign values to the diffusion pressures of both solute and solvent, the latter presents difficulties for in dilute solutions the value approaches infinity. However, in practical problems only differences in diffusion pressure are of significance. Therefore, for convenience in handling such problems, it may be desirable to assign the pure solvent in some standard state an arbitrary value which may be used as a base line for further calculations. We follow MEYER, who states (1945, footnote, page 151) "The diffusion pressure of pure water at atmospheric pressure and at the same temperature as the water, the diffusion pressure of which is to be designated, is conveniently taken as the zero point on the diffusion pressure scale." Using this convention, with a solution having an activity of 1 mol per liter, when $TP = 0$, $OP = DPD = 22.4$ atmospheres (neglecting dissociation, hydration, association, etc.).

If solutes in the liquid state followed the gas law one could readily calculate an ideal diffusion pressure for any substance by the formula $\frac{1000d}{M} \cdot 22.4$, in which d = density and M = molecular weight. This would give water a diffusion pressure of 1243.2 atm. at 0° C., the value for ethyl alcohol would be 383.7 atm., glycerine 306.5 atm., sucrose 103.9 atm. The actual deviation from such a law is shown in FIGURE 16, where calculated and observed values for osmotic pressure are plotted against concentrations. Curve C represents the ideal values obtained by equating OP to $\frac{1000d}{MW} \cdot 22.4$ for sucrose. This follows the van't Hoff law. Curve B shows the values calculated according to MORSE, and curve A the observed values of FRAZER and MYRICK given in TABLE 8.

If water at atmospheric pressure is assigned a diffusion pressure value of zero and water in all aqueous solutions at that pressure negative values (DPD's), solutes may be assigned zero values at zero or any other specified concentration and positive values (TP's) at all higher concentrations. By this convention, solutions may be assigned osmotic pressure values in the common units of pressure. It should be realized, however, that both of these conventions are arbitrary and somewhat illogical for they fail to take into consideration the numerical relations between solute and solvent molecules that have been shown to bear some relationship to their relative diffusion pressures.

The Diffusion Pressure of the Solvent:— The concept of the diffusion pressure of the solvent, *i.e.,* water, is often difficult for the student to grasp. While a solution in a beaker shows no evidence of its potential capacity for work, if placed in an osmometer in contact across the semipermeable membrane with pure solvent it will lift a piston. The pure solvent in the beaker exhibits no such capacity.

Referring back to FIGURE 14, if the solution S is removed and the membrane is placed in contact with a very large reservoir of dry air, water will evaporate from the surface of the membrane, the pressure in W will lower and P_1 will move to the right if left free. If water is allowed to continue evaporating and the piston P_1 is held in a fixed position the pressure in W will lower until a tension of many atmospheres is developed providing the water and apparatus contain no bubbles or unwet surface upon which a vapor phase may be initiated. In fact the cohesion of water, calculated to be in the neighborhood of 17,000 atmospheres, is the limiting factor in determining the pull which the molecules will develop as a result of evaporation from the surface. In practice tensions of from 100 to 300 atmospheres have actually been demonstrated. This is the mechanism which the plant utilizes to supply water to its uppermost parts. It is a practical demonstration of the diffusion pressure of the water molecules.

The equilibrium vapor pressure of the water molecules above the membrane constitutes a measure of the diffusion pressure of the water inside. The relation between the diffusion pressure deficit of the water inside the membrane and the vapor pressure lowering is given by the equation

$$DPD = \frac{RT \ln \frac{p_o}{p}}{\overline{V}} \qquad (10)$$

If the base line for establishing DPD values is obtained by setting the diffusion pressure of pure water at atmospheric pressure equal to zero, DPD values for water may be calculated. HOMAN, YOUNG, and SHULL (1934) give a series of such values terming them "stromogenic tensions." MEYER and ANDERSON (1939) give a more detailed series (p. 207, Table 24). TABLE 18 presents values at 20° C. calculated by the above equation. Each atmosphere of diffusion pressure deficit shown in the fourth column is equivalent to a column of water over 30 feet in height. This indicates that in the case of the experiment mentioned above, if air having a relative humidity of 99 per cent were used in contact with the membrane of FIGURE 14 evaporation would support a column of water approximately 400 feet in height; an atmosphere at 98 per cent would maintain a column 800 feet high and lower humidities would support columns of proportionate height. This concept of the diffusion pressure or driving force of water is extremely useful in problems of plant physiology as it provides a basis for the entrance of water into plants, its movement to the leaves, and its evaporation into the air. It should also prove valuable to the animal physiologist and soil scientist.

TABLE 18. — *Relation between relative humidity, vapor pressure, and diffusion pressure deficit of atmospheric moisture at 20° C.: —*

RELATIVE HUMIDITY per cent	VAPOR PRESSURE mm. Hg.	$LOG_e \frac{p_o}{p}$	DIFFUSION PRESSURE DEFICIT in atmospheres
100	17.54	.00000	00.00
99	17.36	.01004	13.43
98	17.19	.02019	26.89
97	17.01	.03043	40.53
96	16.84	.04075	54.28
94	16.49	.06184	82.38
92	16.14	.08332	110.99
90	15.79	.10535	140.33
85	14.91	.16245	214.00
80	14.03	.22314	297.24
75	13.16	.28765	383.17
70	12.28	.35662	475.04
60	10.52	.51078	680.39
50	8.77	.69314	923.31
40	7.02	.91629	1220.56
30	5.26	1.20396	1603.76
20	3.51	1.60943	2143.87
10	1.75	2.30258	3067.19

In spite of the arbitrary assignment of zero for the base line of water, it is evident that pure water has a very high diffusion pressure. It is this high energy that causes water molecules to break away from the surface in the process of evaporation; it is manifested in Brownian movement; it is the same high energy that causes water to enter the solution in the osmometer through the differentially permeable membrane. The arbitrary assignment of zero diffusion pressure to the solvent in many considerations of osmotic pressure has probably been largely responsible for the erroneous concept that the solvent does not enter into the energy relations of the process of osmosis but simply supplies space for the dispersion of the solute molecules. It should be evident from the above discussion that the excess energy of the pure solvent molecules over that of the solvent molecules in solution is the cause of osmosis. And after osmosis has occurred and the solution has become more dilute, the only way to return to the original state is to put energy back into the system either as heat to evaporate water from the solution until it is at its original concentration, or as mechanical energy to press pure water from the solution through the differentially permeable membrane.

Although this discussion of the mechanism of osmosis may be long and involved, it seems to be necessary to clarify certain aspects. Osmosis, as it relates to cell turgor, is of paramount importance for an understanding of water relations. The ability of the cell to absorb and retain water is critical in its function in the plant. Upon this ability depends its turgidity, its form and size, its relation to the mineral nutrients supplied by the environment, its capacity to expand and grow, and, in the final analysis, its power to compete for water and so to survive. From this standpoint the biologist needs to understand the mechanics of osmosis, the function of membranes, and the energy relations of aqueous osmotic systems as related to living cells.

Summary:— A simple gas osmometer is a convenient mechanism to illustrate the principles of osmosis. When a gas osmometer is in equilibrium across the membrane with the pure gas to which the membrane is permeable, it seems evident that the partial pressure of that gas on the two sides of the membrane is equal and that the excess pressure of the confined gas is due to its partial pressure.

In the liquid state when a solute is added to a solvent, the diffusion pressure of both is reduced. If the solution is now placed in an osmometer and the latter surrounded by the liquid to which the membrane is permeable (the solvent), this liquid moves in until the diffusion pressure of solvent on the inside attains its initial value, that of the pure liquid outside.

The difference in pressure between the solution inside and the pure solvent outside is commonly termed the osmotic pressure of the solution. Turgor pressure at water equilibrium is probably a better designation. HALDANE has shown that the reduction in diffusion pressure of the solvent resulting from the addition of a solute also equals the osmotic pressure of the solution. This difference is more correctly termed the diffusion pressure deficit of the solvent in the solution. A more valuable definition of osmotic pressure is contained in the following equation:

$$OP = DPD + TP$$

Only when TP = O does DPD = OP, and when DPD = O does TP = OP. At all intermediate stages the three terms are needed to describe an osmotic system.

The "solvent" and "solute" pressure theories concern the two extreme states of the osmometer, namely when TP = O and when DPD = O. A complete consideration of osmosis must include all intermediate states as well.

The energy responsible for entry of water into an osmometer is resident in the molecules of the pure solvent. The force expressed by the turgor pressure is due to energy of the solute molecules, energy transmitted to them from the entering solvent molecules.

Arbitrary reference levels for measuring changes in diffusion pressure of both solute and solvent must be established. A customary practice is to set the level of diffusion pressure of the solvent under atmospheric pressure at zero; that of the solute at zero concentration at zero. Though illogical, this is convenient; it should be understood that it is merely an expedient.

The diffusion pressure of the solvent may be demonstrated by allowing it to evaporate through a membrane permeable only to liquid when wet; the energy of the molecules is exhibited by the great lifting force shown. Addition of a solute reduces this pressure and the only way to recover it is to put energy back as by evaporating and condensing it again in pure form, or by forcing pure solvent from an osmometer by pressure upon the solution.

Chapter VI

WATER AS A PLANT COMPONENT — INTRACELLULAR DISTRIBUTION OF WATER

Introduction:— Because water occurs so commonly, it is often taken for granted and little attention is paid to its properties. Especially is this true in biology where water may make up the bulk of the living organism. The content and character of water are too often considered subsidiary to the properties of other structural components and its role in the structure and function of the organism neglected.

The foregoing chapters have stressed the unusual properties of water, not only as an individual chemical compound but as a solvent of other compounds. In the living organism water must play a vital role in determining the nature of the physiological environment wherein metabolism takes place and various functions are carried on. The intermolecular forces between individual water molecules and between water molecules and molecules of other structural materials such as cellulose, pectin, lignin, etc., must have an important influence in the design of the physical mechanism of such complex organisms as plants. In fact, water, as the liquid medium for growth, provides an essential continuity for the transport of solutes, the transmission of impulses, and the coordination of correlative influences that distinguish the organized plant from a mass of individual cells.

The continuity of the protoplasm may rightfully be considered the critical mechanism in the above coordination. However, certain structural features such as the moist cell walls upon which CO_2 molecules are absorbed in leaves and the thoroughly wet pectic surfaces of root hairs that provide intimate contact with colloids in the soil for ion exchange, constitute connections between the protoplasm and these colloids that cannot be neglected.

And, finally, the very character of life itself may depend upon the unique properties of water and the interrelations between water molecules and those of proteins, lipoids, carbohydrates, and the various mineral elements that go to make up the living organism.

As a beginning to the presentation of the water relations of plants it seems proper to consider the water of cells, its distribution, the forces determining its absorption, movement and loss, and the dynamics of balance between these forces.

Anatomy of Cells:— It would be impossible to give detailed consideration to the water relations of the great number of cell types found in plants, a few of which are shown in Figure 17. The complexity of form and function as related to specialization, adaptation, and division of labor among cells and tissues makes generalization difficult. As a compromise an attempt will be made to treat in detail a common cell type with occasional reference to important exceptions. The type selected is the mature, active, vacuolated parenchyma cell common to the pith, phloem, and cortex, and also occurring in the xylem of succulent organs. Though more highly specialized, the mesophyll cell of the leaf may be considered to fall within this same category. Such a cell is conveniently described under three phases: *cell wall*—the enclosing membrane, somewhat elastic but having considerable tensile strength; *protoplasm*—the semi-fluid living substance including cytoplasm, nucleus, plastids, and other inclusions; and *vacuole*—the central region, filled with cell sap.

In certain water storage cells, such as those making up most of the leaf and stem tissue of succulents, the vacuoles may be relatively large, the protoplasm and cell wall consisting of thin layers. In others, for example the meristematic cells of stem and root tips, the vacuoles are small and scattered. In these the protoplasmic phase pre-

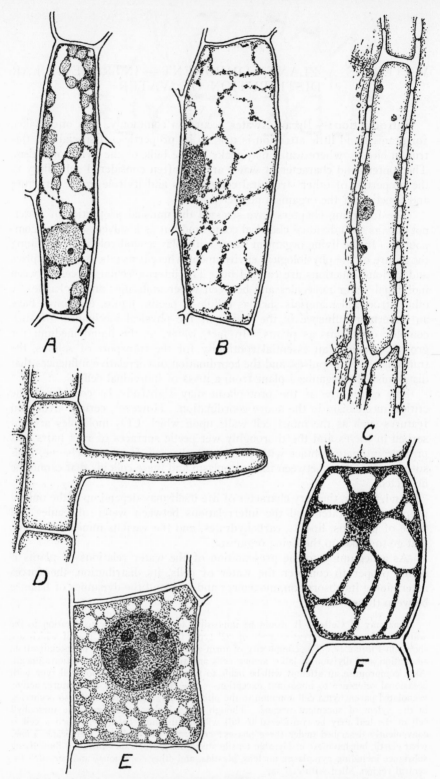

Fig. 17.—Several types of parenchyma cells found in plants. These cells are A, *Elodea* leaf parenchyma, B, *Iris* leaf parenchyma, C, tobacco phloem parenchyma, D, a root hair, E, a meristematic cell from the root tip of onion, and F, a stamen hair from *Tradescantia*.

dominates and most of the cell's water is held as part of the living substance. In cells that have lost their living function and possess little more than a cell wall skeleton, such as vessel segments, tracheids, and sclereids, water may be present only in the imbibed state in the wall; it may fill the lumen or not, depending upon the condition of the tissue. These are some of the extreme variations; others will be mentioned later.

While the cell is usually described as the unit of plant structure and function, the so-called building block, it is becoming increasingly evident that caution is demanded in such usage. The classical cell theory is being replaced by the concept that the organism as a whole is the important unit, and that the interconnected protoplasts constitute an integrated mechanism representing a higher order of organization than any summation of the individual parts. This concept has been used by MÜNCH (1930) in consideration of the mechanism of solute movement in plants, his term for the interconnected protoplasm being the *symplast* as contrasted with the *apoplast*—the sum total of non-living substances of the plant. This change has resulted from the realization that a plant cell cannot be considered an independent entity but rather that it is a highly coordinated part of the whole (symplast), connected to adjacent cells by protoplasmic strands and also by continuous water. At the same time, in spite of its interconnections, each cell maintains a certain degree of individuality. The use of cells as functional units in experimental work (plasmolysis, etc.) is a matter of convenience. The reliability of the results of such work often depends to a large extent upon the degree of injury to the cells from isolation of the tissue.

Water Content:— Water is included among the components of all plants but the variation in composition is so great that it is impossible to give general figures for the content. One example that might be considered typical of many field crops is corn, which LATSHAW and MILLER (1924) found to contain 71.4 per cent water when harvested at the time the grain matured. Many forage crops contain 75 to 80 per cent moisture when cut for hay, and fruit and vegetable crops contain even more water. The water content of plants usually shows a periodic diurnal variation and a progressive decrease with maturity. PISEK and CARTELLIERI (1931, 1932) found the water content in the leaves of a number of herbaceous mountain plants growing in full sun to be 69 to 83 per cent of the fresh weight; for certain shade plants it was greater, 80 to 86 per cent. Leaves of trees generally contain less water than those of herbaceous species. The authors just cited reported (1939) a range from 50 to 70 per cent (of fresh weight) for youngest and oldest leaves of *Fagus sylvatica*. Water in the trunks of trees is lower in amount than in leaves. GIBBS (1935) gives figures varying in the range 40 to 55 per cent of wet weight for trunks of quaking aspen.

At the lower extreme of water content, some of the simpler plants can survive almost complete desiccation during long dry periods. SCOFIELD and YARMAN (1943) report values for the lichen *Umbilicaria* as low as 6.1 per cent of the fresh weight; for the terrestrial alga *Pleurococcus,* FRITSCH (1922) found a lower limit of about 5 per cent.

A general idea as to the water content of certain plant organs used as food materials may be had from TABLE 19.

Binding Forces:— The absorption and retention of water by plant cells depend upon forces that have been, for convenience, termed osmotic, imbibitional, and chemical. Whether or not there is any fundamental difference between them, the net effect of all these forces, including ionic, covalent, dipole, and hydrogen bonds, microcapillary forces, and the colligative effect of solutes, is to lower the free energy and hence the diffusion pressure of water.

Osmotic pressure has been treated in detail in the two preceding chapters. As previously stated, the addition of a solute to a solvent causes an

TABLE 19. — *Water content, in per cent of fresh weight, of some common food materials* (*data of* CHATFIELD *and* ADAMS, 1940) : —

PLANT	WATER CONTENT AS PER CENT OF FRESH WEIGHT
Lettuce (inner leaves)	94.8
Tomato (red, ripe fruit)	94.1
Radish (edible portion root)	93.6
Cabbage (edible portion)	92.4
Watermelon (fruit flesh)	92.1
Carrot (edible portion root)	88.2
Onion (edible portion bulb)	87.5
Apple (edible portion fruit)	84.1
Potato (whole tuber)	77.8
Prune (fresh, flesh and skin)	76.5
Field corn (dry whole grain)	11.0
Common bean (dry seeds)	10.5
Barley (hulless type grain)	10.2
Peanut (raw, with skin)	5.1

increase in the average distance between the solvent molecules and hence a lowering of the diffusion pressure of the solvent. Forces of attraction between solute and solvent molecules cause further diffusion pressure lowering. Any such lowering measurable by separating the solution from the pure solvent by a membrane permeable only to the solvent will be considered as due to osmotic force.

Imbibitional forces result from the attraction between solvent molecules and colloidal substances. Their magnitude may be such that the diffusion pressure of the imbibed water is lowered to the extent of hundreds of atmospheres. Most plant colloids are of the hydrophilic type, that is, they have a strong attraction for water. Because of their structure, colloids are characterized by a high surface : mass relation and surface energy undoubtedly enters into the binding or immobilization of water molecules.

The absorption of water by a hydrophilic colloid results in swelling, and pressures of great magnitude may be exerted by swelling seeds, wood, etc. Imbibitional forces are of great importance in the retention of water by cell wall substances. The initial pull developed as a result of evaporation of water from the mesophyll of leaves is imbibitional in nature and only after transmission of this pull or deficit through the continuous aqueous phase of cell walls, protoplasm, and vacuole do the osmotic and hydrostatic aspects of transpiration pull become manifest.

By chemically bound water is meant that water which enters into true hydrate formation. Depending upon the nature of the substances involved, this water has also been termed water of constitution and water of crystallization. In dealing with cellulose and similar colloidal materials the concept of chemically bound water may be difficult to visualize. Such water we understand to be that which differs from surface bound water only in that it combines in definite proportion to the bonding material as if it were localized in and limited by the lattice structure.

Water of Cell Walls:— The water retaining function of the plant cell wall is closely tied up with its chemical and physical makeup. The wall is pictured as consisting of three layers:

1) The middle lamella, or intercellular substance. This consists almost entirely of pectins and lignins deposited by the cytoplasm.

2) The primary wall, the first wall layer containing cellulose. This wall is infiltrated by pectic materials, and is characterized by its ability to undergo increase in surface area, and to exhibit elasticity, plasticity, and reversible changes in thickness. It may also contain lignin.

3) The secondary wall, a thickening layer deposited on the primary wall. It is composed of cellulose, lignin, and sometimes other materials. It is not capable of reversible changes in thickness.

Both primary and secondary walls are believed to be composed of a skeletal framework or matrix of cellulose forming a continuous system, the interstices of which form another continuous system, of pores or micro-capillaries (BAILEY, 1938). Filling these may be found a variety of substances, namely water, pectic materials, lignin, hemicelluloses, cutin, suberin, and sometimes small amounts of other organic or inorganic substances. Resins, gums, tannins, callose, fats, oils, pigments, ethereal oils, proteins, phospholipids, and salts of sodium, potassium, and silicon have been identified. Very young primary walls may contain protoplasm in the intermicellar system (FREY-WYSSLING, 1939).

Most of the important advances made in recent years toward an understanding of cell wall properties have dealt with fibers of various origins—wood, cotton, ramie and flax, materials with thick secondary walls and of high cellulose content. Hence much of the information does not directly relate to the problems of primary cell walls.

Agreement has been reached that the ultimate units composing cellulose are long chains of glucose residues, the so-called "molecules" of cellulose. However, the number of residues in any chain has not been established with certainty. Estimates vary from 50 to several thousand, or possibly the number is indefinite. Due to unavoidable degradation of the cellulose in preparing samples for particle size analysis, the more likely figure is doubtless in the thousands.

It is further agreed that these chains or molecules are aggregated parallel to one another into groups called micelles, but the manner of grouping is in question. One theory holds that the glucose chains form elongated submicroscopic micelles. Another theory states that the chains are aggregated into definite microscopically visible cellulose particles, separated by infiltrating substances (FARR, 1944). FREY-WYSSLING has proposed (*see* 1939) that the micelles are made up of very long slender cellulose chains, which are arranged in a manner such that there are alternately crystalline and amorphous regions. In the latter, the chains are not sufficiently close or parallel to form a crystal lattice. Aggregates of micelles, termed fibrils, may be observed under the microscope in many fibers. These are the smallest visible structures in the cell wall. Their orientation within the wall may explain many of the physical properties of cellulose.

The forces binding water to cellulose have been considered as residing in the amorphous regions of the micelle and in the intermicellar amorphous material. The forces holding the glucose residues together in the chain are strong primary valence (covalent) linkages between carbon and oxygen. The forces binding the chains together in the micelles are hydrogen bonds, the weaker attractions of OH dipoles, and the permanent electric moment of the C-O-C groups (MARK, 1944). In the crystalline regions, the lattice energy is such that water does not cause a separation of the chains. Swelling consequently would be due entirely to the increase of the distance between the micelles resulting from the absorption of water by the amorphous material filling the interstices, and by the binding of water by such OH groups as are exposed on the micellar surface. But in the amorphous regions of the micelle, where the chains are somewhat curled and arranged in a random manner, water can enter to cause swelling. This has recently been demonstrated by HERMANS and WEIDINGER (1946).

According to STAMM (1936), there are three principal ways in which water is held by cell walls: (*a*) *water of constitution,* (*b*) *surface adsorbed water, and* (*c*) *capillary condensed water.* No sharp line separates (*a*) from (*b*), nor (*b*) from (*c*). The graphical relation between water content of the cellulosic material and relative water vapor pressure of the surrounding atmosphere is represented by a smooth sigmoid curve (FIGURE 10). According to BABBITT (1942), the initial portion (first water taken up) of the adsorption isotherm of cotton fibers is best explained by a monomolecular adsorption, the middle portion by a polymolecular surface orientation. Finally, capillary condensation predominates to produce the steep upper portion of the curve.

Often it is not possible to distinguish between adsorptive and chemical binding of water. BULL (1943, p. 214) has clearly stated the viewpoint that there are varying affinities between adsorbent and adsorbate particles due to the degree to which the latter are exposed on the surface, and the resulting degree to which their force fields have been satisfied. The forces are the same for both types of binding.

From the above description, it is obvious that cell wall material is highly colloidal and characterized by immense internal surface. STAMM (1936) states that the internal surface of one gram of cellulose is between one and ten million square centimeters. On much of this surface must be exposed the polar OH groups of which there are three per glucose unit. These hydroxyls are hydrophilic and experiment has shown that potentially each may coordinate up to three water molecules.

Studies on sorption of water vapor by cellulose have indicated only one half to two thirds of the theoretical water uptake, based on that expected by the attraction of one water molecule by each hydroxyl (STAMM, 1944). Since only an estimated half of the OH groups are on the micellar surface, and some are used in bonding the cellulose together, STAMM estimates that only about one out of four hydroxyls is effective in holding a water molecule, an amount of surface bound water which he states is equal to a moisture content of about 8 per cent. From this it is apparent that not a great amount of water is held on the surface of the micelles.

The intimate relation between the cellulose fibrils and the infiltrating substances would suggest a partial satisfaction of OH bonds by attraction between the two materials. The subsidiary substances of the nature of pectic compounds, hemicelluloses, and gums are more hydrophilic than cellulose, and like cellulose, are polymeric substances composed of chains of sugar or uronic residues. Hence in the primary wall particularly they would account for considerable uptake of water.

Water condensed in the smallest capillary spaces is held relatively firmly, but as the water content increases the successive increments of water filling the increasingly larger capillaries may be considered as approaching the nature of water in bulk, mechanically held.

In studies on hydration of cellulose a strong hysteresis is noted, more water being held by cellulose that has not been subject to drying. URQU-HART (1929) attributes this to the condition of the secondary valence bonds of the hydroxyl groups of the cellulose molecules.   In the original water soaked condition these bonds are saturated; when the cellulose is dried these groups are freed of water and, as a result of shrinkage, pairs are drawn together so that the individual groups of adjacent cellulose molecules mutually satisfy each other.   Upon remoistening, some of the bonds originally binding water are not readily freed for water absorption.   This results in reduced uptake.   Other factors affecting hydration of cell walls are the presence of the infiltrating materials listed above (page 63) the osmotic and imbibitional properties of the protoplast, the presence of ions and molecules passing through or along the walls, and the hydrostatic status of water in the tissue.   The latter is considered important for cells with thick walls, as in certain marine algae (DE ZEEUW, 1939).

The ability of cell walls to hold water in competition with the evaporating power of the air in the stomatal chambers of leaves and the colloids of the soil is of great importance in the economy of the plant.   Apparently the imbibition process in living plants is completely reversible for even after severe wilting, if the plant is supplied with water the wall shows no appreciable damage except where collapse and death of cells has destroyed the organized structure.   Though considerable water may be lost from the walls, they apparently can maintain enough to retain their normal properties.   No hysteresis effects comparable with those noted for dried cotton fibers have been observed in connection with wilting of plants.

The amount of water held by cell walls may be considerable.   CRAFTS (1931) found that phloem walls of potato stolon were relatively thick in their natural condition, and that their loss of volume on drying indicated a high water content.   While considerable shrinkage resulted when they were dried in alcohol, drying in air at 80° C. produced a 50 per cent reduction in volume (TABLE 20).   This indicates a minimum water content of 50 per cent in these walls.

TABLE 20. — *Walls of the phloem of potato stolon expressed as percentage of total cross section of the phloem:* —

FRESH	DEHYDRATED IN ALCOHOL	DEHYDRATED IN AIR AT 80° C.
36.8 ± 0.44	25.8 ± 0.55	18.5 ± 0.32

The above is cited to illustrate the condition in one type of tissue.

Water held by hydrogen linkages along the cellulose chains of cell walls is probably relatively immobile.   On the other hand, considerable water must exist in microcapillaries between the fibrils and this water should be fairly free.   Such water plays an important role in water movement along cell walls.   This movement occurs during absorption by roots, from root hairs across the cortex and into the xylem.   It also takes place laterally through the wood, across the cambium, and in the bark.   It undoubtedly accounts for flow from the last tracheids at the bundle ends to the mesophyll of leaves.   And it probably occurs in a large measure during development of fruits, tubers, and other storage organs.   The microstructure of many cell walls seems highly adapted to such water movement.

Protoplasmic Water:— Considering the properties of protoplasm, it is remarkable that its water content often attains values above 90 per cent; and that an average value for many plant cells may be as high as 85 per cent.

Furthermore, account should be taken of the fact that the water content may vary between wide limits. Some evidence suggests that changes of physiological significance occur only at certain critical contents. For instance SPONSLER, BATH and ELLIS (1940) state that the distance between polypeptide chains of gelatin increases markedly at 33 per cent but remains constant from that water content up to one of about 90 per cent. Probably most remarkable is the fact that the thin layer of protoplasm of a highly vacuolated cell may control the movement of salts and hence of water against gradients of a hundred fold or more where the protoplasm itself is so highly hydrated.

Chemically, protoplasm is a heterogeneous mixture of water, proteins, phosphatides, lipids, sugar, salts, and other compounds. Protein makes up about two-thirds of the non-aqueous substances.

Proteins are composed of amino acids united through peptide linkages. A peptide chain may contain several hundred amino acid residues arranged somewhat as follows:

$$\begin{array}{ccccccc}
R^I & H & O & R^{III} & H & O & \\
| & | & \| & | & | & \| & \\
C & N & H C & C & N & H C & \\
/|\diagdown/ & \diagdown/|\diagdown & / & /|\diagdown/ & \diagdown/|\diagdown & / \\
H C & C & N H C & C & N & \\
\| & | & | & \| & | & | \\
O & R^{II} & H & O & R^{IV} & H
\end{array}$$

In the protoplasm these chains are probably coiled or folded into various shapes and sizes. When spread in a film they are stretched out more nearly straight. The R residues consist of, or bear, both hydrophilic and hydrophobic groups. Oxygen and nitrogen atoms coordinate water by virtue of their ability to form hydrogen bonds. Each oxygen may hold 2 water molecules, and the NH groups a like number. OH and NH_2 groups potentially hold three molecules each and COOH groups four. Furthermore, layers of water molecules may form bridges between the backbones of adjacent polypeptide chains to produce a vein of strongly bonded water separating the two chains by the width of a water molecule. Hydration centers on the side chains are fewer and attractive forces somewhat weaker than on the backbone.

From x-ray data on gelatin (SPONSLER, BATH and ELLIS, 1940), the spacing between backbone layers is constant at 4.4 Å up until a hydration of about 33 per cent is reached, at which time the spacing increases to 7.0 Å, which holds up to a water content of 90 per cent. Other properties of proteins that change as water content passes through the critical range of 30 to 35 per cent are heat of imbibition, imbibition pressure, freezing point, expansion upon freezing, etc. When less than 30 per cent water is present in proteins the freedom of movement of water molecules is apparently restricted.

There is speculation as to the grouping of the chains of a protein, the shape of the particles or fibrils formed, the degree of continuity, and the forces holding them together. SPONSLER (1940) and SPONSLER and BATH (1942) picture an enormous number of molecular and submicroscopic particles to be present in protoplasm, grading in size up to visibility. These are composed mostly of protein displaying various shapes, monolayers, packets, etc. The chain is the fundamental unit of structure just as in cellulose, the principal difference being that the protein molecule is looped or folded. These units are aggregated into (*a*) super molecules, small packets consisting of monolayer polypeptide chains folded back and forth, or groups of monolayers of shorter length, in size about 50 Å on a side; (*b*) compact aggregates, due to grouping of the supermolecules, particles that may possibly be visible with the ultramicroscope; and (*c*) associations of super molecules and compact aggregates with water channels between. Such groups may be microscopic in size.

Forces accounting for the grouping of the chains into particles, and of the particles into the various aggregates, are attributed by SPONSLER to several types of bonds: primary valence (*e.g.,* cystine) bonds; electrostatic forces due to ions, etc.; hydrogen bonds; and van der Waals forces of cohesion. The complex aggregates are probably porous structures, interpenetrated by water channels, which widen in certain regions to form submicroscopic vacuoles of varying size. Composing the walls of these vacuoles, which, according to SPONSLER, WARBURG has termed "reaction chambers," are the active groups which are intimately tied up with respiratory and other vital reactions, including hydration phenomena.

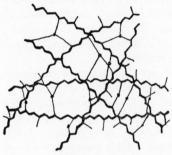

FIG. 18.—Protein structure pictured by FREY-WYSSLING (1940).

FREY - WYSSLING (1940) has proposed a structure for proteins combining corpuscular and reticulate properties. His structure is more rigid and continuous than that visualized by SPONSLER, consisting of loosely interwoven molecular strands of protein chains (FIGURE 18). The high water content is related to reticulate structure; fluidity and viscosity changes are explained by shifting bonds.

BERNAL (1940) proposes that long particles, aggregates of polypeptide chains, are oriented into spindle-shaped bodies termed tactoids which can have either positive or negative charges.

Any postulated structure must conform with the many extraordinary properties exhibited by protoplasm. Among these are elasticity, plasticity, viscosity (and the ability to vary in this respect with no change in concentration), anisotropy, a widely variable imbibitional capacity, rigidity, tensile strength, adhesiveness, thixotropy, and differential permeability. All of these properties are dependent on or related to the amount of water present, and to the types of forces responsible for the retention of water. Because protoplasm may exist in the liquid state, the gel state, and in intermediate states, and may flow or stream, its structure cannot be described in general terms. It neither conforms to a reticulate structure nor a corpuscular one but at times appears to shift from one to the other. Rigidity must be due to the presence of a submicroscopic framework wherein the molecules are coordinated to a lattice structure. Hydrogen bonds may account for such coordination.

Fluidity, according to modern theory of liquid structure, should result from a breaking down of the lattice to a closer packed structure in which points of abnormal coordination constituting cavities occur. In simple liquids these cavities have been pictured as providing space for the rotation of paired molecules in a mechanism postulated to account for viscous flow (HIRSCHFELDER, STEVENSON, and EYRING, 1937). If one attempts to apply this theory to fluid protoplasm, he might visualize pairing and rotation of water molecules, inorganic ions, and simple organic molecules, as occurs in simple liquids. Long-chain molecules may be pictured as bending in such regions, globular molecules as turning or shifting. Involved also must be a loosening of the framework to allow structural units to glide by each other, separated by layers of water molecules in which true viscous flow occurs.

In streaming protoplasm viscous flow can be observed not only along the moving strands but also at the surfaces of plastids, nuclei, vacuoles, and other cellular structures. Such flow must result in the breaking and shifting of many bonds and the activation energy of streaming required to overcome cohesional and lattice forces is presumably derived from cellular oxidations. FREY-WYSSLING (1938) proposes that the high content of water in protoplasm may be due not alone to the retention of water by the hydrophilic groups, but to the fact that the meshes produced by the polypeptide framework are of considerable size, making possible the holding of water and its dissolved salts in these meshes unattached to framework bonds. Such water would be comparatively free and might readily move by replacement. He (1940) attributes decrease in water content, such as occurs during dormancy, to gradual narrowing of the meshes and masking of the hydrophilic groups by polar radicles. Such dehydration would occur gradually without disturbing molecular configuration.

The views of LEPESCHKIN (1936, 1938) on the structure of protoplasm are somewhat different. He proposes that water is not present as a dispersion medium, but that it enters into a loose combination with lipoids and proteins, complexes which comprise the dispersion medium and which he has termed "Vitaids." His theory rests on several lines of evidence (a) the relatively rapid movement of lipoid soluble materials through the protoplasm compared to that of water suggesting that water is only one constituent of the dispersion medium and that fats are also a part (b) the typical behavior toward protoplasm of weak acids and other substances, which affect lipoids relatively little. Furthermore, water is believed by Lepeschkin to be absorbed by protoplasm up to a certain point, above which it separates as vacuoles. By placing certain marine foraminifera and algae in dilute sea water he was able to observe vacuolization after limited swelling of the organisms. In addition to the water-protein-lipoid dispersion medium, there is postulated to be a variety of dispersed phases, including substances of a hydrophilic, as well as those of a hydrophobic nature.

M. H. FISCHER (1923) advanced similar views of protoplasmic structure on the basis of studies of phenol-water systems: "It is essentially not a solution of protoplasmic material dissolved in water (like phenol-in-water), but one of reverse type, namely, water dissolved in protoplasmic material (like water-in-phenol)." MASON and PHILLIS (1939) believed that data which they obtained in sap pressing experiments (see later) on cotton leaves seemed to be more in accord with the "Vitaid" hypothesis of LEPESCHKIN, than with the assumption that water forms the dispersion medium.

These ideas of LEPESCHKIN and FISCHER have not had widespread acceptance. BROOKS and BROOKS (1941) reject the viewpoint in question on the basis that "(a) It is improbable that the phenol-water systems are analogous to the other systems mentioned . . . . (b) the abundance and small size of water molecules make it, *a priori*, improbable that they would be completely separated into separate phases by the large and complex protein molecules; (c) water soluble dyes and salts diffuse freely and rapidly within the cell; and (d) the evidence . . . . shows that protoplasm without a special surface membrane is freely miscible with water." CHAMBERS (1944) also regards water as the continuous phase in protoplasm, as evidenced by microinjection experiments. The ready diffusion of aqueous solutions through cytoplasm, the formation of discrete droplets by water immiscible liquids, the rapid freezing of water in cytoplasm when inoculated, all are strong evidence.

We must therefore at present accept the working hypothesis that water forms a continuous phase in protoplasm.

It should be obvious from the foregoing discussion that forces of many types are involved in the hydration of protoplasm, and at present it is impossible to analyse completely the various interrelations of these forces. Keeping in mind the unique nature of the living protoplasm, the intricate and involved processes going on, and the almost insurmountable difficulties presented by the complexity of the energy relations, it seems that a clear picture of protoplasmic function must await years of patient research.

Water in Vacuoles:— Vacuolar sap may consist of as much as 98 per cent water; it has the highest water content of the three cellular phases. In it are found a miscellaneous and variable assortment of sugars, salts, acids, pigments, etc. Its composition among different plants is extremely variable.

The colloid content of vacuolar sap may be appreciable in some species. In conifers, tannins, gums, resins, and other substances have been demonstrated, and some (e.g., ROBERTS and STYLES, 1939) have, correctly we believe, stressed their importance in the water relations of the cell.

The substances which most commonly comprise the hydrophilic colloidal fraction of vacuoles, at least in the higher plants, are proteins, tannins, and mucilages. Tannins may be found combined to some degree with proteins or mucilages. Other colloidal substances of a fatty nature such as lipids, phosphatides, and phytosterols may be present (cf. GUILLIERMOND, 1941, p. 164).

An especially high vacuolar colloid content in petal cells of certain Boraginaceae can be demonstrated (GICKLHORN and WEBER, 1926). Apparently the sap may even solidify. The solidification follows a spontaneous contraction of the vacuole, plasmolysis, or vital staining. On treatment with neutral red solutions the sap separates into two phases, an inner gel and, between the gel and the cytoplasm, an optically clear watery solution. HOFMEISTER (1940a, b), who has recently investigated the problem by micrurgical methods, concludes that the neutral red effect is a precipitation reaction (coacervate formation), while the plasmolytic and vacuolar contraction phenomena are of the nature of syneresis.

Microchemical tests by HOFMEISTER (1940b) on cells of *Symphytum officinale* showed no tannin, protein, or cellulose in the vacuolar sap. Large quantities of pectin, however, were indicated. Other examples of vacuoles containing sap of a jelly-like consistency are known (GUILLIERMOND, 1941, p. 154).

The vacuolar sap of most cells has been considered to be essentially a true solution. The researches of HOAGLAND and DAVIS (1923, 1929), COLLANDER (1939), LUNDEGÅRDH (1940), and others indicate the high content of nutrient salts that occur in solution in plant cells. In addition to salts, sugars are of great importance in determining the water retention of cells. On the other hand, one must recognize the complex nature of the vacuolar contents and the existence of phenomena associated with the colloidal state.

In addition to osmotic water, certain authors suggest that water may be held in vacuoles by entirely different mechanisms in which metabolic energy plays a dominant part (*cf.* BENNET-CLARK, GREENWOOD, and BARKER, 1936; VAN OVERBEEK, 1942). These theories, involving so-called "active" water relations, will be discussed in Chapter VIII.

Methods for Determining Water Partition:— No method has been devised by which the relative amounts of water in cell wall, protoplasm, and vacuole may be determined accurately. A common method has been the expression of sap from whole tissues, either in the living condition or after killing by freezing, boiling, or treatment with ether, etc. The fluid thus obtained must be termed whole cell sap since it is a composite liquid having its origin in all three cellular phases. That such sap is a true or representative sample of vacuolar contents is erroneous even though, for tissues composed of mature vacuolated cells it may consist predominately of vacuolar liquid. Sap expression techniques will be considered in Chapter VII.

Perhaps the most reliable information on the composition of vacuolar sap has been obtained by the use of large cells of certain algae. *Nitella,* with cells up to 1½ inches long and ⅛ inch in diameter, has been used; *Valonia,* a large spherical coenocyte, is even more convenient. These large cells may be broken open and slightly compressed whereupon from a drop to a cubic centimeter or more of sap is obtained. This represents a fairly reliable sample of the vacuolar sap of such plants, and many experiments dealing with permeability and solute absorption have been made using these cells. Recent studies have involved absorption of radioactive isotopes and accurate measures of the partition of these elements have been obtained.

Micrurgical techniques have been devised (*see* for example LIVINGSTON and DUGGAR, 1934) whereby rather pure vacuolar sap may be secured from even small cells, *e.g.,* hair cells of tobacco, by inserting a small hollow needle into the vacuole and drawing out the liquid. The method is laborious and provides very small samples that require analysis by micro methods.

CHIBNALL (1923) treated spinach leaves with ether as a means of separating vacuolar from protoplasmic sap. The cells rapidly plasmolyzed, the vacuoles markedly decreased in volume, and a clear liquid could be obtained on applying pressure. Examination showed no rupture of cells, and the protoplasm remained essentially intact. He admitted that the "vacuolar" liquid contained some protoplasmic constituents, but believed that the expressed sap was almost entirely vacuolar in origin. The ground, pressed residue gave a measure of the protoplasmic and wall sap.

MASON and PHILLIS (1939) estimated the partition of water between the vacuole and protoplasm of the cotton leaf in two ways. First, by determining the concentration of chlorine and potassium in press sap assumed to be vacuolar in origin, in sap assumed to be protoplasmic in origin, and in whole cell sap expressed from tissue that had been frozen. They calculated the amount of water associated with the quantities of Cl^- and K^+ found. Vacuolar sap they designate as that expressed from living leaves where shearing forces are avoided. Protoplasmic sap they take as that originating from the frozen and thawed press cake remaining after expression of vacuolar sap. Second, by plotting the weight of sap (believed to be vacuolar) expressed from living leaves against pressure applied in uniform increments. The total weight of vacuolar sap was calculated by extrapolation.

The authors concluded that only about 30 per cent of the total cell water is present in the vacuoles of cotton leaves. This value seems low and both procedures for its calculation are subject to criticism. The possibility of water in amount disproportional to solute expressed from cell walls and protoplasm, due to the behavior of cell colloids toward water and dissolved substances at the higher pressures seems likely. It also appears certain that some filtration of solutes by the cytoplasm would occur when living cells are submitted to pressure. The fact that solute concentration of the vacuolar sap was only one-fifth that of protoplasmic sap could be explained in this way. Because residues from expression of living leaves absorbed water, even from protoplasmic sap, it seems that the pressures used must have brought about a separation of water from the solutes in the cells, giving a false measure of the concentration of the so-called "vacuolar" sap.

Determination of the volume of each cellular phase will give a rough indication of the partition of water in the cell; there would be little error in assuming that the volume of the vacuole is a measure of its water content; the method is more questionable in the case of the cell wall and cytoplasm.

In many tissues the protoplasm of mature vacuolated cells forms a thin parietal layer, comprising only a small portion of the total volume. Values between 10 and 30 per cent are common in storage parenchyma; palisade cells of leaves have a greater proportion of protoplasm.

Equilibrium Between Phases:— Finally, attention should be drawn to the fact that, at least in active cells, there is a constant trend toward an equilibrium between the forces attracting water to the three cellular phases. We use the word trend because an actual equilibrium probably never obtains, due to varied activities of the living organism of which the cell is a part. With KROGH (1939), we consider "steady state" a better term, but even this is not completely valid.

The most useful concept in a consideration of the mechanics of interphasal water balance, and for the balance between various tissues and organs of the plant is that of MEYER (1938), namely *diffusion pressure deficit*. As explained in Chapter V, water, regardless of its state, location, or temperature, has a definite diffusion pressure. When this diffusion pressure is decreased, as by addition of solutes or imbibants, by decrease in turgor or temperature, or by any other means, it develops, with respect to its own previous state, or with respect to water in any phase which has not undergone change, a difference in diffusion pressure. The difference may be termed a deficit if the previous state is designated as standard. For convenience, this term is contracted to DPD.

With this concept in mind it is not difficult to explain the maintenance of a dynamic equilibrium in plant cells. If water is evaporated from the cell wall, the DPD of water in the wall will increase, and water will move in from the protoplasm to make up at least a part of the deficit. In turn, water will leave the vacuole to satisfy the DPD of water in the protoplasm. And if water is moving through an adjacent tracheid there will be a movement to satisfy the developing deficits in all three cellular phases.

Other activities which may change the DPD of water in cells and shift the equilibrium are: *1*) water exchange with other cells; *2*) solute metabolism, including condensation, hydrolysis, accumulation, or loss; *3*) water metabolism, anabolic (*e.g.,* photosynthesis) or catabolic (*e.g.,* respiration); *4*) changes in turgor; and *5*) changes in hydrophily of the protoplasm. Under certain conditions the volume of the protoplasm may increase at the expense of water in the vacuole, a phenomenon known as vacuolar contraction. As a consequence the solute concentration in the vacuole increases; presumably water moves into the cell to satisfy the DPD gradient. Contraction of the protoplasm may occur under other conditions. Chloroplasts of *Spirogyra* readily contract to give up water to the rest of the cell (OSTERHOUT, 1945). This may occur normally, or it may be induced experimentally through the action of certain salts.

The DPD concept emphasizes the fact that water in the free state under atmospheric pressure has a greater diffusion pressure than does solvent water in vacuoles, imbibed water in cell walls and protoplasm, or water under tension in the xylem. Thus water tends to move along gradients of diffusion pressure from regions where it is relatively free to those where it is highly bonded or relatively deficient. Considering the individual cell and its aqueous medium, such movement is opposed by turgor within the cell and hydrostatic tension outside, and between these forces the dynamic equilibrium known as water balance is in constant flux. Scarcely an activity takes place in the plant which does not in some way influence this balance.

Summary:— Water plays a vital role in determining the nature of the environment wherein various cell functions are carried on. It forms a continuum in which transport of solutes and stimuli occur. The protoplasm also constitutes an interconnected unit termed the symplast.

Water makes up as much as 75 to 90 per cent of the total mass of many common plants. Water is retained in cells by osmotic, imbibitional, and chemical forces, all of which lower its free energy. At their extremes and in simple systems these three types of forces are distinct and are easily distinguished; in complex systems, however, they overlap. Various types of bonds are involved in the hydration of cells among which the hydrogen bond is probably predominant.

Plant cell walls may consist of pectins, lignins, cellulose, and a number of other infiltrating substances. Cellulose and pectin have strong affinities for water. Water also exists in the microcapillaries of the cell walls. Much of this water is relatively free, and it may translocate during absorption and movement of water in the plant.

Protoplasm may consist largely of water. Yet it may regulate the movement and accumulation of solutes and hence of water. Certain evidence indicates that a protoplasmic water content of around 30 to 35 per cent is critical; water held at lower contents is less mobile. Proteins are pictured as forming interconnected chain structures similar to, but more complex than, those of cellulose. Many types of radicles, both hydrophilic and hydrophobic, may be included in protein structure. Hydrated protein may have sol or gel structure with the molecules in various states of aggregation. Protoplasm may have similar but more complex structure. It may shift from reticulate to corpuscular structure, or from a lattice having a high degree of coordination to a fluid containing holes resulting from abnormal coordination. Capillary forces may also come into play, holding water in the structural meshwork of protoplasm.

Vacuolar sap is high in water but it also contains sugars, salts, acids, pigments, tannin, protein, gums, resins, fats, etc. Water is held osmotically by the solutes in the vacuole. The osmotic pressure also reflects an equilibrium with inbibitional forces in those cells in which vacuolar colloids occur. Active forces have been postulated by some to account for the high water content of vacuoles in certain plants.

Vacuolar sap from large algal cells has been used in studies on sap composition and solute uptake. Sap from smaller cells has been withdrawn micrurgically for analysis. Sap obtained by pressure may contain materials from cell walls, protoplasm, and vacuole, and it does not give an accurate indication of concentration in any of the three phases.

A tendency toward water equilibrium in the three cell phases is maintained by a tendency for diffusion pressure equilibrium. Factors that shift this equilibrium are loss or gain of water, solute metabolism, water metabolism, changes in turgor, and changes in the hydrophily of the protoplasm.

Chapter VII

THE OSMOTIC QUANTITIES OF PLANT CELLS

A Description of the Quantities and of their Interrelations:— The osmotic quantities of plant cells are *osmotic pressure* (OP), *diffusion pressure deficit* (DPD), and *turgor pressure* (TP). That the dynamics of water movement and retention can be explained by these three quantities has been shown by the work of THODAY (1918) and HÖFLER (1920), and later by BECK (1928), URSPRUNG (1935), MEYER (1938), and others. A diagram that has proved extremely valuable in presenting these concepts and their interrelations is shown in FIGURE 19. One fundamental equation necessary to the interpretation of this figure is

$$OP = DPD + TP \qquad (1)$$

This diagram resembles FIGURE 15 of Chapter V with the exception that the diffusion pressure deficits are shown as positive quantities and are

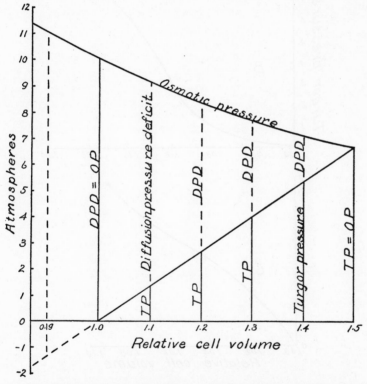

FIG. 19.—A diagrammatic presentation of the relations among osmotic pressure, diffusion pressure deficit, and turgor pressure as applied to plant cells. Redrawn with modification from MEYER and ANDERSON (1939).

placed above the base line. The curved upper boundary labeled *osmotic pressure* designates the concept used by MEYER (1945), that is, the index of the value which the sum DPD + TP may attain in the cell. It is sloping to account for the increase in volume and decrease in concentration that occurs as water passes into the cell between the states of limiting plasmolysis and full turgor. It is curved because the relation between osmotic pressure and change in volume is hyperbolic ($OP_2 = OP_1 \cdot \frac{V_1}{V_2}$), where subscript 1 represents the initial state and 2 the subsequent state.

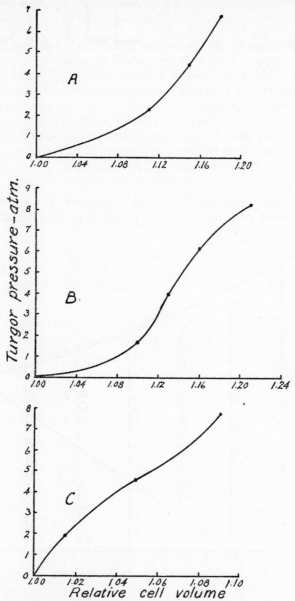

FIG. 20.—Three forms of TP-volume curves for plant cells. A, curve for cells having walls of high tensile strength. B and C, curves showing complex relations between elasticity and tensile strength.

Starting at the condition of limiting plasmolysis (relative cell volume 1.0) the DPD is high and equals the osmotic pressure of the cell contents. There is no turgor at this point. As water is taken up by the cell, turgor increases due to the opposing force which the cell wall exerts on the cell contents.

The TP-volume relation in FIGURE 19 is represented by a straight line, a relation which holds only if the cell wall is perfectly elastic. Such is not usually the case and FIGURE 20 shows three such curves derived from experimental results. The first (FIGURE 20A) shows a curve that bends upward with increasing volume. This represents a condition exemplified by a rubber film where, as the elastic limit is approached, the high tensile strength limits expansion. Another example would be a group of spherical cells surrounded by a tissue of great tensile strength such as the epidermis of a leaf or the bark around a stem. As such cells expand and fully occupy the space within the limiting tissue the force of wall pressure that opposes turgor is shifted to the confining influence of the stronger tissue and expansion is limited.

The inverse curve (bending downward) would represent a situation such as exists with a bubble where the film becomes thinner with stretching and, losing in tensile strength, finally bursts. The second curve (FIGURE 20B) starts like the first but shifts to the inverse form at the condition of full turgor. The third (FIGURE 20C) appears to start by bending downward and then changes as if the tensile strength were increasing. Other physiological processes may be involved and the time element also may influence the form of this curve. If the DPD of the external environment is rapidly reduced as occurs experimentally when flaccid cells are immersed in water, the shape of the TP curve may be concave upward because time is not allowed for plastic stretching. As full turgor is approached the slow extensibility of the wall causes an increasing slope. HÖFLER (1920), ERNEST (1934c), and BROYER (1946) present such curves.

A particularly good example of this behavior was observed in *Nitella* cells by STOWE (from TAMIYA, 1938).

With increasing volume of the cell the DPD decreases rapidly because of dilution of the cell sap and increase in turgor pressure, both of which increase the diffusion pressure of water in the cell. Any curvature in the TP line will be reflected in the DPD since the two are related.

HASMAN (1943) used the weight method in plotting DPD curves exhibited by storage tissues of potato tuber and roots of beet and carrot. Using molarities of KNO_3 and sucrose solutions as abscissae, she found that positive parts of the curves may be straight, concave upwards or concave downwards. Various causes are discussed.

The osmotic pressure also decreases as the cell expands and its contents are diluted. At full-turgor cell volume and TP are at a maximum; osmotic pressure reaches a minimum and DPD = 0. In this state the diffusion pressure of water in the cell equals that of pure water at the same temperature and at the reference pressure.

From this discussion it is evident that there is danger of oversimplifying the relations between the osmotic quantities of the cell. The diagrams shown are useful only when the time period required for the volume change involved is short. Under such conditions plastic stretching and the actual expansion due to growth are minimized so that they can be neglected.

Under certain conditions the turgor pressure may pass the zero reference level and become subatmospheric; in such an event the DPD is increased over its value at incipient plasmolysis. It seems doubtful if this reduction in pressure can go very low in cells such as root hairs, mesophyll, and the like because of the nonrigid condition of the walls; as the pressure drops below atmospheric such cells will fold, wrinkle, or collapse and the pressure remain approximately constant. In rigid, thick-walled xylem conductors, on the other hand, tensions of many atmospheres have been pictured in tall trees and plants suffering permanent wilting. The contents of such cells are virtually pure water and a dynamic equilibrium exists between the water in such cells and that in the more concentrated vacuolar sap of surrounding parenchyma. Tension in the xylem depends upon the ability of water to exist in a metastable state when no unwet surface is present on which the vapor phase may initiate. The ability of living parenchyma to retain water in competition with forces of such magnitude depends upon the osmotic and imbibitional character of their constituents.

It follows from the discussion in Chapter VI that if a complete picture of the water relations of the cell is to be embraced by the three terms OP, DPD, and TP, it is necessary to include under OP all forces leading to water absorption by the cell, *i.e.,* leading to a lowering of the DP of water; where tension exists, its value must be added to the OP. Under TP are included all forces acting in the opposite direction. DPD then represents any difference occurring between these forces, and finds expression as a net force causing water to enter the cell.

Some prefer to treat problems of plant water relations on a thermodynamic basis, following the general scheme presented on page 51. One such treatment (EDLEFSEN, 1941; EDLEFSEN and ANDERSON, 1943) deals particularly with the use of soil moisture by plants, and interprets the movement of water on a free energy basis. Water tends to move in a direction such that its free energy is lowered. The partial specific free energy of water in a solution is a function of several components: various force fields (gravitational, electrical, adsorptive); dissolved material giving the solution an osmotic value; and hydrostatic pressure.

BROYER (1946) has applied these principles directly to the problem of cell water relations in a comprehensive treatment. He aptly describes the free energy concept as applied to movement of water through the plant as follows: "The fundamental principle underlying the movement of materials is that each molecule possesses a total internal energy equal to the sum of its internal kinetic and potential energies . . . . and the molal (or partial molal) free energy is equal to the product of the mean free energy of the particles and the number of particles in one mole. A system is subject to spontaneous change if there is any conceivable process whereby the internal energy of the constituent molecules can be effectively reduced. The action, here especially that concerned with translation of the particle in space—its escaping tendency—which could be produced by such a conceivable process is determined by the internal free energy of the individual molecules. The free energy of the particles may be modified by any change in condition of the external environment."

Distinction is made between those partial specific free energies which effect movement of water into the cell, and those producing outward movement. The difference and sign represent the magnitude of the escaping tendency gradient, and the direction of water movement. Thus

$$\text{NIF} \qquad = \qquad \Sigma\,\text{IF} \qquad - \qquad \Sigma\,\text{EF} \qquad (2)$$

| Net influx specific free energy | Sum of influx specific free energies | Sum of efflux specific free energies |

The principal partial specific free energies identified are

> osmotic solute specific free energy,
> hydrostatic specific free energy,
> metabolic specific free energy,
> non-metabolic specific free energy (effect of colloids).

Each of these may act inwardly or outwardly depending upon the state of the cell and external conditions.

The relationship between the osmotic specific free energies (F) and osmotic pressure (P) is given by BROYER as

$$P = p - p^\circ = \frac{\bar{f} - f^\circ}{\underline{V}^\circ\,(1.013 \times 10^9)} = F, \qquad (3)$$

where

$\overline{f}$ = partial molal free energy of water in the given state, in ergs;

f^o = molal free energy in its standard state, in ergs;

$\underline{V}^o$ = the molal volume of water in its standard state, in liters;

$\underline{p}^o$ = the pressure on the water in its standard or reference state, in atmospheres;

p = the pressure on the medium in the given state, necessary to make $\overline{f}$ equal to f^o, in atmospheres.

The osmotic "solute" specific free energy is therefore equal to the change in free energy brought about by the formation of the solution (addition of solute to solvent). In the state as defined, the free energy change due to solute is equal in magnitude to the DPD of water in the solution at the reference pressure, or to the TP of the system at water equilibrium, both of which are numerically equal to the osmotic pressure as indicated by FIGURE 15 of Chapter V. As with diffusion pressures, free energies are not determined; only the differences between the given and some arbitrarily chosen standard state are considered.

Another system is that employed by BROOKS and BROOKS (1941). The terms and concepts selected to explain movement of water and solutes are *fugacity* and *activity*. Fugacity (f) is defined as a corrected vapor pressure, corrected for deviation from ideal gas behavior. Activity (a) is defined as a corrected concentration, and proportional to a fugacity ratio, $a = \frac{f}{f^o}$, where f^o is the fugacity in an arbitrarily chosen standard state. The close connection between these two quantities is apparent, since both are functions of partial molal free energy of a constituent in a solution, and from the fact that both are used as measures of what is qualitatively termed the "escaping tendency." By definition f^o may be set equal to one, whereupon the activity numerically equals the fugacity.

The use of "fugacity gradients," "activity gradients," "escaping tendency gradients," in explanations of water and solute movement in osmotic phenomena, is sound, and the concepts which these terms represent are essential in a clear understanding of the problems.

In addition to the above terms, Brooks and Brooks use osmotic pressure, but they have given it a meaning different than that used in this volume (*cf.* Chapter V), tending to identify osmotic pressure gradients with activity gradients (1941, p. 6, 32). In animal cells, where there is little or no effect of turgor on the activity of water in the cell, this may be justified. But the significant turgor in plant cells requires a clear distinction between these two quantities. Osmotic pressure, in our usage, is not a function of pressure, except to the extent that concentrations may be altered. Activity is a definite function of pressure.

There is much to be said for the adoption by physiologists of the terminology of physical chemistry. It would have a unifying effect and would provide a series of accurately defined units for expressing quantitative results. On the other hand, since the methods of measurement remain the same and the same numerical values must be relied upon, no new or more accurate information is acquired. Measurement of the forces involved in movement and retention of water by plants does not submit to highly accurate methods and certain qualitative aspects such as the health and vigor of tissues do not come within the scope of physico-chemical determination. There are many plant functions that cannot yet be measured by physical or chemical methods.

Furthermore, compared with the OP = TP + DPD system, the physico-chemical terminology is not more simple. The concept of DPD which is now accepted by many plant physiologists (MEYER, 1945) is represented, at least partially, in the terms net influx specific free energy, activity gradient, fugacity gradient, and escaping tendency gradient. And, finally, in view of the inadequate preparation of undergraduate students in biology, it may be premature to attempt a thermodynamic treatment of biological systems, except at the graduate level.

Membranes and Permeability:— In order that the osmotic pressure of a solution may find expression as turgor, there must be a membrane having differential properties in the osmotic system. Ideally a differentially permeable membrane is one that allows the passage of solvent but not of solute. In the living cell this role is largely played by the protoplasm, which is relatively permeable to water, but much less permeable to solutes. The selective capacity of the cell is believed due, more specifically, to two "plasma" membranes. One, termed the *ectoplast* (or *plasmalemma*), comprises the outer limiting layer of the cytoplasm immediately within the cell wall; the other is the *tonoplast,* the inner limiting layer bathed by vacuolar sap.

While these membranes are too thin to be detected microscopically, evidence for their existence has been obtained in several ways. More convincing is the micro-injection of aqueous solutions of certain dyes, which distribute themselves throughout the protoplasm, but do not pass out of the cell (CHAMBERS, 1944). Micrurgical manipulations have demonstrated the tough elasticity of these layers. SEIFRIZ (1928), using onion scale tissue, was able to strip off the protoplast from the vacuole by means of a micro-needle, leaving a free floating sac, limited by what appeared to be the tonoplast. The appearance of such structures is evidently rather common (ZIRKLE, 1937). They are often produced on thin sectioning of tissue; those from red beetroot retain pigmented vacuolar sap, and several may be produced by cutting one cell. KÜSTER (1928) has further described these structures as *vacuolar envelopes* (Vacuolenhüllen), and gives methods for isolating them from ripe berries of several species of *Solanum*. Whether the limiting membranes of these structures actually represent only the tonoplast is questionable. When such structures break under the microscope, a very thin membranous remnant is left. If the tonoplast consists of a membrane but a few molecules in thickness, as some have postulated, it seems doubtful if any such remnant would be detectable.

The phenomenon termed "Intrabilität," leading to vacuolar contraction, suggests a differential permeability between the inner and outer membranes. Various substances such as dyes are absorbed freely from the bathing solution by the protoplasm but do not diffuse into the vacuole. This has been presented as evidence that the ectoplast is permeable to such substances but the tonoplast is not (*cf.* OSTERHOUT, 1943). As pointed out by STILES (1937), other factors—adsorption, solubility, and partition coefficients—also could conceivably contribute to this effect. Electrical measurements have demonstrated a difference in behavior of the two protoplasmic surfaces (OSTERHOUT and HARRIS, 1927).

There has been hesitancy on the part of some to accept the existence of these membranes (FISCHER, 1921; LEPESCHKIN, 1938). To some extent the confusion has been a result of failure to accurately define what is meant by the term "membrane." If reference is made to definite visibly distinct layers, then there is little supporting evidence from plant cells. But it is not necessary to postulate such structures. At the limiting surface or interface of any complex solution there is a tendency for orientation and accumulation of substances which act to reduce the interfacial tension. Consequently, the chemical and physical properties of the interface will differ from those in the body of the solution. The composition of this surface will, therefore, depend on the substances present in the solution. In this sense it is difficult to visualize the absence of membranes.

The composition of the plasma membrane has not been established with certainty. The best evidence points to an association of protein and lipoid (DAVSON and DANIELLI, 1943). The lipoid molecules are believed to form a film in such a way that they have a certain freedom of orientation. Adsorbed to this film is the protein layer, composed of long polypeptide chains, cross-linked so that a heterogeneous pore or sieve effect is obtained. The hydrocarbon groups of the chains are oriented so as to be in the oil layer, thus acting as anchors; the polar water soluble groups remain in the aqueous phase. The forces holding the complex (protein-fat-water) together must be of an exceedingly intricate nature. Other substances may be present at the surface in addition to the three indicated. The complexity is increased when one considers that the composition may differ from plant to plant, varying with internal and external conditions.

A similar view is the *lipoid-sieve* theory of COLLANDER and BÄRLUND (1933). A lipoid-protein mosaic is postulated as comprising the surface of the protoplasm, a view which tends to reconcile the essential features of the "sieve" and "lipoid" theories. On such a basis many of the results of permeability experiments may be explained, especially when the molecular volume of the permeating substances is considered. Details may be found in books by DAVSON and DANIELLI, and by HÖBER (1945).

Artificial membranes of many sorts have been tested in attempts to simulate such properties of the protoplasm. And membranes have rendered valuable service in the physical measurement of osmotic pressure (MORSE, 1914; TINKER, 1917). Among artificial membranes that have been used, some certainly partake of the nature of sieves for the pore size can be regulated in their preparation (ELFORD, 1937; SOLLNER, ABRAMS, and CARR, 1941); others act as selective solvents, for instance water between layers of chloroform and ether (MEYER and ANDERSON, 1939), or oil between aqueous phases (OVERTON, 1902); air or other gases in a closed container will act as selective diffusion media for passage of solvents between solutions of different concentrations.

From the complex nature of protoplasm, as described in Chapter VI, it seems possible that all mechanisms that are compatible with a continuous liquid system may be involved in the protoplasm. Furthermore, from studies on the nature of chemical bonds (PAULING, 1939; REMICK, 1943) it seems that electrostatic and other bonding forces, by repelling some compounds, holding others in close association with the constituents of a membrane, and allowing free passage of others, may play a role in differential permeability. Ultimately the properties of all membranes must be explainable in terms of the chemical and physical properties of their constituent molecules.

Permeability to Solutes:— The limiting surfaces of protoplasts were long considered to be readily permeable to solutes, and absorption was pictured as taking place by diffusion. Since the memorable work of HOAGLAND and DAVIS (1923), BROOKS (1929), STEWARD (1932), COLLANDER (1939), LUNDEGÅRDH (1940), and many others, it is now recognized that most solutes enter the plant as a result of an active absorption process utilizing metabolic energy and often acting against strong gradients in concentration. Demonstration of active solute absorption can be accomplished using vital stains that accumulate in cells to concentrations far above that of the bathing solution.

Thus, whereas the cell walls are pictured as readily permeable, the cytoplasmic layer has distinctive properties which make it different from any artificial membrane that has been prepared. And careful researches have established a long list of environmental and internal factors that determine the permeability and absorptive capacity of plant cells for solutes (HOAGLAND, 1944). Principal among these are oxygen supply, temperature, organic nutrients, the status of the cells with respect to previously absorbed solutes, and the nature and concentration of solutes in the external medium.

In the absorption of nutrient ions from soils, not only the solutes present in the soil solution but the composition of clay colloids in intimate contact with root surfaces is involved. Studies by JENNY and OVERSTREET (1939) show that contact exchange phenomena may enable the roots to take up ions from the solid phase, their release into solution being accomplished only after they have reached the vacuoles of the root cells. Though the protoplasm itself may not extend through the walls of root hairs to come into actual contact with the soil, the presence in the wall of polyuronides provides a highly hydrated matrix along which ions may migrate much as they do in the protoplasm itself.

Thus, it seems that the protoplasm is highly impervious to the outward migration of solutes and that the inward movement is usually effected by an absorptive process that is active and hence not subject to the ordinary laws of diffusion. When the protoplast is subject to adverse conditions such as lack of oxygen, excessive temperature, excessive concentration of hydrogen or hydroxyl ions or toxic substances, or to lack of organic nutrients, its metabolic activity may be so reduced that loss of nutrients occurs. Response to such conditions may be reversible up to a certain point; beyond this, permanent injury occurs and complete loss of control over solute movement indicates death of the cell.

In view of these properties of the living protoplasm, it seems that the term permeability, in the classical sense of a passive control or selective action upon passage of ions or molecules, has little to do with the functioning of the living cell. Most cell walls may be considered permeable to water and salts in the classical sense. And loss of solutes from injured or senescent cells takes place by diffusion. But uptake by the active living cell, and possibly migration via the symplast, are active processes involving the use of metabolic energy.

Permeability to Water:— Water passes through the plasma membranes with relative ease, although its rate may change due to various influences. For example, the protoplasm of young cells appears to be more permeable to water and salts than that of older cells; protoplasm of senescent tissue is again more permeable (MAXIMOV and MOZHAEVA, 1944). Cells in a frost-resistant condition seem to possess increased permeability, and this is proposed as one explanation of hardiness (LEVITT and SCARTH, 1936).

The permeability of cells to water may be determined in several ways: 1) rate of plasmolysis or of deplasmolysis, 2) by change in volume of protoplast (plasmometric method), 3) by change in volume or weight of bulky tissues, 4) by means of conductivity and osmotic pressure measurements of expressed sap. 5) Special methods have been devised for studies on large algal filaments by DE ZEEUW (1939). He determined the water exosmosis from *Chaetomorpha linum* by sensitive refractometric and dilatometric procedures. The first is based on extent of dilution of the external medium, the second on change of cell volume.

The rate of water movement through isolated protoplasts of onion bulb scale was found by LEVITT, SCARTH, and GIBBS (1936) to be 0.3 cubic microns per minute, passing through one square micron of cell surface under a DPD difference of one atmosphere. Such values are commonly termed diffusion constants. Other reported values of diffusion constants are for *Fucus* eggs 0.16 (RESÜHR, 1935); leaf cells of *Salvinia auriculata* 0.55 (HUBER and HÖFLER, 1930); internodal cells of *Tolypellopsis stelligera* 1.08 (PALVA, 1939). The above value of 0.3 represents a linear rate of 20 microns per hour for water movement through the cell membrane.

BRAUNER and BRAUNER (1940) found that exposure to light increased the water permeability of plant tissue and postulated an electro-osmotic mechanism as an explanation. Others (*e.g.*, WEBER, 1929a) have found opposite results, and still others report no apparent effect of light on permeability.

Permeability of cells toward water may vary from cell to cell and from tissue to tissue. HUBER (1933) found for *Vallisneria* leaf a rate 30 to 40 times less in the mesophyll than in the epidermis. L. and M. BRAUNER (1943b) have made a significant contribution toward an understanding of permeability of plant cells to water. They state that passage of water through membranes is determined by two factors, each operating in an opposite direction: (*a*) an "electrostatic valve" effect, a function of the intensity of the electrokinetic potential at the pore walls, and (*b*) a mechanical filter effect. It is shown that, as is true for certain cellophane membranes, the permeability to water exhibited by plant cells is determined largely by factor (*a*) above. Permeability is thus greatest at the iso-electric point of the protoplasm; hydration and viscosity are minimal at this pH. In dense protein membranes, such as calf's bladder, the degree of hydration (swelling) and water permeability run hand in hand, *i.e.,* factor (*b*) predominates. Contrary to the finding of the above authors, DE HAAN (1933) found that the water permeability of onion bulb scale epidermis increased as the hydration of the protoplasm increased. There are many factors to consider in interpreting permeability phenomena.

Permeability of Cell Walls:— It has been conveniently assumed, in discussing the passage of substances into and out of cells that the cellulose walls are truly permeable to water and solutes alike. Actually all cell walls would be expected to offer some resistance to the passage of water and dissolved materials, but in most instances this resistance is not important when compared to that of the outer surface of the protoplasm. For most parenchyma cells, with normally hydrated walls, this is certainly true. On the other hand, certain cell walls, those containing cutin or suberin (*i.e.,* cork), and those in seed and fruit coats may be almost completely impermeable. Some are clearly differentially permeable. The work of BROWN (1909) showed that barley grains readily absorbed water from a number of salt solutions, but the salt remained excluded. SHULL (1913) lists a number of substances to which the seed coat of cocklebur is impermeable, as well as several which can penetrate. DENNY (1917) found great variation in the passage of water through seed coats and the outer bulb scale of onion. A difficulty resulting from differential permeability of cell walls has been met in plasmolytic studies (*see* page 82).

Osmotic Pressure. Methods of Measuring Osmotic Pressure in Plants. The Plasmolytic Method:— Though discovered previously by PRINGSHEIM and NÄGELI, the plasmolytic method for determining osmotic pressure in plants was not employed until about 1877, when DE VRIES and PFEFFER used it in their studies. Because little equipment is required, and because observation of living cells is fascinating, studies on plasmolysis have been popular with cell physiologists; there is a wealth of literature on the subject. Mention should be made of URSPRUNG's (1938) monograph on the measurement of osmotic properties of cells, in which practically all important findings are reviewed. Other general works which may be consulted are BRAUNER (1932), STRUGGER (1935), KÜSTER (1935), HÖBER (1945), and the periodical Protoplasma which contains one or more papers on plasmolysis in almost every issue.

Plant cells immersed in hypertonic solutions exhibit plasmolysis. This phenomenon is characterized by separation of the protoplasm from the cell wall due to loss of water from the cell contents and contraction of the vacuole and surrounding cytoplasm. Movement of the water is caused by the gradient of diffusion pressure established when the tissue is immersed in hypertonic solution. Onset of plasmolysis, due to excess shrinkage on the part of the protoplast over shrinkage of the cell wall, depends upon the relative elasticity and rigidity of these two phases. Cell walls are usually the more rigid.

An external solution which reduces the turgor of the cell to zero, but does not cause plasmolysis, is said to be *isotonic* with respect to the cell sap; the cell assumes the condition of *limiting plasmolysis*. The osmotic pressure of the bathing solution at this state is designated by the symbol Og. In practice the condition of limiting plasmolysis is detected with difficulty; a slightly more advanced stage known as *incipient plasmolysis* wherein the protoplasm first begins to draw away from the walls is used as a standard reference state. Since this is taken for the condition of isotonicity, there is by definition a slight difference between the true osmotic pressure of the flaccid cell, and that measured at incipient plasmolysis.

Limitations of the Plasmolytic Method:— Although the plasmolytic method has been criticised as involving too many errors, many of the important cell-water concepts have been developed by its use. It has several advantages: *1*) measurements on single cells are possible, *2*) intact living cells may be investigated, *3*) permeability and other types of studies may be made in conjunction with the method. The following criticisms have been offered to its use: *1*) the actual measurement is restricted to the state of incipient plasmolysis. Only by correcting for the change in volume may values be computed for cells in any state of turgor. — *2*) Permeability changes may be involved, which, while of interest from the standpoint of permeability, may bring about errors due either to absorption of the plasmolyzing solute or to loss of cell solutes or both. — *3*) It may be inapplicable to cells possessing large protoplasm: vacuole ratios (OPPENHEIMER, 1932a). — *4*) Adhesion of the cytoplasm to the cell wall, at least for certain types of cells, allegedly may result in excessive osmotic pressure values (BUHMANN, 1935). — *5*) The cell wall may be so impermeable to the solute of the plasmolyzing solution that it crinkles (HUBER and HÖFLER, 1930; PRINGSHEIM, 1931). — *6*) The exact determination of incipient plasmolysis is often difficult because of inability to observe the very first separation of the cytoplasm from the wall. — *7*) Mechanical shock from cutting or isolation of sections may produce abnormal conditions in the protoplasm (LUCKÉ and McCUTCHEON, 1932).—*8*) Sap released from cut cells may exert injurious effects on intact cells.—*9*) There is no critical point in the plasmolysis time curve (ERNEST, 1935).—*10*) Plastic stretching or shrinking of cell walls may invalidate the results. (OPPENHEIMER, 1930b).

Because of the long list of possible errors, one may question the accuracy of measurements made by this method. However, some of the criticisms are unjustified; errors involved in others are so small as to be insignificant. Material may be selected that does not suffer from all of the disadvantages noted. Tissues with pigmented vacuoles have been popular because incipient plasmolysis is easily recognized. The leaf epidermis of *Rhoeo discolor* is a classical material.

As a plasmolyzing substance, sucrose has been almost universally employed. It is nontoxic, does not appreciably penetrate the protoplasm, and its physical and chemical properties are well known. BECK (1927), after critically comparing sucrose with potassium nitrate solutions, concluded that results obtained with the latter were unreliable because of an excessive penetration into the cells. Many of the early plasmolytic data were obtained through the use of KNO_3. PETERS (1942) states that "sucrose appears to be more completely excluded from cells than any of the other substances." To mannitol has been ascribed similar properties (COLLANDER and BÄRLUND, 1933; van OVERBEEK, 1942). Sodium chloride, calcium chloride (and their mixture), glycerin, and urea have also been employed. The time necessary for equilibrium between the cell contents and external solution has been variously reported to be from 20 minutes to 2 hours. ERNEST (1935) objects to the plasmolytic method on the ground that there is no critical point for incipient plasmolysis in the plasmolysis-time curve, and that the time necessary for equilibrium may be so great that changes occur, introducing errors. This is opposed by BENNET-CLARK, GREEN-WOOD, and BARKER (1936), who point out that after 30 minutes the amount of water still to be transferred is insignificant. *See also* OPPENHEIMER, 1936.) Generally, for suitable tissues and under proper conditions, water transfer in plasmolysis tests should attain equilibrium in 30 minutes. Red beetroot cells have been shown to remain in a condition of incipient plasmolysis for 16 hours with no detectable change (CURRIER, 1944a).

Penetration of sucrose or loss of solutes are more likely to occur where cells are bathed in hypertonic solutions or pure water than in isotonic solutions (MEYER and WALLACE, 1941). STEWARD (1928) found that potato tissue discs placed even in distilled water failed to lose significant quantities of solutes during reasonably long periods. As an indication of the low permeability of cells to sucrose, HUBER and HÖFLER (1930) calculated the permeability of stem cells of *Majanthemum* for water to be 10,000 times greater than for sucrose.

That adhesion of the cytoplasm to the walls occurs in certain cells upon plasmolysis has been frequently reported (literature by BUHMANN, 1935). SCARTH (1923) observed that the protoplast of *Spirogyra* separated from the wall smoothly when plasmolyzed with salts of monovalent alkaline earths, but di- and trivalent cations increasingly produced adhesion. Exposure to very dilute solutions of di- and trivalent salts, followed by plasmolysis in a solution of the monovalent salt, similarly resulted in adhesion. The effects were reversible and could be removed by washing in water. Methylene blue was found to completely prevent the trivalent salt effect, and to remove the effect once established. Scarth suggested that in some cases the adhesion may be due to the imparting of a positive charge to the cell wall, which would attract the protoplasm, and that this may be accompanied by changes in viscosity or adhesive properties of the protoplasm.

Quantitative estimations of the magnitude of adhesion pressure were sought by BUHMANN (*loc. cit.*). Values found for leaves of *Rhoeo discolor* were of the order of 1 atm., for *Bergenia cordifolia* 1-3 atm., *Hookeria lucens* 3-6 atm., and for *Pinus laricio* 5-10 atm. Her method involved 1) determination of the limiting plasmolysis value, POg, 2) plasmolysis in hypertonic solution, 3) redetermination of the limiting plasmolysis value, DOg, this time approaching it from the plasmolyzed state, 4) complete deplasmolysis in hypotonic solution, and 5) again determining the limiting plasmolysis, ROg. It was assumed that the POg, DOg, and ROg values should be identical in the absence of adhesion. Actually, POg values appeared to be generally higher. ROg values slightly exceeded DOg values; this was attributed to a new, but weaker, adhesion with the wall.

BUHMANN's adhesion values for beetroot tissue amounted to one to three atmospheres (TABLE 21). Using the same tissue and a similar technique, one of us obtained somewhat lower values as shown in TABLE 33, Chapter VIII (CURRIER, 1944a). A complicating factor in such tests involving de- and replasmolysis relates to the extensible nature of the cell wall. Walls exhibit, in varying degree, both elasticity and plasticity, the latter defined as "the ability to undergo permanent irreversible changes in size and shape" (HEYN, 1940). Cells whose walls exhibit excessive plasticity during severe plasmolysis or deplasmolysis are not suitable material for this type of experiment.

TABLE 21. — *Measurement of adhesion pressure in Beta vulgaris root (data of* BUHMANN, *1935) :* —

PLASMOLYSIS (PO_g) atm.	DEPLASMOLYSIS (DO_g) atm.	ADHESION PRESSURE atm.
19.61	16.35	3.26
18.13	15.64	2.49
18.87	17.42	1.45
18.13	17.06	1.07

Such plastic stretching has been observed in beetroot tissue by PRINGSHEIM (1931). Some representative data are presented in TABLE 22. Stretching would be expected to affect measurements of Og. Sections of beet tissue soaked in tap water for an hour gave an Og value as much as

TABLE 22.— *Longitudinal strips of beetroot (Futterrübe) 14 cm. long, soaked for various times in water, then overnight in 0.5 M KNO3. Change in length is expressed in per cent of initial length (data of* PRINGSHEIM, *1931) :*—

HOURS IN WATER	0	1	2	2.5	3	4	5	6	7
cm.	14.00	14.50	14.77	14.75	14.75	14.75	14.80	14.85	14.95
%	0	+3.6	+5.3	+5.3	+5.3	+5.3	+5.7	+6.1	+6.8

Now overnight in 0.5 M KNO_3 : —

cm.	13.62	13.82	13.82	13.90	13.90	13.87	13.95	13.95	14.05
%	—2.7	—1.3	—1.3	—0.7	—0.7	—0.9	—0.04	—0.04	+0.04

5.7 atmospheres less than sections not soaked in this way. TABLE 23 shows these results. Unless otherwise stated, the symbol Og refers to the osmotic pressure at limiting plasmolysis approached from the normal state. This is interpreted as due to plastic stretching of the cell wall, causing plasmolysis to set in at a greater than normal cell volume. Such an interpretation neglects any error caused by loss of vacuolar solutes during soaking. Complete absence of anthocyanin in the tap water is taken for evidence that no injury was present. Presumably loss of solutes was slight, if present at all during the one-hour period.

TABLE 23. — *Effect of water saturation on O_g values* (CURRIER, 1944a) : —

Og (USUAL METHOD) ATM.	Og (WATER SATURATED) ATM.	DIFFERENCE ATM.
14.5	12.3	2.2
22.6	16.9	5.7
17.5	12.3	5.2

Volume change studies on isolated mesophyll cells of *Sedum nicaense* have shown that considerable plastic stretching of these cells occurs upon soaking. Incipient plasmolysis of such cells often occurs at cell volumes greater than normal (CURRIER, 1943). MARTENS (1931) demonstrated a marked extensibility in staminal hairs of *Tradescantia virginica,* amounting to increases in length of 100 to 150 per cent for cells freed of their cuticle. The review by HEYN (1940) and URSPRUNG's monograph (1938) may be consulted for a discussion of plastic and elastic stretching of cell walls.

Similarly it seems certain from the work of DELF (1916) and PRINGSHEIM (1931) that plasmolysis in strongly hypertonic solutions causes plastic shrinking of cell walls, tending to increase somewhat the DOg value in comparison with Og values.

GASSER (1942) was unable to demonstrate adhesion pressure in several plants which he investigated. BENNET-CLARK, GREENWOOD, and BARKER (1936) definitely oppose the idea that it may invalidate plasmolytic measurements, at least for the plant material used (*see* TABLE 30). They give the following reasons: "the magnitude of the difference [between cryoscopic and plasmolytic measurements of OP] is too great; deformation of the cell wall such as is demanded by the adhesion view is not observed; it should be impossible to observe cells in equilibrium in the condition of limiting plasmolysis, which in actual fact are seen in large numbers."

Sufficient evidence has been reported to indicate that adhesion does occur but it probably has not been a serious factor in most of the measurements made by the plasmolytic method. Actually the nature of the association between the cell wall and cytoplasm is not well understood. If, as has been suggested, the wall is a living part of the cell, there is good reason to postulate an intimate structural bond between the two. BALAZS (1943), investigating epidermal cells, believes that the fine threads connecting the separated protoplast with the wall (Chodat-Hecht filaments) are derived from the wall and not from the protoplast. Careful observation of plasmolysed onion bulb cells on the other hand indicates that these threads may be continuous with the plasmodesmata of pits and hence have an intimate relation with the protoplasmic connections normally present.

L. and M. BRAUNER (1943b) believe that there is no general explanation for the adhesion of protoplasm to walls, since various conditions may act to produce different behavior in the same material.

Of the various kinds of plants to which plasmolytic methods have been applied, the marine algae (*Phaeophyceae, Rhodophyceae*) have perhaps yielded the most unreliable data (KOTTE, 1915; HÖFLER, 1930, 1931; HOFFMAN, 1932; BUNNING, 1935). The trouble appears to lie in a relatively high permeability towards the plasmolyzing solute, in marked swelling of the wall and protoplasm, depending on the solution employed, in volume changes that are difficult to measure due to irregular shapes of cells, and in a strong adhesion of the protoplasm to the wall. According to DE ZEEUW (1939) the wall swells as plasmolysis is approached due both to release of turgor pressure, and to the imbibing of the relatively pure water passing through from the vacuole. The relationship may be more than adhesion; BUNNING (1935) states that the protoplasm may permeate from one third to one half of the wall in *Callithamnion roseum.* It is therefore not surprising that plasmolysis is injurious to these plants.

Plasmolytic Method—Experimental Procedure:— A recommended procedure for determining the limiting plasmolysis value Og of a tissue is as follows: sections of tissue are cut to such a thickness that one to four layers of intact cells remain. They are quickly distributed among graded, weight molar sucrose solutions, the concentrations of which vary by steps of 0.02 to 0.05 M. Infiltration by means of a vacuum pump will shorten the time necessary to attain equilibrium and will reduce optical difficulties. After 30 minutes (or longer, if necessary) the sections are examined microscopically for evidence of plasmolysis. The concentration range of the solutions should be chosen so that no plasmolysis occurs in the more dilute while the highest causes plasmolysis of all cells. Between the two extremes, sections will show plasmolysis of some cells, but not of others. By carefully scrutinizing 100 cells of each section under high power, and plotting the number of plasmolyzed cells against the sugar concentration, a curve may be drawn from which the concentration effecting plasmolysis of 50 per cent of the cells may be found. FIGURE 21 shows such curves. This concentration value is taken as the Og value for the section. It should be clear that it is an average value since each cell behaves somewhat differently. The degree of precision obtainable by this method can be of the order of ± 0.1 atmosphere.

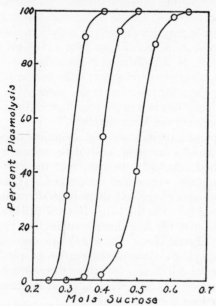

FIG. 21.—The relation between concentration of plasmolyzing solution and degree of plasmolysis. Curves showing the 50 per cent value.

The assignment of OP values to sucrose solutions may be based on: *1*) osmometric measurements (MORSE, 1914; BERKELEY and HARTLEY, 1916; FRAZER and MYRICK, 1916); *2*) vapor pressure measurements (BERKELEY, HARTLEY, and BURTON, 1919); *3*) freezing point data (Int. Crit. Tables, 1933); or *4*) formulas corrected for the anomalous behavior of aqueous sucrose solutions (*see* discussion in Chapter IV). Study of data from these four sources shows that the vapor pressure data most nearly agree with the directly measured values. Freezing point data are a close second; values calculated from concentrations require correcting, particularly above 1 molal. At concentrations below this, no great error is introduced by any of these methods. Physiologists owe a great debt of gratitude to the workers listed above who painstakingly determined by direct methods highly accurate values for the osmotic pressures of sucrose and other solutions over so wide a range of concentrations. Tables of osmotic pressure values of volume molar sucrose solutions at 20° C. may be found in MOLZ (1926) and URSPRUNG (1938, page 1275). It may be concluded from MORSE's work that while sucrose solutions do not obey the ideal gas law equation with respect to concentration, they do for temperature, at least from 0° C. to 25° C. The correction factor for plasmolytic experiments carried out at 20° C. amounts to $\frac{293.1}{273.1} = 1.073$.

DE VRIES in 1888 proposed the name isotonic coefficient to describe the relative molar amounts of substances forming isotonic solutions. Thus a molal solution of KNO₃ exhibits a greater osmotic pressure than a molal solution of sucrose. This

TABLE 24. — *Isotonic coefficients of various salts calculated on a weight molar basis. Sucrose = 1.00 (data of FITTING, 1917) : —*

SALTS TO WHICH RHOEO CELLS ARE RELATIVELY PERMEABLE			SALTS TO WHICH RHOEO CELLS ARE RELATIVELY IMPERMEABLE		
Salt	By plasmolysis	By cryoscopy	Salt	By plasmolysis	By cryoscopy
KNO₃	1.69	1.78	MgSO₄	1.05	1.1
KCl	1.74	1.84	Mg(NO₃)₂	2.54	2.55
KBr	1.14-5	1.84	Ca(NO₃)₂	2.43	2.4
KClO₂	1.73	1.75	Ba(NO₃)₂	2.23	2.22
K₂SO₄	2.27	2.36	BaCl₂	2.42	2.46
NaNO₃	1.7	1.80-2	MgCl₂	2.49	2.64
NaCl	1.71	1.84	Sr(NO₃)₂	2.35	2.43 (?)
LiNO₃	1.83 (?)	1.77-8	SrCl₂	2.49	2.55
LiCl	1.8	1.85-7	CaCl₂	2.46	2.59

results from the dissociation of the former into ions resulting in a greater number of solute particles per unit volume. With sucrose taken as one, FITTING (1917) calculated isotonic coefficients of many solutes by comparing their ability to produce limiting plasmolysis in leaf cells of *Rhoeo discolor*. TABLE 24 lists some of his values, as well as those calculated from freezing point measurement. There is good agreement in most instances. DE VRIES used this method to determine the molecular weight of raffinose.

Further Uses of Plasmolysis:— In addition to osmotic pressure measurements, the plasmolytic method may be used in permeability studies to determine the effect of solutes on the behavior of protoplasm, and as a criterion of the physiological state of cells.

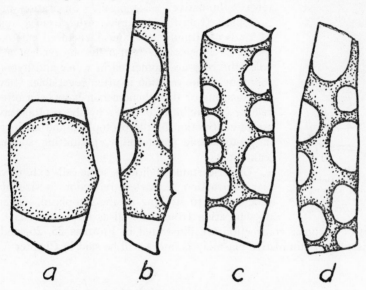

FIG. 22.—Plasmolysis types as illustrated by STRUGGER (1935). Convex plasmolysis, a; concave plasmolysis, b; "krampf" plasmolysis, c and d.

The form which the cytoplasm assumes upon contraction and separation from the wall is usually indicative of its viscosity (WEBER, 1924), which in turn may reflect other conditions in the cell. Its form is also related to the nature and concentration of solutes in the plasmolyzing solution, and often is characteristic for any one type of cell. FIGURE 22 illustrates some of the forms which have been described. *Convex* plasmolysis (FIGURE 22a) is attended by, or is the result of, low viscosity, and the separation from the wall appears to progress smoothly and without perceptible adhesion. It is generally observed in normal uninjured cells, and particularly in mature cells. *Concave* plasmolysis (FIGURE 22b) indicates a relatively high viscosity, where the separation occurs with more difficulty. The form identified as *spasmodic* ("Krampf") by the German workers (FIGURE 22c and d) is an advanced concave type which indicates an even higher viscosity. WEBER (1925) made the interesting observation that guard cells of *Vicia faba* in the closed condition exhibit a convex form when plasmolyzed, while those in the open condition showed the concave or spasmodic form.

Several forms of plasmolysis are allegedly due to differential permeability of ectoplast and tonoplast. Solutes may diffuse into the protoplasm but not into the vacuole ("Intrabilität").

In *cap* plasmolysis (FIGURE 23) the cytoplasm swells markedly at the ends of the cell, where there has been separation from the wall. This effect can be induced by using a plasmolyzing solution containing salts of K, Na or Li (HÖFLER, 1939). Calcium salts antagonize the action. In *tonoplast* plasmolysis (FIGURE 24) two or more distinct vacuolar membranes are formed. Still other types, limited to certain kinds of cells, have been described. STRUGGER (1935) is a source of literature on plasmolysis types.

Several types of response are included under the term "stimulative" plasmolysis. Separation of the protoplast from the wall may result from a number of kinds of stimuli: mechanical, chemical, photo, and thermal. Plasmolysis is usually observed at a time when the cells are immersed in water and hypotonic solutions. The reaction is often reversible. Several explanations of this phenomenon have been offered: release of imbibitional water by the protoplasm, an active contraction of the protoplast, and an increase in protoplasmic permeability, permitting solutes to leak out.

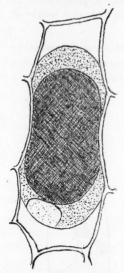

FIG. 23.—Onion epidermal cell showing cap plasmolysis. R e d r a w n from STRUGGER (1935).

Under certain conditions, some cells exhibit vacuolar contraction, a marked reduction in size of the vacuole due to swelling of the cytoplasm. There is no separation from the wall as in plasmolysis. Examples of vacuolar contraction are illustrated in FIGURES 25, 26, and 27. Of this, and of stimulative plasmolysis, more will be said in Chapter VIII.

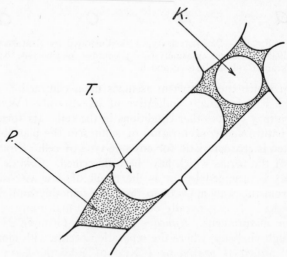

FIG. 24.—Tonoplast plasmolysis of onion epidermis. K, the hyaline, strongly swollen nucleus; P, the cytoplasm, and T, the tonoplast. (STRUGGER, 1935).

It seems obvious from this and the previous discussion of plasmolysis that the protoplasm cannot be regarded as merely a thin membrane permitting passive diffusion of water to and from the vacuole. In all experimental work with plasmolytic methods or vital staining, utmost care must be taken against unconscious injury of the cells by use of unanalysed "tap" and "distilled" water. Where cells are to endure long exposure, salt solutions should be buffered to a favorable pH value and physiologically balanced with respect to uni- and bivalent cations. Toxic solutes should be avoided as far as possible and temperature and light should be regulated to avoid injury of the cells.

While plasmolytic methods are of interest in the study of cell processes, plasmolysis is not of normal occurrence in plant tissues. There may be exceptions, *e.g.,* spore formation in certain algae (GROSS, 1940). Generally, it is considered to be injurious to cells, either by rupture of the plasmodesmata connecting them and by rupture of whatever union exists between the unpitted wall and the protoplasm, or by effecting certain colloidal changes in the protoplasm. SCARTH (1941) presents evidence that the degree to which a cell may be plasmolyzed without undue injury "is determined by the point at which an irreversible stiffening, presumably coagulation, of the protoplasm occurs," and that "the immediate cause of death is usually the rupture of the rigid ectoplasm on deplasmolysis." BENNET-CLARK and BEXON (1943) have shown that there is a rapid increase in the respiratory rate on plasmolysis of beetroot

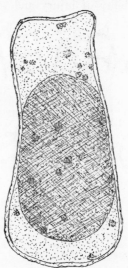

FIG. 25. — Vacuole contraction in a cell of the fruit flesh of *Ligustrum vulgare.* Redrawn from STRUGGER (1935).

cells. The question as to whether osmotic pressure determined at limiting plasmolysis could be converted to the value at normal volume merely by considering volume change has always been troublesome to the investigator. An increased respiration rate is one of the first definite indications that marked changes do occur during plasmolysis. Such a response may effect, or may be the result of, other reactions which conceivably are involved in the water balance of the cell.

Returning to the plasmolytic measurement of osmotic pressure, it can be safely stated that the anomalies discussed above are not often observed when proper precautions are taken and when suitable material is employed. As a rule, best results are obtained where the plasmolysis form is convex.

FIG. 26. — Vacuole contraction in an onion epidermal cell having the vacuole strongly stained with neutral red. Drawn from a photograph by STRUGGER (1935).

The Plasmometric Method:—Introduced by HÖFLER (1917) this procedure is adaptable to certain types of cells. The technique involves rather strong plasmolysis, followed by measurement of the respective volumes of cell and protoplast. The value of Og is obtained from the following relationship:

$$Og = OP \text{ of plasmolyzing sol.} \times \frac{\text{Vol. of protoplast}}{\text{Vol. of turgorless cell}}$$

The method is claimed to be highly accurate, and may be more suitable for single cells than the limiting plasmolysis method. However, there are certain disadvantages. Only cells of regular shape whose volume may be determined with fair accuracy are suitable. Large cells with a low protoplasm/vacuole ratio are recommended. The possibility of injury and subsequent changes due to strong plasmolysis must be considered. LEVITT and SCARTH (1936) used the plasmometric method to investigate the bound water content of hardened and unhardened cells. It is a preferred procedure in permeability studies, but may not necessarily indicate permeability in the normal state.

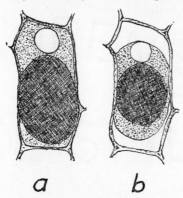

Cryoscopy:— The cryoscopic method has been widely used for indirect measurement of osmotic pressure in plants. It involves the determination of the freezing point of expressed cell sap, the osmotic pressure being directly proportional to the freezing point lowering. The important investigations of DIXON and ATKINS (1913) in England, WALTER (1931b) in Germany, and HARRIS (1934) in this country utilized this method and have contributed to its improvement.

FIG. 27.—Vacuole contraction as shown by leaf cells of *Elodea canadensis* after staining with neutral red. Unplasmolyzed cell, a; plasmolyzed, b. Redrawn from STRUGGER (1935).

The following advantages over the plasmolytic method may be noted: *1*) measurements may be made at normal cell volume; *2*) no errors due to change in permeability are encountered; *3*) changes resulting from injury due to shock are avoided; *4*) determination of average OP values of whole tissues or organs is possible; *5*) freezing point lowerings may be determined with a high degree of accuracy.

Possible errors and limitations of the method include: *1*) inherent difficulties connected with expression of plant saps. Small samples from a single tissue type are more significant than large mixed samples. With any sample, dilution of the vacuolar sap by water liberated by alteration in physical organization of colloidal matter may constitute a real limitation (NEWTON, BROWN, and MARTIN, 1926; MEYER, 1928; JACCARD and FREY-WYSSLING, 1934; ROBERTS and STYLES, 1939; KERR and ANDERSON, 1944; CURRIER, 1944a). WALTER and WEISMANN (1935) consider this not to be a source of error.—*2*) If killing is accomplished by heat, water loss from the sample may result in too great a depression.—*3*) Chemical changes such as hydrolysis, mostly enzymatic in nature, may increase the amount of osmotically active solutes. Condensation reactions or production of volatile substances might lower the osmotic concentration.—*4*) Contamination of sap by contents of vascular elements is a possible source of error.—*5*) Use of different pressures for expression of sap may give discordant results because varying amounts of water of imbibition from protoplasm and walls are included in the samples. — *6*) Filtration, and adsorption of solutes by dead cellular membranes during pressing may result in lower values. There is evidence to the contrary (*e.g.* THREN, 1934) but more information is needed.—*7*) The press metal may have a catalytic action on the sap.

When these errors are all reduced to a minimum, valuable data can be obtained by the cryoscopic method. In spite of its drawbacks it is the most practical method for measuring the osmotic pressure of bulk tissue.

Expression of Sap:— DIXON and ATKINS (1913) recommended that sap be expressed from tissues that have been frozen; if the tissue is not killed in some manner filtration of solutes by the living cell membranes may lead to low values. The successive fractions of expressed sap from untreated tissue show a progressive increase in OP. GORTNER, LAWRENCE, and HARRIS (1916) showed that while this is true for most plants, for some the concentration remains constant.

Other means of rendering the cell membranes permeable prior to sap expression are: grinding (HIBBARD and HARRINGTON, 1913; NEWTON, BROWN, and MARTIN, 1926; SAYRE and MORRIS, 1932) ; and exposure to toxic vapors (CHIBNALL, 1923; GOLDSMITH and SMITH, 1926). Heating the samples (THREN, 1934; DONEEN, 1934; MALLORY,

1934) gives satisfactory results, and in some cases may be preferred. Freezing is the method commonly employed, and the use of liquid air or dry ice is recommended. While for some plants an ice-salt bath at —15° to —20° C. is sufficient (GORTNER and HARRIS, 1914), for others such as the needles of *Pinus rigida* in the winter condition the lower temperature of dry ice is required (MEYER, 1929). BROYER (1939) has reviewed methods of sap extraction.

Hydraulic presses are commonly employed in connection with press cylinders of various design. FIGURE 28 shows a semi-micro press cylinder useful in expressing sap in volumes of 0.5 to 5.0 ml. In order to gain the desired precision, the magnitude of

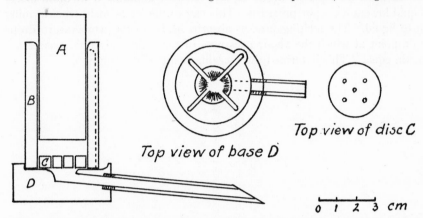

FIG. 28.—Press cylinder outfit used to express small amounts of sap from plant tissue. From CURRIER (1943), modified after BROYER and FURNSTAL (1941).

the pressure used should be known within narrow limits. This has special significance in dealing with cells where the proportion of cell wall and protoplasm to vacuole is high. The possibility of imbibed water diluting the expressed sap was considered by MOSEBACH (1936) to be a major error in cryoscopic investigations of certain brown and red marine algae. Pressures should be expressed in common units, as pounds per square inch, based on the area of the press cylinder. Pressures of 10,000 to 16,000 pounds per square inch are recommended.

The Cryoscope:— Various cryoscope designs are available. The German workers have preferred the BURIAN-DRUCKER (1909) apparatus, which accommodates 1.5 ml. of sap, and the DRUCKER-SCHREINER (1913) adapted for small volumes (about 0.005 ml.). The latter is less accurate and not as generally useful as the first. FIGURE 29 shows a semi-micro cryoscope accommodating 0.5 to 1.0 ml. of liquid. MOSEBACH (1940) designed an apparatus which employs a fraction of a drop of sap obtained from succulent tissue without pressing. The sap is frozen in a capillary tube, and the melting point is accurately observed by means of a horizontal microscope. Where larger amounts of sap are available (15-25 ml.) the standard method described in manuals of physical chemistry is suitable. With this a differential thermometer of the Beckman type, or a Haidenhain thermometer with a fixed zero point may be employed.

All of the above apparatus depends upon a mercury thermometer for determination of the freezing point. Another method employs the thermoelectric principle, and several designs are available (DIXON, 1911; HERRICK, 1934). In this procedure a fine wire thermocouple consisting of two kinds of metal is inserted into the solution, another is held in a reference liquid at constant temperature. The difference in temperature causes current to flow through the circuit and this is measured by a sensitive galvanometer.

Where freezing points of "living" tissues are to be determined the thermocouple has been preferred. However, because the thermocouple point requires rupture of cells, whereby the needle is flooded with sap from a limited number of cells which freezes ahead of the uninjured cells, WALTER and WEISMANN (1935) claim that a mercury thermometer inserted into a relatively dry cavity in the tissue gives a truer freezing point value. Regardless of which method is employed, the data obtained in the freezing of "living" tissues is difficult to interpret. This problem is further considered in Chapter VIII.

MAIR, GLASGOW, and ROSSINI (1941) successfully employed a platinum resistance thermometer for measuring freezing points of hydrocarbons. Their paper should be consulted for discussion of the theoretical aspects of freezing point measurements.

Physical Principles:— The principle involved in the cryoscopic method is that the presence of a solute lowers the vapor pressure (and diffusion pressure) of a solvent. Since the vapor pressure of water is equal to that of ice when both phases are in equilibrium, the addition of a solute to the liquid lowers its vapor pressure. This causes the ice to melt, transforming it to liquid. The melting process absorbs heat and the temperature drops to a point at which the vapor pressures of the solid and liquid phases are again equal. This is termed the freezing point of the solution.

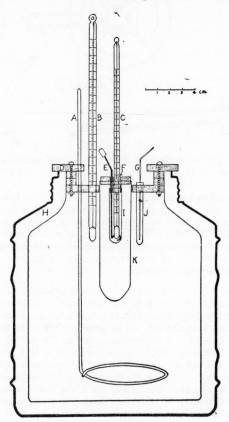

FIG. 29.—Construction of cryoscopic apparatus. The insulated vessel H is fitted with a top D with holes drilled to receive a heavy wire stirrer A, an ordinary thermometer B to record bath temperature, a glass air jacket K, and a small glass tube I closed at one end, in which a piece of capillary tubing G containing water may be frozen. Within the air jacket the sample tube I is held in place by a cork fitted with holes to receive the freezing point thermometer C and a fine wire stirrer E, as well as a small hole F for inserting the frozen capillary to initiate crystallization.

Raoult's law states that the vapor pressure of water is lowered in proportion to the mol fraction of solute added.

$$\frac{p_0 - p}{p} = \frac{n_2}{n_1 + n_2} \qquad (4)$$

where p_0 and p are the vapor pressure of pure solvent and solution and n_1 is the number of mols of solvent containing n_2 mols of solute.

Vapor pressure: temperature curves of dilute solutions are approximately parallel with those of pure water. Therefore, for dilute solutions

$$\frac{T_0 - T}{p_0 - p} = a \text{ constant } (K) \tag{5}$$

where T_0 and T are the freezing temperatures of pure solvent and solution. If $\frac{T_0 - T}{K}$ be substituted for $p_0 - p$ in Raoult's law, then

$$\frac{T_0 - T}{K p_0} = \frac{n_2}{n_1 + n_2} \tag{6}$$

or

$$T_0 - T = K p_0 \frac{n_2}{n_1 + n_2} \tag{7}$$

For dilute aqueous solutions K has been determined to be $1.86°$ C. per mol of undissociated solute. Where the solute is an electrolyte, dissociation into ions increases the total number of particles, each of which has an equal effect in lowering the vapor pressure of the solvent. Since the ratio of the number of solute particles to the number of solvent particles is the important factor in determining the freezing point of the solution, electrolytes are more effective than nonelectrolytes. It has been noted earlier that a molal solution of KNO_3 has a much lower freezing point than has a molal sucrose solution; if ionization were complete, and other factors did not interfere, the lowering would be twice as great. Before the introduction of the activity concept, freezing point determinations were used to measure the so-called "degree of ionization." More recently they are used to measure activities, the discrepancy between theoretical and actual measured activity being ascribed to the influence of intermolecular force fields upon the escaping tendency of the molecules.

Conversion of the freezing-point lowering of a solution to osmotic pressure values at $0°$ C. is easily accomplished by the following relation:

$$OP = \frac{\Delta}{1.86} \cdot 22.4 \tag{8}$$

or

$$OP = 12.04 \, \Delta \tag{9}$$

where $\Delta =$ freezing-point depression.

Lewis (1908) offers the more accurate form of this equation

$$OP = 12.06 \, \Delta - 0.021 \, \Delta^2 \tag{10}$$

which has been used by Harris and Gortner (1914) and Harris (1915) to compile a table of values convenient for converting freezing point data to osmotic pressures. In correcting for change in osmotic pressure from $0°$ to, for example, $20°$ C., the assumption is made that expressed tissue saps, like sucrose solutions, obey the gas law for change in temperature. The validity of this assumption is of special importance where the sap is high in colloids.

Freezing-Point Determination:— The procedure generally used for determining the freezing point of expressed sap is as follows. The sap is placed in a small tube, and a thermometer is inserted with the bulb immersed, together with a small wire stirrer. This tube is placed within another larger tube, providing a dead air space to preclude too rapid cooling. The jacket tube is now immersed in a freezing mixture, usually ice and salt, and the temperature of the sample slowly falls; stirring is continuous. Upon crystallization, the mercury column rises abruptly, steadies, remains constant for a short time, then falls slowly. The plateau, or highest temperature reached is recorded as the observed freezing point. Crystallization at temperatures below the freezing point can be readily induced by introducing the tip of a fine glass capillary containing ice into the solution.

The value so obtained is not the true freezing point, because of (*a*) supercooling of the solution, and (*b*) absorption of heat by the apparatus. HARRIS and GORTNER (1914) proposed a correction for the supercooling. Since crystallization usually begins at a temperature lower than the true freezing point, the liquid phase at the observed freezing point, in equilibrium with the ice crystals, is more concentrated than it would be at the true freezing point. Since one eightieth of the weight of water solidifies per degree of undercooling,

$$\frac{\left(V - \dfrac{uV}{80}\right)\Delta^1}{V} = \Delta \tag{11}$$

or

$$\Delta = \Delta^1 - 0.0125\ u\ \Delta^1 \tag{12}$$

where Δ^1 and Δ = observed and true freezing point depressions, V = volume of solution, and u = number of degrees of undercooling. This correction has been widely used in cryoscopy. If undercooling can be avoided by salting with ice crystals, jarring, etc., the correction is unnecessary.

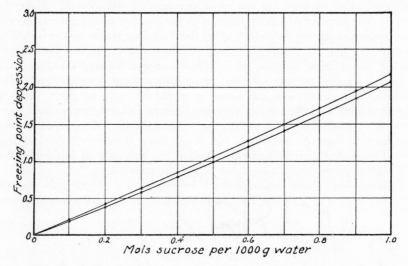

Fig. 30.—Calibration curve for the apparatus shown in figure 29. The lower curve was constructed from data from the International Critical Tables (1933); the upper curve presents the observed values.

An approximate correction for heat capacity effects may also be calculated if the following values are known: *1*) the weight and heat capacity of glass sample tube, thermometer, and stirrer in contact with the solution; *2*) volume of solution; *3*) temperature at which freezing begins; *4*) temperature of bath; and *5*) observed freezing point. The heat capacity effect is small and the correction unnecessary where the volume of solution is large in comparison with the volume of the thermometer and glass. For small amounts the error may be serious.

By use of a modified procedure (CURRIER, 1944*b*), it has been found possible to eliminate these two corrections. The semimicro apparatus (FIGURE 29) was standardized by recording the observed freezing points of carefully prepared molal sucrose solutions, ranging in concentration from 0.1 M to 1.0 M in steps of 0.1 M, and comparing them with the accurately known theoretical values (Int. Crit. Tables, 1933). The results of this comparison are shown in FIGURE 30. By referring an observed value to this graph, the corrected value may be obtained at once. The increasing discrepancy between Δ obs. and Δ corr., as the solutions become more concentrated, is not due to supercooling effects as the correction for supercooling, when calculated according to HARRIS and GORTNER's formula, remains at about 0.01° C. for all concentrations. The probable explanation is that with increasingly concentrated solutions a greater amount of heat is lost to the system because crystallization is slower, and the time required to reach the apparent freezing point is longer. WALTER (1931*a*) recommended that in the cryoscopic determination the amount of supercooling be constant and approximately 1° C. This procedure requires a preliminary trial to determine where freezing must begin to be 1° C. below the freezing point.

As proof of the validity of correcting observed freezing point values as described, freezing curves, such as that shown in FIGURE 31, were constructed according to the recommendations of MAIR, GLASGOW, and ROSSINI (1941). Extrapolation of the part of the curve where thermodynamic equilibrium exists between the solid and liquid phases of the system, back to the initial downward part of the curve, gives a close approximation of the true freezing point. The above authors point out that in a strict sense the true freezing point is slightly higher than this, but they have proved that the difference is insignificant when the amount of supercooling is small in comparison with the head of temperature (difference between the temperature of freezing bath and that of the test solution). With a head of 10° to 15° C., this error was found to be insignificant in the determinations made as described. True freezing points of both sucrose solutions and beet juice, obtained by plotting freezing curves, agree with those corrected by means of the calibration curve of FIGURE 30.

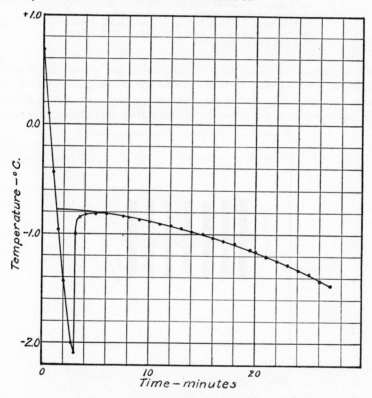

FIG. 31.—Freezing curve constructed according to recommendations of MAIR, GLASGOW, and ROSSINI (1941). Extrapolation of the latter portion back to the initial downward line gives a close approximation of the true freezing point of the solution.

In dealing with plant saps of high viscosity, separation of ice may occur more slowly, resulting in a slower rise of the mercury column and a greater proportion of heat lost to the system. Under these circumstances a calibration curve prepared by use of sucrose may not be valid. The error would likewise not be corrected by use of the formula for supercooling. Where doubt exists, comparison of freezing curves like that of FIGURE 31 with similar curves for sucrose solution will indicate the error involved.

Vapor Pressure Methods:— A unique method for determining osmotic pressure is the vapor pressure method devised by BARGER (1904, 1924) for the purpose of calculating molecular weights, and adapted by HALKET (1913) to plant saps. Small glass capillaries of uniform bore are prepared, and into them are drawn, first, a droplet of unknown (sap), followed by an air space, then by a droplet of sucrose solution of known concentration, and so on. Each tube then contains alternating layers of sap, air, sugar solution, air, sap, etc. (FIGURE 32). The tubes are sealed in

FIG. 32.—The Barger Halket method for determining the osmotic pressure of plant sap. Capillary tubes contain alternate columns of standard sucrose solutions and sap. In this figure the black columns represent stock solution, the clear columns sap. Each tube contains stock solution of a different concentration.

a flame and mounted on a slide. Several tubes are prepared for each determination, each varying with respect to the concentration of the sugar solution. By means of a binocular microscope and micrometer, the length of the sap columns is measured before and after equilibrium has been at-

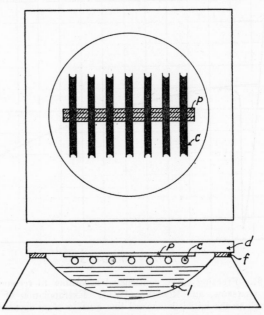

FIG. 33.—Osmotic pressure determination by the method of URSPRUNG and BLUM (1930). Standard reference solutions are contained in capillary tubes c, attached to a cover glass d by plastic cement p. The cover glass with attached capillaries is sealed on top of a shallow dish by grease f. The depression in the dish contains the expressed sap I.

tained. The results are placed on a graph, and that concentration that produces no change in the length of the sap columns is considered to be isotonic with the sap, *i.e.,* having equal vapor pressure and osmotic pressure. The method depends upon the diffusion of water vapor through air, which acts like a semi-permeable membrane. Though the method is tedious and subject to error from mixing of the droplets and movement of films along the walls of the capillaries, it is useful where only small volumes of sap are available. WILDERVANCK (1932) preferred it over other methods for determining the osmotic pressure of *Nitella translucens* sap.

Modifications of this method are described by SIGNER (1930) and by BERL, *et al.* (1930). The capillary method of URSPRUNG and BLUM (1930) differs in that the expressed sap or other solution to be investigated is placed in the shallow depression of a small moisture chamber, and that the standard reference solutions are contained in a series of capillaries attached to an upper glass cover (FIGURE 33). Technical details may be found in the original paper.

Procedures have been perfected for measuring osmotic pressure thermoelectrically, based upon differences in vapor pressure between the solution to be investigated and some standard reference solution (HILL, 1930; BALDES and JOHNSON, 1939). Either a sensitive thermopile or thermocouple is used, and very small amounts of liquid can be investigated. The principle involved (*cf.* BALDES, 1939) is that differences in temperature between the two droplets under standard conditions for evaporation can be measured by a delicate galvanometer. This reading is converted to vapor pressure or osmotic pressure by standardizing the apparatus with known solutions. ROEPKE (1942) has provided refinements in apparatus and method.

Osmometric Methods:— Direct determination of osmotic pressure by means of osmometers is not particularly adaptable to plant saps. BOURDILLON (1939) describes a micro apparatus utilizing a flat horizontal membrane, which will accommodate as little as 0.2 cc. of protein solution in concentrations down to 0.025 mm. BLEGEN and BRANDT REHBERG (1938) used specially prepared collodion tubes. Results compared well with HILL's vapor pressure method. Ordinarily osmometric procedures are successful only where the sample is a fairly pure colloidal solution, where significant amounts of dissolved electrolytes are absent. LEVITT (1946) has investigated the colloid osmotic pressure of proteins extracted from potato tuber tissue in this manner.

Other Methods for Osmotic Pressure:— The "simplified" or "minimum cell volume" method, designed by URSPRUNG (1923), consists of measuring the change in length of strips of tissue immersed in solutions (usually sucrose) of varying concentration. The lowest concentration of sugar that produces minimum length is considered to be isotonic with the cell sap at limiting plasmolysis. There are two serious objections to the method. First, it is not valid to assume that a tissue strip in equilibrium with the most dilute solution effecting "minimum cell volume" is in a condition of limiting plasmolysis. There is assumed to be a point, as the concentration is increased, where shrinkage ceases, and volume remains constant. TABLE 25 shows, however, that within the concentration range used, potato tissue may continue to shrink with increasing concentration of the bathing solution. Although a constant condition is approached, the fact that higher and higher concentrations are capable of causing reduction in imbibition of the walls indicates that the method cannot produce highly accurate results. On the other hand the simplified method is a valuable means of determining DPD values at normal volume (see later).

The second objection is that change in length of a tissue is not always a true indication of change in volume. Many strips exhibit distortion

TABLE 25. — *Change in volume of potato tuber tissue cylinders immersed 8 hours in sucrose solutions of varying concentration at 20-22° C. Values are based on normal volume* (CURRIER, 1943) : —

CONC. OF SOLUTION	PER CENT CHANGE
Tap water	+12.4
0.1 M	+ 6.5
0.2	+ 3.4
0.3	+ 0.8
0.4	— 9.6
0.5	—19.5*
0.6	—21.9
0.7	—27.6
0.8	—33.0
1.0	—33.6

* All cells plasmolyzed at this point.

when permitted to swell or to shrink. Especially is this true of epidermis with its cuticle on one side. That of *Sedum nicaense* has been shown to decrease in the two surface dimensions upon swelling (increase in total volume) in water. TABLE 26 shows the measurements.

TABLE 26. — *Changes in dimensions of epidermal strips from Sedum nicaense leaves. Values are arbitrary units* (CURRIER, 1943) : —

NORMAL			SATURATED			INCIP. PLASMOL.		
L	W	D	L	W	D	L	W	D
7.75	4.00	1.01	7.30	3.90	1.35	7.70	4.00	0.84
9.21	4.21	0.90	8.86	4.00	1.24	9.00	4.10	0.73
10.85	2.14	1.00	10.78	2.08	1.37	10.70	2.14	0.81
5.71	2.36	...	5.85	2.43	...	5.85	2.50	...
6.94	2.00	...	6.85	2.07	...	6.78	2.14	...

L = Length; W = Width; D = Depth or thickness.

The simplified method may theoretically be extended to measurement of all three osmotic quantities in the following manner. Letting O = osmotic pressure of the tissue, DPD = diffusion pressure deficit of water in the tissue, T = turgor pressure of the tissue, V = volume of the tissue, and the subscripts g = limiting plasmolysis, n = normal state, and s = water saturation, the following relations should be valid.

$$Og = OP \text{ of plasmolyticum causing minimum volume} \tag{13}$$

$$On = Og \cdot \frac{Vg}{Vn} \tag{14}$$

$$Os = Og \cdot \frac{Vg}{Vs} \tag{15}$$

$$DPDg = Og \tag{16}$$

$$DPDn = On - Tn = OP \text{ of plasmolyticum causing no change in Vn} \tag{17}$$

$$DPDs = zero \tag{18}$$

$$Tg = zero \tag{19}$$

$$Tn = Ts \cdot \frac{(Vn - Vg)}{(Vs - Vg)} = On - DPDn \tag{20}$$

$$Ts = Os \tag{21}$$

This method proves convenient for rapid estimation of approximate values for these states of a given tissue.

The Magnitude and Variation of Osmotic Pressure in Plants:—
To secure quantitative data relative to the role of osmotic pressure in plant
functions, and in plant distribution, an enormous number of measurements
have been made. Many were obtained by plasmolytic methods, especially
where it was necessary to work with single cells. The cryoscopic procedure has been preferred by ecologists, since it is more adaptable to field
conditions and because average values of plant organs and whole plants are
more easily obtained. In such studies, osmotic pressure data are used as a
criterion of the plant's ability to withdraw water from the soil, and to retain it against the evaporative capacity of the atmosphere. For reasons
already presented, neither the plasmolytic nor cryoscopic method is without
objection. The former indicates the absorptive capacity at limiting plasmolysis only; the latter must rely on total expressed sap with the obvious
associated errors. In both, the normal turgor pressure is unknown. It
would appear that the simplified method theoretically would be expected
to give the most valuable ecological data, but from a practical viewpoint the
cryoscopic procedure is to be preferred.

Osmotic pressures of plant tissues have been found to vary from values
of around one atmosphere to an extreme of 202.5 atm. reported for the
expressed sap of *Atriplex confertifolia,* growing in an alkali region of
Utah (HARRIS, 1934, p. 70). The sap contained 67.33 grams of chloride
per liter. However, most mesophytes exhibit concentrations within the
range of 5 to 30 atmospheres. Desert species yield higher, hydrophytes
usually lower values than mesophytes. It should be stated that these generalizations represent averages or trends. Exceptions must be expected because of the multiplicity of factors exerting an effect on sap concentration.

Contiguous cells, even in a homogeneous tissue, may not have identical
cell sap concentrations. Regardless of protoplasmic connections, each cell
maintains a structural and functional individuality, reflected in one way by
the osmotic pressure of its contents. Plasmolytic studies clearly demonstrate this fact; all cells do not reach incipient plasmolysis simultaneously,
but Og values distribute themselves in a typical S-shaped curve (FIGURE
21). It is usually found that Og values are greater for small than for large
cells within a single tissue.

Gradients of osmotic pressure have been reported within individual
tissues. While such gradients may be real, they are constantly changing,
and may even reverse in direction due to seasonal and diurnal changes and
to environmental and internal factors.

URSPRUNG and BLUM (1916a) reported a radial gradient in the cortical region of *Helleborus foetidus* root, and in xylem parenchyma of *Fagus
sylvatica* stem, the Og values increasing toward the center. Vertical gradients were found in the stem of *Urtica dioica,* Og increasing from tip to base
for all tissues. A gradient decreasing downwardly was reported for root
tissues of *Helleborus, Urtica,* and *Fagus.*

There may be considerable variation in osmotic pressure among the tissues composing an organ. The distribution of Og values among leaf tissues
assumes the following pattern: palisade parenchyma > spongy parenchyma
> upper epidermis > lower epidermis (URSPRUNG and BLUM, 1916a;
BUHMANN, 1935).

URSPRUNG and BLUM found for root tissues of *Helleborus, Urtica* and
Fagus highest Og values in xylem and phloem parenchyma, and in companion cells; lowest in the outer cortical region and epidermis.

In nonwoody stems of *Helleborus* and *Urtica,* minimum values appeared in epidermis, cortex, and pith, with highest values in xylem and phloem parenchyma, companion cells, and cambium. Woody twigs (*Fagus*) showed highest concentrations in xylem parenchyma cells, lowest in phloem parenchyma.

Averages of values exhibited by leaf, stem, and root tissues of four plants are shown in TABLE 27. Figures represent "osmotic values," *i.e.,* number of mols of KNO_3 (per liter of solution) isotonic with the cell sap at incipient plasmolysis. (Note, however, remarks concerning KNO_3 as a plasmolyzing agent, page 82).

TABLE 27. — *Osmotic pressure of various tissues determined plasmolytically, expressed as mols of KNO_3 per liter of solution. Data of* URSPRUNG *and* BLUM (1916a). *For conversion to atmospheres, osmotic pressure values of KNO_3 solutions* (URSPRUNG, 1938, p. 1290) *are included:* —

	Helleborus	Urtica	Fagus	Sedum acre
Epidermis	.484	.473	.371	.278
Spongy parenchyma	.575	.635	.571	} .330
Palisade parenchyma	.871	1.015	1.017	
Outer cortex	.522	.472	.671	.348
Inner cortex	.532	.495	.679	.377
Phloem parenchyma	...	.518	.573	...
Companion cells	.577	.556	.722	.492
Cambium	.558	.548	.634	.411
Xylem parenchyma	.567	.59	.983	.495
Pith	.521	.471	...	...
Rays, cortex	...	...	.869	...
Rays, wood	...	...	.938	...

KNO_3 solutions at 20° C. : —

Concentration volume molar	OP atm.	Concentration volume molar	OP atm.
0.1	4.3	0.7	27.0
0.2	8.3	0.8	30.5
0.3	12.3	0.9	33.9
0.4	16.1	1.0	37.2
0.5	19.8	1.1	40.4
0.6	23.4	1.2	43.5

Sap contained in the conducting elements of the xylem is very dilute. MAXIMOV (1929a, p. 54) reports osmotic pressures in root sap (exudate) of *Xanthium strumarium, Impatiens balsamina,* and *Zea mays* of 0.67, 0.36, and 1.46 atm. respectively. VAN OVERBEEK (1942) recorded 0.42 atm. for the initial exudate of decapitated "low salt" tomato plants, 1.32 atm. for "high salt" plants. The dry matter content of xylem exudate of squash was found to vary between 0.102 and 0.23 per cent (CRAFTS, 1936). STOCK-ING (1945) determined a value of 1.9 atm. for this plant growing in culture solution. CRAFTS (1932) found an average of 7.0 atm. in the phloem exudate of pumpkin and cucumber.

Variation of osmotic pressure among different organs of plants has been studied. Values exhibited by leaves generally exceed those of roots (HANNIG, 1912; DIXON and ATKINS, 1916); older leaves exceed young leaves (DIXON and ATKINS, 1912; KORSTIAN, 1924; GAIL and CONE, 1929). Illuminated leaves show a higher OP than those growing in the shade (DIXON and ATKINS, 1912; LUTMAN, 1919; HALMA and HAAS,

1928; MARSH, 1941). Fruit tree leaves exhibit a higher OP than the immature fruits (CHANDLER, 1914).

With respect to average osmotic pressures of entire plants, individuals of unlike species growing under the same environmental conditions may display significant differences in sap concentration (HARRIS, 1934).

In general, a decrease in osmotic pressure is expected in the sequence trees, shrubs, herbs (HARRIS and LAWRENCE, 1916). Winter annuals show a decrease over perennial herbs. Succulents and hydrophytes are characterized by rather low, xerophytes by high sap concentrations; mesophytes lie between (MAXIMOV, 1929a, p. 274).

Many studies have dealt with the effect of environmental factors on osmotic pressure. Any change or condition leading to the development of a water deficit in the plant is generally attended by an increase in sap concentration. The OP tends to vary directly with the concentration of the soil solution, and is increased by those factors which cause the plant to transpire at a greater rate.

The cell sap concentration of leaves generally varies from a maximum in the early afternoon to a minimum in the early morning hours (STODDART, 1935; MARSH, 1940). The rise during the daytime is due both to photosynthetic activity and to increasing water deficit within the leaves. Such fluctuations are less pronounced in roots than in aerial organs.

In addition to diurnal variation, plants show annual or seasonal fluctuations in OP. In some—certain conifers for example—the sap concentration may be higher during the winter months (GAIL, 1926; MEYER, 1928). In others, a maximum is reached in the summer (MALLERY, 1934). According to MARSH (1940), the osmotic pressure of lowland prairie species which he examined increased during the growing season about one half over that at early summer; for upland species the concentration doubled or tripled.

The variation in osmotic pressure as a result of extended water deficit may be very great. GASSER (1942) used the limiting plasmolytic method to determine the direction and extent of changes in Og of detached plant organs (mainly leaves) placed under conditions which permitted slow water loss. In an extreme instance, cells of the terrestrial alga *Trentepohlia aurea* increased in Og from 123.4 atm. to 291.4 atm. in 33 days. Out of 95 plant species, 69 indicated a rise of 15 to 223 per cent of the initial value. The rest either showed no change or a slight decrease. Where a condition of water excess was induced by placing the leaves in moist air, 72 out of 87 plants exhibited a decrease in Og, within a range of 5.3 to 66 per cent of the initial value.

The changes in Og (the author uses Sz_g) are ascribed to processes embraced by the term *osmotic regulation,* wherein the solute concentration varies due to hydrolysis or synthesis of polysaccharides, and by exosmosis or endosmosis of solutes. The responses shown can possibly be attributed in some degree to plastic stretching or shrinking of the walls which were not conclusively shown to be inoperative. However, it is not unlikely that other factors, as suggested by the author, are primarily responsible for the changes observed.

Diffusion Pressure Deficit. Methods of Measuring DPD: — The diffusion pressure deficit of the water in plant cells is a measure of the ability of those cells to absorb water. Its value may be measured directly, or it may be obtained by difference if the osmotic and turgor pressures of the cells are known. When TP = zero, as at limiting plasmolysis, OP = DPD, but at all other states the hydrostatic pressure or turgor of the cells lowers the DPD of the water in the cells. At full turgor, or what is termed water saturation, the diffusion pressure of water in the cell sap is equal to that of pure water at the same temperature, and the DPD = zero. Cells in the normal state are neither at full turgor nor at limiting plasmolysis; procedures employed in estimating DPD must be applicable to cells in a state of partial turgor. The following methods have been used in DPD measurements. In all of them, the water absorbing power of cells, tissues, or organs is balanced by various means, such that there is no change in size, weight, turgor, or vapor pressure.

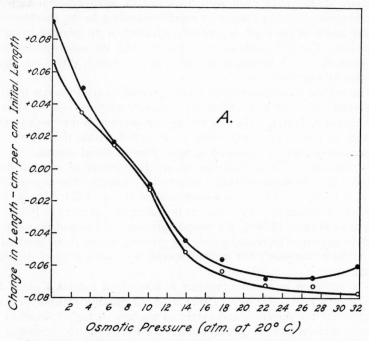

Fig. 34A.— Diffusion pressure deficit values determined by the volume method. (Meyer and Wallace, 1941).

The Cell Method:— Although the idea was suggested by de Vries (1884), this method was first employed in actual measurements by Ursprung and Blum (1916b). A thin section of tissue, a bit of thin leaf, or any cells that may be observed under the microscope may be used. The tissue is placed in paraffin oil on a slide to prevent evaporation of water. One or more cells are selected, and their surface outlines are drawn on paper by means of a camera lucida. The tissue is then placed in sucrose solutions of varying concentration until one is found in which the cells do not change in volume. The OP of the solution causing no change in volume is recorded as equivalent to the DPD of the cells.

This method has certain weaknesses. Ernest (1931) has pointed out that upon removing a tissue section from a plant organ, a change in equilibrium conditions occurs and volume measurements may become invalid. In fact, gradients in DPD may be reversed due to changing intercellular pressures and to the osmotic effect of sap liberated by sectioning on the cells. She further demonstrated that water-saturated tissue, on sectioning, can absorb yet more water due to partial removal of intercellular pressure. Thus DPD values measured may be too high. Ernest (1931, 1934a, b) used an epidermal strip method, whereby intact mesophyll cells adhere to the epidermis, and found leaves of *Iris* and *Crocus,* among others, to be suitable material. It has been pointed out by Oppenheimer (1936), however, that even here there is a release of intercellular pressure. This author (1930a, 1932a, b) further criticises the cell method. Volume changes are difficult to detect and are often so small as to be insignificant within the range of experimental error. Changes in the three dimensions are often disproportional, so that volumes determined by surface measurements are erroneous.

It therefore appears that values obtained by this method and reported in the literature are open to some question.

Strip or Simplified Method:— The advantage of the strip method (URSPRUNG, 1923) is that the measurement embraces hundreds of cells and is more successful in estimating the average DPD of organs. Tissue strips in size approximately 20 mm. long and 2 mm. wide are removed from leaves, stems, or fleshy storage organs. Filaments and slender roots are cut into suitable lengths. Vascular elements should not run parallel or at right angles. The length of the sections in paraffin oil is immediately determined by means of a microscope and a stage micrometer; the strips are then transferred to a series of sugar solutions. The DPD of the water in the tissue is

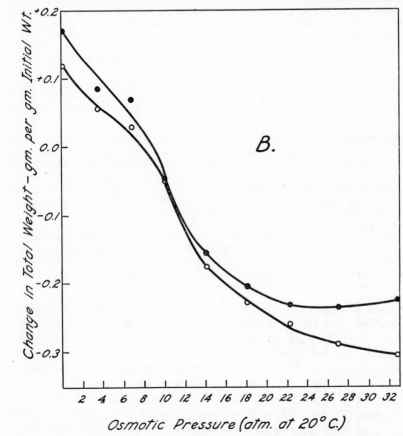

FIG. 34B.— Diffusion pressure deficit values determined by the weight method. (MEYER and WALLACE, 1941).

equivalent to the OP of that solution which effects no change in length. Usually 30 to 45 minutes is sufficient time; often 5 to 10 minutes is enough.

A simple modification of the above method is useful where massive tissues are studied (LYON, 1936). Cylinders of tissue 5 to 10 mm. in diameter and several centimeters long are removed from organs by means of a cork borer, and are immediately measured for length by means of a binocular dissecting microscope fitted with an ocular micrometer. They are then distributed among sucrose solutions of varying concentration. After several hours, the solution in which the cylinders show no change in length is assumed to be equal in DPD to the tissue. In place of tissue cylinders, square sticks may be used, prepared by means of a double-bladed knife (LYON, 1940). Check strips are kept in paraffin oil.

Instead of measuring length changes, volumes may be determined by an immersion method. Cylinders of tissue upon removal from organs are immediately immersed in calibrated glass tubes partially filled with sugar solutions. A diameter of 10 mm. is a convenient size for the tubes. The sugar solutions are in a graded series of known concentrations and temperature is held constant. The difference in liquid level before and after immersion of the cylinder is recorded as the initial volume of each cylinder. The cylinders are next transferred to larger volumes of the same solutions and are permitted to come to equilibrium, the time being related to the diameter. For beetroot cylinders 9 mm. in diameter and 28 mm. long, 8 hours were found to be sufficient (CURRIER, 1943). The cylinders are then freed of excess moisture, and their volumes again determined. Absence of any change in volume is assumed to mean that the cylinder is immersed in a sucrose solution equivalent to the DPD of water in the tissue. If such a solution is not included, a graph may be prepared from which a fairly accurate estimate of the DPD may be made. Errors due to non-uniform swelling of the tissue are eliminated by this immersion method.

Change in volume of a tissue piece may be affected by intercellular air. Increase in turgor reduces the size of the intercellular spaces, as evidenced by the escape of gas bubbles. Thus, the actual change in cell volume would be greater than that indicated by tissue measurements. Similarly, the spaces might increase in size on shrinkage of the tissue, giving low values. There should be no error in DPD measurements where no, or only slight, volume change occurs.

While the simplified or strip method involves fewer errors than the cell method, there remain the difficulties due to removal of intercellular pressure at the cut surfaces, and the low order of volume change of some tissues due to inelastic walls. The suitability of each tissue must be determined in advance.

The Weight Method:— This method involves the same principle, that is a sugar concentration is sought which produces neither gain nor loss in weight of water by the tissue. A major source of error is in reproducing comparable conditions of surface moisture at the time of weighing the tissue pieces. Also, any surface active material released from cut or injured cells that reduces the surface tension of the sugar solutions to a point where wetting of the intercellular capillary spaces takes place will introduce an error. This infiltration can be quite significant under some conditions (ASHBY and WOLF, 1947).

MEYER and WALLACE (1941) found that the volume method (based on change in length) and the weight method gave practically the same results when applied to potato tuber tissue (FIGURE 34). Also that permeation of sugar into or loss of solutes from the tissues at concentrations near the DPD were insignificant, and even at other concentrations were not sufficient to change the trend of results.

Other Methods for DPD:— STOCKING (1945) devised a procedure for studying the DPD of water in tissues of intact plants growing in the field. Using squash plants, he injected sugar solutions of known concentrations into the hollow petioles of leaves of comparable size and age. At periodic intervals thereafter he withdrew small samples of the solutions and determined their concentrations using an Abbé hand refractometer. Not only could he measure the DPD of water in the tissues at a given time, but he could follow changes throughout a considerable period, dependent mainly upon the volume of solution that could be held by the hollow petiole. From his data he determined the diurnal trend in water deficit in the leaves and calculated tensions in the xylem that corresponded to these. Values varying between 0.2 and 9.1 atm. were calculated.

A method for examining the DPD or water absorbing power of relatively intact root tissue is credited to SABININ (1925). When plants growing in water culture are excised above the root they usually exhibit exudation as a result of the phenomenon termed "root pressure." If sucrose or mannitol is dissolved in the solution surrounding the roots, exudation ceases and if a potometer is affixed to the bleeding stem it will be found that the movement of water through the root may be reversed. By carefully adjusting the concentration of the bathing solution until movement ceases entirely, a value will be obtained that might be considered in equilibrium with the DPD of the root system. However, VAN OVERBEEK (1942) has shown by cryoscopic determination of the osmotic concentration of the exudate and of the bathing solution that an active mechanism may be involved, amounting to as much as 71 per cent of the average root pressure (*see also* Chapter IX, page 150). WHITE (1938) also postulates an active component in absorption of water by roots. Probably the method is more valuable in studies on the physiological activity of roots than in osmotic pressure or DPD determinations.

Several other techniques have been employed in DPD measurements:

a) Hard leaf method (URSPRUNG and BLUM, 1927). This method is adapted to such structures as sclerophyllous leaves, conifer needles, grass leaves, and horsetails. Changes in thickness instead of length are determined.

b) Lever method (URSPRUNG and BLUM, 1930). A modification of the above; changes in thickness are indicated by a delicate pointer.

c) Tissue tension (DE VRIES, 1884). Release of tension on splitting a growing shoot tip produces a curvature which can be sketched on paper (LIVINGSTON, 1906) or projected (BOUILLENNE, 1932).

d) "Schlieren" method (ARCICHOVSKIJ and OSSIPOV, 1931*a*), whereby the concentration of the reference solution is balanced against that of the plant sap so that their refractive indices are the same. This method is designed for use on growing stems.

e) Potometer method (NORDHAUSEN, 1921; ARCICHOVSKIJ and others, 1931). In this a reference solution is brought into contact with the tissue being studied and change in volume is registered on a potometer tube. This method is adapted to measuring the DPD of water in tissues of attached stems.

f) Vapor pressure methods. Here the vapor pressure of water in the air in a small enclosed chamber is regulated such that there is no change in volume of a tissue piece (usually area or length is measured) (URSPRUNG and BLUM, 1930; RENNER, 1932) ; or weight (ARCICHOVSKIJ and ARCICHOVSKAJA, 1931) of cells. The difficulties inherent in the method are related to temperature control of the apparatus and the rather long duration of time required for equilibrium. If the tissue is weighed, condensation of water in the intercellular spaces may give trouble.

Methods for DPD determination in intact organs and whole plants will be discussed in more detail in Chapter IX.

The Magnitude and Fluctuation of DPD Values:— Diffusion pressure deficit values lie in the same general range as that found for osmotic pressures. The latter are commonly employed as an index of maximum or potential DPD's which can be developed in cells. Although in most cells the DPD should not ordinarily exceed the OP, instances have been reported where this seemed to be true. PISEK and CARTELLIERI (1931) noted such a result in leaves of several plants, and for the most part in the afternoon. In their opinion, the simplified method, used for DPD, yielded values which were too high, especially when leaves in a wilted or nearly wilted condition were measured. KERR and ANDERSON (1944), finding that DPD values exceeded OP values in developing cotton seeds, concluded that imbibitional phenomena were the cause, and that cryoscopic values were too low.

That a considerable proportion of the DPD may at times be due to the development of high tensions has been emphasized by some. Such negative wall pressures, in intact leaves of trees, especially during periods of abnormally high water loss, may exceed the influence of osmotic effects on the DPD (*see* CHU, 1936).

The variation, in particular the diurnal variation, is much greater for DPD than for OP. This is made clear by visualizing a cell which at limiting plasmolysis exhibits an OP of a given value, say 20 atm. As water is absorbed, the OP decreases from 20 to perhaps 16 atm., while the DPD decreases from 20 to 0 atm. In cells where tensions can develop, a greater range is possible. Thus it becomes evident why OP values obtained by use of the cryoscopic or plasmolytic methods fail to reveal the actual capacity of the cells to absorb water.

The effect of environment on DPD is therefore more pronounced than on OP. The important external factors are soil moisture, atmospheric humidity, and light. Li (1929), using leaves of *Syringa oblata,* concluded from statistical studies that from 6:30 A.M. to 10 A.M. light and relative humidity exert an important effect, while from 10 A.M. to 2 P.M. light becomes insignificant. Temperature was considered relatively unimportant in its effect on DPD.

Although this statement is true for purely liquid systems where DPD varies as absolute temperature in systems involving the atmosphere, temperature, through its relation to the degree of saturation, may have a profound effect upon transpiration and hence upon the DPD of the tissues. For further discussion of this point *see* page 190 and Figure 52, Chapter X. Table 28 indicates the effect on DPD of varying amounts of moist soil.

Table 28. — *Effect of varying soil moisture supply upon the DPD of plant tissues* (Molz, 1926) : —

Amount of water given daily to individual plants for period of 2 weeks	Variation in suction force of the leaves of each *Bellis perennis* plant after receiving the given amounts of water daily for 2 weeks
150 g.	+1.37 atm.
75 g.	+2.40 atm.
50 g.	+3.81 atm.
5 g.	+4.20 atm.

Wide diurnal fluctuations in DPD values of plant cells have been reported as might be expected. The maximum is reached about noon or in the early afternoon (Molz, 1926; Li, 1929; Herrick, 1933) under most conditions.

Table 29. — *Osmotic quantities in the hypocotyl of Helianthus annuus seedlings, determined at normal volume* (data of Beck and Andrus, 1943) : —

Zone	Millimeters from base of cotyledons	O_n Epid.	O_n Cortex	DPD_n Epid.	DPD_n Cortex	TP_n Epid.	TP_n Cortex
1	0-5	7.3	11.35	5.3	11.15	2.0	0.23
2	5-10	6.64	11.14	5.2	10.93	1.44	0.21
3	10-15	6.49	10.72	5.1	10.60	1.39	0.12
4	15-20	6.14	9.52	4.9	9.40	1.14	0.12
5	20-25	6.05	9.37	4.0	8.95	2.05	0.42
6	25-30	6.08	8.47	3.7	8.20	2.28	...
7	30-35	6.08	8.02	3.4	7.60	2.58	0.42

Meyer and Wallace (1941) found DPD values of approximately 8 atm. in potato tuber tissue. This closely approached the OP of the expressed sap measured cryoscopically, indicating a low order of turgor. Lyon (1942) obtained values of roughly the same magnitude but found considerably higher OP values, using the minimum cell volume (simplified) method.

Gradients of DPD are often of interest to the physiologist in studies of translocation and other functions. Beck and Andrus (1943) measured values for *Helianthus annuus* seedlings. DPD's (suction tensions) were determined, by use of Ursprung's simplified method, in seven zones of the hypocotyl, as indicated in Table 29. It will be noted that the values decrease consistently from the region at the base of the cotyledons to a region 35 mm. below. This is true for both the epidermis and cortex. Values of the other two osmotic quantities are also included in the table for comparison.

Turgor of Plant Cells:— Turgor plays several important roles in the structure and function of the plant. Because no rigid skeleton is possessed by herbaceous plants nor by the tender parts of woody species, the swollen condition of the cells acting against the restraining influence of the cell walls provides support. Growth of plants is related to turgor expansion of their cells. Plant movements of various sorts may be due to changes in turgor. Opening and closing of stomata are the result of turgor variation of the guard cells. Seed dispersal may be facilitated in certain species by "exploding" of fruits (*e.g.,* the squirting cucumber). Quality of many succulent vegetables such as celery, lettuce, cucumbers, and the like may be related to their state of turgor so that some extremely important problems confront the handlers of fresh vegetables, problems related to water loss at varying humidity and temperature. Severe losses are sometimes caused by splitting of certain fruits and vegetables, for example cherries, watermelons, and tomatoes. Complete explanations for this are not known, but excess water and high humidity are causative factors in that they result in high turgor states. Anatomical factors are also involved (Kenney and Porter, 1941). The keeping qualities of cut flowers depend on the maintenance of turgor, and this presents serious problems to the commercial florist.

Finally, it has been observed that plants do not thrive and their cells do not function properly when their turgor is low or lacking. Although this may relate more directly to the low water content of such plants and the effects of water deficit upon hydration of the protoplasm, imbibition of the walls, and concentrations of solutes in the protoplasm and vacuoles, study of water deficient plants emphasizes the intimate and complex relations existing among these several factors. Therefore, though water deficiency and the attendant wilting may injure plants in more important ways than through loss of turgor, the state of turgor of the plant is a valuable index of its water content and supply, and hence of its physiological well-being.

Intercellular pressure (A) may be regarded as an additional osmotic quantity, related in the following manner:

$$OP = DPD + TP \pm A. \tag{22}$$

It seems best, however, to consider this factor simply a component of turgor pressure whenever cells are associated in a tissue.

Measurement of Turgor:— Few direct measurements of cell turgor have been made. Values of 3 to 10 atm. were obtained by a manometric procedure in the massive-celled *Nitella* (Arens, 1939). Overbeck (1930) measured the turgor of the fruit of the squirting cucumber by means of a manometer. He found a value of 2.4 atm., which was sufficient to throw the seeds 12.7 meters. Most measurements of turgor are made by difference, using the simplified method, to determine OP and DPD values. In the normal state, OP measured cryoscopically and DPD determined by the simplified method enables one to calculate turgor pressure from the relation $TP = OP - DPD$; and at water saturation, the cryoscopic value is a measure of the degree of turgor. In both of these instances, the accuracy of the measurement depends on the extent to which expressed sap is representative of vacuolar contents.

BENNET-CLARK and BEXON (1940) investigated turgor pressures of leaves by determining the amount of added pressure necessary to express juice from the cells. In this method a round piece of leaf is placed horizontally between two solid brass cylinders. Weights are added to the upper cylinder until liquid is first exuded by the cells into the intercellular spaces. A horizontally placed microscope is employed to detect this point. The pressure imposed was believed to be equal to the turgor pressure (and hence equal also to OP) of those cells possessing the lowest osmotic pressure. For this reason it was termed the "minimum hydrostatic pressure" of the fully turgid leaf.

The method operates on the assumption that cell sap exudes only when the externally imposed pressure equals the osmotic pressure of the vacuole. However, this can be true only when the cells are initially in a turgorless condition; otherwise the observed values would be low. It must also be assumed that the elastic stretching of the wall is equal throughout the tissue. The authors state that ". . . application of a pressure lower than the hydrostatic pressure of the contents of the fully turgid tissue expresses no juice." It would seem that any amount of pressure, when applied to fully turgid cells, would express some liquid, although admittedly more from cells having low osmotic pressures. Therefore, the method of BENNET-CLARK and BEXON can hardly be considered critical for determining turgor pressure. Furthermore, the technical difficulties involved would seem almost insurmountable.

The term *plasmoptysis* designates the bursting of cells due to the inability of the cell wall to resist turgor pressure. The phenomenon has been observed on immersing cells in water (pollen grains, ripe pulp cells of watermelon fruit, certain marine algae). Some solvents such as alcohol may cause bursting due to rapid entry into the cells. In other instances, swelling of the protoplasmic and cell wall colloids may be the cause. This has been demonstrated in barley root hairs by immersion in a weak acetic acid solution (STRUGGER, 1935).

Intercellular Movement of Water:— It has been clearly pointed out (MEYER, 1938) that the DPD gradient existing between two cells is the cause of water movement from one to the other; the osmotic pressure difference may not enter the problem. Under certain conditions it is possible for water to move from a cell with a relatively high to one with a relatively low osmotic pressure due to the existence in the first cell of a higher turgor than in the second. The diagram of FIGURE 35 illustrates an example.

URSPRUNG and BLUM (1916b) pointed out that the concentration of osmotically active solutes in a cell is not necessarily the determiner of water movement, for if the cell is saturated with water it has no further ability to absorb; water, on the other hand, may pass through such cells hindered only by the resistance to movement through the membranes involved. Absorption of water by roots undoubtedly involves movement across tissues that vary in osmotic concentration, and finally, the water is delivered into xylem vessels where the concentration of solutes, though higher than in the soil, may be much lower than in the cortical cells across which the water has moved. PRIESTLEY (1920) and CRAFTS and BROYER (1938) have attempted to picture mechanisms to explain the uptake of water by roots (*cf.* Chapter IX, pages 149 and 150).

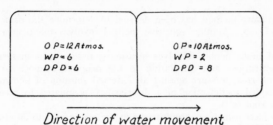

Direction of water movement

FIG. 35.—Diagrammatic illustration of water movement along a gradient of DPD. (MEYER, 1938).

Summary:— The osmotic quantities of plant cells are osmotic pressure, diffusion pressure deficit, and turgor pressure. The dynamics of water movement and retention can be explained in terms of these quantities.

As with an osmometer also with cells the relation OP = DPD + TP is fundamental to an understanding of osmotic relations. Under certain conditions of water stress TP may pass the zero level and pressure may become subatmospheric.

Under OP all forces leading to water absorption by the cell are included. When tension exists, its value must be added to the OP. Increase in hydrophily of the protoplasm results in water uptake. The OP of the vacuolar sap reflects the integrated resultant of the interaction of all forces causing water to enter the cell. Under TP are included forces acting in the opposite direction.

In order that osmotic pressure of a solution may find expression in turgor a differentially permeable membrane must separate the solution from a more dilute solution or from pure solvent. In the cell the protoplasm serves as this membrane. Its selective capacity is believed due to two cytoplasmic membranes, the ectoplast, and the tonoplast. These are pictured as a complex of lipoid and protein. Some physical membranes act as sieves, others as selective solvents. The lipoid-sieve theory combines the essential features of both to explain the permeability of protoplasm.

Active absorption is responsible for most solute uptake by the cells of living plants. Essential to this process are oxygen supply, temperature, organic nutrients, the salt status of the cell, and the nature and concentration of solutes in the external medium.

Some ions may be taken up from the solid phase of the soil by contact exchange. Polyuronides in the root hair walls make a connecting medium between the soil and the cell protoplasm capable of ion transfer. The passive permeability of cells to ions does not account for active absorption by living cells.

Cells are generally readily permeable to water. Cells may vary among themselves with respect to water permeability.

Tugor is contingent upon osmotic water uptake; absorption and movement are dependent upon osmosis. An external solution which reduces turgor to zero is said to be isotonic with respect to the cell sap. Such a solution is used in determining the osmotic pressure of the cell by the plasmolytic method.

Many objections have been raised to the plasmolytic method, nevertheless it has proved valuable in studies of cell physiology. Some of the more pertinent criticisms of the method involve adhesion of the protoplast to the wall, plastic stretching of the wall, and the technical difficulties in correctly observing the critical state of incipient plasmolysis. By plotting the number of plasmolyzed cells against sugar concentration an average OP value for many cells may be obtained.

Several forms of plasmolysis have been observed, the more important being convex and concave. Plasmolysis may follow chemical or physical stimulation. Vacuole contraction is another type of response.

The plasmometric method involves strong plasmolysis followed by measurement of cell and protoplast. Osmotic pressure is calculated from these.

The cryoscopic method is widely used. It is relatively free of errors but involves the expression of sap and this has definite limitations. A differential thermometer is used to determine freezing point lowering of sap; a thermocouple is usually used to find the freezing point of living cells. From the freezing point lowering the osmotic pressure can be calculated by a simple formula.

Errors in cryoscopy involve supercooling and absorption of heat by the apparatus. Methods are available to correct both of these; by a calibration technic they may be avoided.

A vapor pressure method has been devised to determine the osmotic pressure of small samples of sap. Another sensitive method involves the temperature lowering due to evaporation.

A simplified tissue method involves measuring tissue strips in series of solutions of graded concentrations and calculating to the original volume. Another method involves balancing root pressure against an external solution of known concentration. This method has led to detection of a discrepancy postulated to result from active water uptake by root cells.

Most plants have osmotic concentrations in the range of 5 to 30 atmospheres. An extreme value of 202.5 atm. has been recorded. The distribution of osmotic pressure values in the leaf assumes the following pattern: palisade parenchyma $>$ spongy parenchyma $>$ upper epidermis $>$ lower epidermis. Xylem sap is very dilute. Phloem exudate has a higher concentration.

Diffusion pressure deficits of cells and tissues may be determined by surrounding them with solutions which cause no change in volume or in weight. Another method is to inject a solution into the hollow petiole or stem and follow changes in concentration. Variations in DPD resulting from diurnal fluctuation in transpiration may be followed by this method. Several other methods have been described.

Changes in DPD values are greater than in OP values. They result from variations in soil moisture, humidity, and light. Cell walls of some xerophytes show little elasticity, hence DPD values fluctuate sharply and water is conserved.

Turgor plays an important role in growth and development of plants. Quality of vegetables depends on turgor. Growth hormones may act through turgor expansion.

Direct measurement of turgor is difficult. Values from 3 to 10 atm. have been recorded. Intercellular water movement follows DPD gradients; it may be independent of OP.

Chapter VIII

ACTIVE CELL WATER RELATIONS

Introduction:— Recent developments, most within the last decade, necessitate re-examination of certain aspects of cell water relations. Specifically considerable doubt has been cast on the classical concept of the mechanism of uptake and retention of water by plant cells. This classical view has been fully discussed in the two preceding chapters. Simply stated, it holds that water is retained in the vacuole osmotically by reason of the presence of solutes in the sap; that at limiting plasmolysis the osmotic pressure of the sap is equal to that of the bathing solution; and that, at full turgor, the hydrostatic pressure developed in the vacuole is equal to the osmotic pressure of the vacuolar sap. In simpler terms, for the range from full turgor to incipient plasmolysis, DPD = OP — TP. The protoplasm is considered to be passive in its behavior to water; it constitutes a thin layer, differentially permeable, retaining solutes within the vacuole but permitting ready passage of water.

Most interpretations of cell water studies have rested upon these assumptions. However, sufficient evidence has now accumulated to cause serious doubt concerning the passivity of protoplasm with respect to water movement and retention. Plant physiologists are asking themselves *1*) do some living cells retain in their vacuoles more water than can be accounted for by their solute content; *2*) what role does metabolism play in water exchanges; *3*) exactly how does protoplasm function in the water balance of cells; *4*) how do certain alleged vital water functions relate to other physiological processes—namely absorption, movement, and loss of water? Concisely, we would like to know if protoplasm can act differentially toward both water and solutes. Secretion of water is particularly difficult to visualize in view of the high content of water in the protoplasm itself.

Some of the early workers in plant physiology attempted to explain certain aspects of water absorption and translocation on the basis of a vital control of water (HALES, 1738; KNIGHT, 1801; GODLEWSKI, 1884; JANSE, 1913; BOSE, 1923), but the evidence has never been considered valid. In the present chapter current research leading to evidence for active control of water will be presented and discussed.

The water specifically referred to in the phrase "active water relations" we consider to be that water which may be transported or retained against an apparent diffusion pressure gradient, by processes requiring the expenditure of metabolic energy. It includes water held in the protoplasm by forces involved in living processes which may bring about a separation of water and solutes. Practically, it is reflected in an apparent inequality between the DPD and the quantity OP — TP. A distinction is thus attempted between active forces and passive (osmotic) forces, a distinction which is difficult in the present state of knowledge, and which may of necessity be somewhat arbitrary.

Evidence from Plasmolytic and Cryoscopic Measurements:— To determine the nature of the forces accounting for turgor, promising results have been obtained by comparing the osmotic pressure of the living cells measured plasmolytically (Pg) with that of the expressed cell sap measured cryoscopically (On). From such experiments BENNET-CLARK, GREEN-WOOD, and BARKER (1936) were led to the conclusion that the protoplasm of certain cells, using metabolic energy, was able to "secrete" water into their vacuoles. It follows from this conclusion that such cells could retain, within their vacuoles, more water than would be expected from purely osmotic forces. Using root tissues of *Beta vulgaris* and *Brassica napobrassica,* and petioles of *Begonia rex, Rheum rhaponticum* and *Caladium bicolor* they measured cryoscopically the osmotic pressure of the expressed sap. After correcting these values for change in volume (Vn to Vg) they compared them with values obtained plasmolytically. As shown in TABLE 30, marked discrepancies occurred, particularly in *Beta, Brassica,* and *Begonia.* Thus Og was greater than On $\cdot \frac{Vn}{Vg}$ by significant amounts. This discrepancy BENNET-CLARK, GREENWOOD, and BARKER attributed to a force termed "water secretion." In place of the classical equation DPD = OP — TP they proposed DPD = OP — TP + X, and X they described as "an unknown additional pressure sending water into the cell."

TABLE 30. — *Cryoscopic and plasmolytic measurement of osmotic pressure in various plants (data of* BENNET-CLARK, GREENWOOD *and* BARKER, 1936). *Values are atmospheres at 20° C., and in most instances represent averages of several tests:* —

PLANT	OP FROM FREEZING POINT DEPRESSION (On)	OP FROM PLASMOLYSIS (Og)	X (Og — On · Vn/Vg*)
Beta vulgaris A	15.5	23.4	7.1
Beta vulgaris B	9.5	12.6	2.6
Beta vulgaris C	12.0	18.4	5.8
Brassica napobrassica A	11.4	17.8	5.9
Brassica napobrassica B	11.85	17.0	4.6
Begonia rex A	5.3	8.0	2.4
Begonia rex B	5.5	8.0	2.2
Rheum rhaponticum A	7.5	8.1	0.2
Rheum rhaponticum B	8.6	9.5	0.5
Caladium bicolor A	5.8	5.5	—0.5
Caladium bicolor B	5.8	6.4	0.4

* A constant factor of 1.05 was employed in calculations to correct for shrinkage from Vn to Vg.

The discrepancies for *Caladium* and *Rheum* range from —0.5 atm. to +0.5 atm., values that probably are not significant. For *Begonia, Brassica* and *Beta* on the other hand the discrepancies are all positive and range from 2.2 to 7.1 atm., values that are highly significant and constitute from 25 to 30 per cent of the DPD at limiting plasmolysis. These results are of importance in pointing out the magnitude of errors that may occur in the usual interpretation of such experiments; they are of greater importance in that they challenge the accepted views of the mechanics of water absorption and retention by cells and call for re-examination of the data upon which these views were built. In a later paper (BENNET-CLARK and BEXON, 1940) the nature of the secretion process is treated in more detail, the proposition being made that it does not constitute an exception to the physico-chemical laws of diffusion but rather that water is transported into the vacuole by the concurrent diffusion of another component which acts as a "carrier." Discussion of the theoretical considerations of the secretion theory is presented later.

Studies dealing with growth processes in tomato have led WENT (1944) to admit the possibility of a non-osmotic force contributing to the DPD of cells. Sap from killed leaves had an OP (determined cryoscopically) of slightly over 9 atm., while a sucrose solution of about 25 atm. was required for plasmolysis of mesophyll cells.

The presence of hydrophilic colloids in the vacuole has been advanced as an explanation of discrepancies between the plasmolytic and cryoscopic methods for determining osmotic pressures. For ten species of conifers whose expressed cell sap was low in mucilaginous colloids ROBERTS and STYLES (1939) found fairly good agreement between the two methods; the average discrepancy amounted to 2.6 atm. in favor of the plasmolytic determination. On the other hand, plasmolytic values were around 14 atm. higher, or over 40 per cent of the DPD for seven species possessing much colloid. The colloid content was measured by the somewhat questionable method of comparing outflow times for sap through a capillary tube. Other substances, for example sugars, also have marked effects upon viscosity and further analyses of the saps would have aided in interpreting the data. Although this method possibly involves an error, the fact that cryoscopic values of the two groups of conifers were of the same order of magnitude is evidence that colloids are probably responsible for the viscosity differences. While recognizing water secretion as a possibility, ROBERTS and STYLES favor the presence of colloids in the sap as an explanation for the differences obtained. They believed that the plasmolytic method embraces, in addition to osmotic pressure of the cell sap, swelling pressures developed by vacuolar colloids which the cryoscopic procedure fails to measure. The difficulty of distinguishing between osmotic and imbibitional forces in complex solutions was emphasized in Chapter III. Although ROBERTS and STYLES did not make it clear, it should be emphasized that in order for the above explanation to be valid, water must have been removed from the colloid during preparation of sap for the cryoscopic determination.

Using leaves of several tree species, MAXIMOV and LOMINADZE (1916) compared osmotic pressure values of pressed sap determined by the Barger-Halket capillarimetric method with plasmolytic values. The latter values averaged 1.7 atm. higher than those of the pressed sap and this discrepancy accounts for a force representing about 8 per cent of the water absorbing power (DPD) of the cells at limiting plasmolysis. Though one may question the use of whole leaves for expression of sap while only epidermis is used for plasmolytic measurements, the fact shown by URSPRUNG and BLUM (1916a), BUHMANN (1935), and others that the osmotic pressure of the mesophyll exceeds that of the epidermis, indicates that the discrepancy found was too low.

Comparisons of the plasmolytic and Barger methods in studies on *Nitella,* where volume changes were considered, gave almost identical values (WILDERVANCK, 1932). Similar results were obtained by comparing plasmolytic and cryoscopic methods (CURRIER, 1943). It is perhaps significant that in this case sap may be obtained without pressing, so that it is almost identical with vacuolar sap in the intact cells.

OPPENHEIMER (1932a) thought that good agreement between plasmolytic and cryoscopic osmotic pressure values could be obtained if suitable plant materials were employed, and when the various sources of error were accounted for. He investigated twelve plants, employing mostly leaf tissues. With a few exceptions his values agreed within 1.5 atm. In most instances the plasmolytic value was the higher of the two.

This discrepancy was attributed to various causes: *1*) adhesion of the protoplast to the wall; *2*) the slight difference in osmotic pressure between a solution effecting limiting plasmolysis and that causing incipient plasmolysis; *3*) time of treatment, insufficient or excessive; *4*) failure to account for the volume change between the normal and incipiently plasmolyzed states; *5*) excessive proportion of protoplasm in the cells; *6*) inelastic stretching of cell walls.

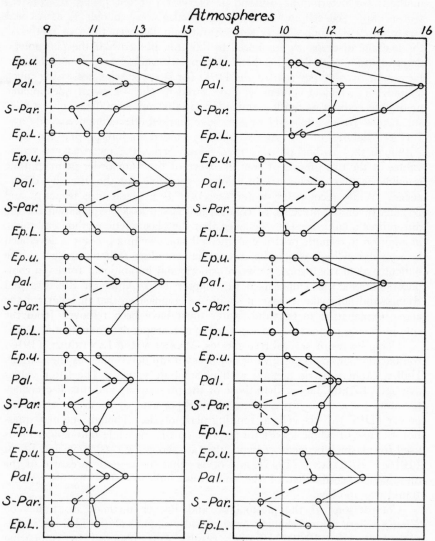

Fig. 36.—Osmotic pressure values of leaf cells of *Bergenia cordifolia*. Solid lines represent initial plasmolysis, dashed lines deplasmolysis, and dotted lines cryoscopic values on the expressed sap. (BUHMANN, 1935).

The sampling error involved in making plasmolytic tests usually one day after the cryoscopic tests, and using different leaves for each, may have influenced these results. Epidermis was chosen for many of the plasmolytic determinations; these were compared with cryoscopic values obtained on sap expressed from many whole leaves. OPPENHEIMER'S discrepancies would probably have been greater had he used a mean plasmolytic value for mesophyll and epidermis.

A somewhat different interpretation was offered by BUHMANN (1935). Investigating various types of tissues, discrepancies varying from a fraction of an atmosphere to as much as 60 atmospheres were found. Plasmolytic values were, on the average, in the order of 5 to 7 atmospheres higher than the cryoscopic. The discrepancies were ascribed to adhesion of the cytoplasm to the cell wall, producing a delay, and hence an overestimation of the OP at incipient plasmolysis. For a discussion of the adhesion problem, *see* Chapter VII. FIGURE 36 shows a series of measurements on four tissues of *Bergenia cordifolia* leaves showing values of PO_g, DO_g, and cryoscopic O_n. In *Pinus laricio* where, in one instance, the discrepancy attained a value of 60 atm., BUHMANN attributed 13.5 to 27 atm. to adhesion.

Using *Beta vulgaris* root, and neglecting change in volume, BUHMANN found discrepancies in the plasmolytic and cryoscopic values ranging from 5.25 to 7.78 atm., the plasmolytic values being higher. Adhesion pressure amounted to 1.07 to 3.26 atm. An unusually high shrinkage ($V_n/V_g =$ 1.22 to 1.36) was reported for this tissue which, when applied as a further correction, produced good agreement between plasmolytic and cryoscopic values.

In a study of the water relations of red beet root tissue one of the present authors (CURRIER, 1944*a*) verified the occurrence of plasmolytic-cryoscopic discrepancies (PCD's) in measurements of osmotic pressure. However, there were unexpected variations among different lots of beets tested. After volume corrections had been applied, the value at limiting plasmolysis exceeded the cryoscopic value by as much as 5.9 atm. for two of the lots tested; for other beets the average discrepancy did not exceed one atmsphere. In some instances the cryoscopic value was the higher one, but here the difference rarely exceeded a fraction of an atmosphere (TABLES 31 and 32).

TABLE 31. — *Description of beets employed in PCD determinations, and periods during which tests were made:* —

LOT	VARIETY	AGE IN WEEKS	STAGE OF GROWTH	TIME OF TESTS
A	Detroit	35-36	Pre-bolting	Mar. 15-22
B	Detroit	59-63	Dormant	Apr. 23-May 21
C	Detroit	59-63	Bolting	Apr. 23-May 21
D	Crosby	36	Bolting	May 23-26
E	Detroit	17-18	Vegetative	July 7-15
F	Crosby	7-25	Vegetative	May 21-Sept. 13
G	Detroit	20-22	Vegetative	July 13-29
H	Detroit	15-31	Vegetative	Sept. 15-Jan. 3

The excessive plasmolytic values could not be attributed to any of the explanations previously offered. Using a technique similar to that of BUHMANN (1935), no significant adhesion pressure could be detected (TABLE 33). The method involved the use of plasmolyzing and deplasmolyzing solutions having osmotic pressures about 4 atm. greater and less respectively than the predetermined limiting plasmolysis value, which insured complete plasmolysis and deplasmolysis without stretching or shrinking the wall to any great extent. Adhesion pressure values lay within 0.5 atm., and were no greater for beets exhibiting a +PCD (plasmolytic value > cryoscopic value corrected for volume) than for those having a —PCD (cryoscopic > plasmolytic). Nor was there visible evidence that the cyto-plasm adhered to the wall.

With one exception, the highest +PCD values were found in beets yielding the most concentrated expressed sap (Lots D, E, G), the lowest PCD's in beets with least concentrated saps (Lots B, C, F). Lot A, with the highest average discrepancy, had a relatively dilute sap.

TABLE 32. — *Summarized results of plasmolytic and cryoscopic tests on various lots of beets:* —

Lot	NUMBER OF EXPERI-MENTS	AVERAGE OSMOTIC PRESSURE		CHANGE IN VOLUME		AVERAGE PCD[b]	AVERAGE DEVIATION PCD[b]
		Plasmolytic	Cryoscopic	Average	Range		
		atm.	atm.	%	%	atm.	atm.
A	4	16.2	10.4	3.0	1.0-5.5	+5.3	0.7
B	9	10.2	9.1	5.2	3.6-11.3	+0.6	0.4
C	6	10.0	8.9	3.2	1.4-4.8	+0.8	0.7
D	8	22.8	17.2	7.3	3.0-10.6	+4.1	0.9
E	4	15.6	13.9	5.4	1.9-7.5	+0.9	1.1
F	21	12.6	12.0	2.7[a]	0-7.7	+0.3	0.8
G	12	17.9	16.1	2.2[a]	0-5.9	+1.4	1.0
H	4	14.5	13.9	4.3	3.5-5.0	0	1.1

[a] Cylinders of four roots of Lot F and of six roots of Lot G were soaked in isotonic sucrose solution prior to sectioning, hence no volume change is involved. When these are not considered, average changes in volume are somewhat higher, 3.3 and 4.4 per cent respectively.

[b] PCD is introduced as a convenient contraction of the term plasmolytic-cryoscopic discrepancy.

The suggestion was made by BENNET-CLARK, GREENWOOD and BARKER (1936) that water secretion may be a function only of potential growing tissues. This does not appear to be true for beet root tissue. Lot F was tested beginning when the plants were 3 weeks old, and continuing until they were 25 weeks old. The youngest plant examined showed a PCD of —0.6 atm. Out of twenty determinations, nine showed negative PCD's and an average discrepancy of near zero. During this growth period, both Og and On increased at about an equal rate.

TABLE 33. — *Results of deplasmolysis and replasmolysis tests on beet root tissue. Atmospheres at 22.5° C.:* —

BEET No.	PCD	PO$_g$	DO$_g$	RO$_g$	PO$_g$-DO$_g$	PO$_g$-RO$_g$
39	—0.1	13.0	12.5	12.8	0.5	0.2
40	+0.7	13.8	13.6	13.6	0.2	0.2
41	—0.1	12.5	12.0	12.2	0.5	0.3
42	—0.3	12.5	12.0	12.2	0.5	0.3
47	—1.0	13.0	12.5	12.5	0.5	0.5
54	—0.8	13.8	13.8	...	0	..
55	+0.2	17.2	16.9	17.4	0.3	—0.2
56	+3.6	19.4	19.3	19.2	0.1	0.2
55a	+1.6	17.7	18.0	17.7	—0.3	0
61	+1.4	16.4	16.3	16.0	0.1	0.4
62	—0.8	14.1	13.6	13.6	0.5	0.5

Plants yielding the highest +PCD values (Lots A and D) were in a prebolting or bolting stage of growth. These lots were fall planted, the others spring planted. That temperature was not directly associated with the discrepancy is shown by the fact that Lot A was subjected to winter temperatures, while D grew under warm greenhouse conditions, yet both yielded high PCD's.

On the basis of this and other experimental evidence presented else-where in this chapter, it was postulated that the discrepancies (PCD's) are related to contamination of expressed sap by liquid held by and expressed from the protoplasm; that the discrepancy may be positive or negative depending on whether the contamination was less or more concentrated than the vacuolar sap; that the nature of the contaminating protoplasmic sap depends on the state of hydration of the cytoplasm; and that where the discrepancy is positive (protoplasmic sap less concentrated than vacuolar) the cells may be in a cold hardy condition. The possibility of dilution by wall imbibed liquid is not precluded; however, morphological differences (cell size, wall thickness) sufficient to account for significant variation in PCD's were not observed.

While this monograph was in press a paper by LEVITT (1947) appeared, in which he throws doubt on the possibility of plant cells maintaining water secretion pressures in excess of about one atmosphere. This conclusion is based on calculations which indicate that there is insufficient energy release, judging from maximum observed respiratory rates, to make such work thermodynamically possible.

In summary, it is evident that with few exceptions, osmotic pressures of plant cells measured plasmolytically exceed those determined cryoscopically, even when volume changes are taken into consideration. Explanation of the discrepancy based on active secretion of water by the protoplasm into the vacuole, adhesion of the cytoplasm to the wall, the presence of colloids in the vacuole, various errors in method, and a high variable imbibitional capacity of the protoplasm, have been suggested.

While admitting that both of these methods of measuring the OP of plant tissues are beset with numerous errors, it is possible that where comparative values are secured from similar plants in different states of growth many errors will cancel out. Additional data are needed.

Interpretation of Sap Expression Data:— The meaning of results of osmotic pressure measurements, where plasmolytic and cryoscopic methods are compared, is confused by the questionable origin of expressed sap. If plasmolytic values could be compared with osmotic pressure determinations on sap known to have originated in the vacuole, the discrepancies, if any, would have greater significance.

Several methods have been devised in an attempt to obtain expressed sap of known origin from plant tissue (*cf*. Chapter VI). Knowledge as to the distribution of solutes and water between the protoplasm and vacuole is greatly needed, for it would be of assistance in many kinds of physiological investigations.

The problem has been attacked by refining the pressing technique. The usual method has been one in which frozen and thawed plant organs, or parts of organs, are wrapped in cheesecloth and pressed, with no particular attention to the arrangement of the individual pieces. MASON and PHILLIS (1939) found that if cotton leaves were carefully stacked, and pressure applied slowly so as to prevent shearing forces, a very dilute sap could be obtained. They postulated that such sap was vacuolar in origin, and that it was expressed through "fissures" produced in the protoplasm. On this basis, in one experiment a difference between plasmolytic and cryoscopic osmotic pressure determinations of 20.4 atm. was found (OP of plasmolyzing solution = 22.8 atm., OP of press sap = 2.4 atm.). This led them to suspect that the water secretion force was "much greater than anything contemplated by BENNET-CLARK, GREENWOOD and BARKER." At the same time they agreed that no actual evidence has been produced to prove that such a process, dependent on metabolic energy, actually exists, and suggested that high imbibitional forces might also be involved.

In other sap-expression experiments designed to shed more light on the proposed water-secretory phenomenon, BENNET-CLARK and BEXON (1940) distinguished between pressure slowly applied, and pressure quickly applied. Leaves containing anthocyanin in their vacuoles were found to be suitable material. Slow increments of pressure applied to carefully stacked leaves produced a colorless sap approaching pure water in composition, up to a certain point which was termed the "break." Here the yield of sap per pressure increment increased, the osmotic pressure was higher, and anthocyanin appeared in the juice. The fraction expressed prior to the break was interpreted to consist primarily of vacuolar water, from which many of the solutes had been filtered by the cellular membranes, and possibly some protoplasmic water. Sap appearing after the "break" was attributed to breakdown of the protoplast.

Sudden increments of pressure, on the other hand, released a sap containing anthocyanin, with a higher osmotic pressure than occurred with slow increments. This was interpreted to be primarily vacuolar in origin. BENNET-CLARK and BEXON feel, with MASON and PHILLIS, that the vacuolar contents are probably liberated through fissures formed in the protoplasm without serious injury thereto. Sap from the killed residue of leaves was considerably more concentrated than the "vacuolar" sap.

Cryoscopic determinations on these various sap fractions gave some interesting results, especially when compared to plasmolytic values. A sample of these is shown in TABLE 34.

TABLE 34. — *Comparison of osmotic pressure values determined plasmolytically and those determined cryoscopically on various fractions of expressed leaf sap (data of* BENNET-CLARK *and* BEXON, *1940)* : —

	Fagus sylvatica	Beta vulgaris	Parthenocissus quinquifolius	Gossypium barbadense
	atm.	atm.	atm.	atm.
Mean plasmolytic value ...	30-32	14	15-16	22
OP cytoplasmic sap	18-24	..	25	17-18
OP vacuolar sap	5-8	7	5-7	9-10
OP entire cell sap	15	9	8-10	12-14

It is evident from these results that even where entire cell sap (from frozen leaves) is used for comparison, the cryoscopic value amounts to only 40-50% of the plasmolytic value. The discrepancies are even greater with respect to "vacuolar" sap. If the inference drawn here is true, that the water absorbing power of the cell markedly exceeds the osmotic pressure of expressed sap, then the plasmolytic method and other procedures involving equilibrium between living cells and bathing solutions are to be preferred in measurements of diffusion pressure deficits but are not suitable for osmotic pressure determinations.

PHILLIS and MASON (1941) postulate three kinds of sap which may be expressed from cotton leaves:

a) *vacuolar sap*, obtained by rapid application of relatively high pressure to carefully stacked living leaves,

b) *injury sap*, the result of rather low pressures for long periods of time, originating partly in the vacuole and to some extent in the protoplasm; they agree with LEPESCHKIN (1937) that pressure first results in vacuolar contraction, but after a time water separates in the form of small vacuoles, and it is this liquid which is believed to compose a portion of injury sap,

c) *death sap,* sap expressed from the killed residue after the vacuolar sap has been expressed, and originating almost entirely in the protoplasm.

PHILLIS and MASON, while in accord with BENNET-CLARK and BEXON that vacuolar sap may be expressed by rapid increments of pressure, differ with reference to the nature of "injury sap." On the basis of volume of liquid obtained, and of the chlorine content of successive fractions, they assume the absence of filtration effects, and prefer to consider the sap a mixture of protoplasmic and vacuolar solutions.

It is not at all clear, if solutes are filtered out at low pressures, why some filtration would not occur at more rapidly exerted high pressures. Similarly, even if fissures are produced in the protoplasm of some cells, it does not appear likely that all cells would be affected in the same way. And if the protoplasm yields liquid when low pressure is applied for a relatively long period, it seems possible that some protoplasmic sap would also be expressed by quick pressure.

More accurate methods for separating the liquid present in the various cellular phases are needed. Until these are found, sap from frozen and thawed tissue may be preferred over that from fresh tissue for use in comparisons with plasmolytic values. Since it generally contains more solutes than that from living tissue, there can be little claim that vacuolar sap from frozen cells is diluted by filtration. Furthermore, there is less variation in concentration with different pressing techniques. The fact remains however that it is whole cell sap from many cells—a mixture, that is worthless in interphasal distribution studies.

While fluid expressed from living tissue usually exhibits a significantly lower osmotic pressure than that from killed tissue, there are some plants for which this is evidently not true. Examples are given by WALTER (1931b, p. 36), and his data are presented in TABLE 35. The plants represented are of a type which one might expect to behave in this manner. Rich in colloids, they hold relatively large amounts of water by imbibitional forces. The equality in osmotic pressure between saps from living and dead tissue could in part be due to the liberation of colloidally bound water on heating or freezing. It could also reflect the anatomy of succulent plants, made up of large thin-walled cells rich in water. Such cells,

TABLE 35. — *Effect of killing tissue on the osmotic pressure of expressed sap (data of* WALTER, *1931b)* : —

TREATMENT	Opuntia phaeacantha	Opuntia versicolor
	atm.	atm.
Living	9.56	10.89
30 min. at 100° C.	9.63	11.54
24 hrs. at —20° C.	9.92	11.10

	Aloe	Rhoeo discolor	Taxus baccata
	atm.	atm.	atm.
Living	5.71	6.48	18.46
100° C. heat	5.33	6.87	18.36
Liquid nitrogen	5.06	6.58	18.40

upon pressing, might easily rupture and yield a sap more nearly like that existing in the vacuoles. It is difficult to see, however, how this would be true for plants such as *Taxus*. Finally, there could be, as Walter suggests, sufficient filtration of solutes in expressing viscous sap from killed tissue to explain the similarily of osmotic pressures obtained.

For purposes of comparison, some representative data to be found in DIXON (1914, p. 177, 182) and in THREN (1934) are presented in TABLES 36 and 37. It is clear that in most instances there is a considerable discrepancy between the concentrations of sap from living and killed tissues. Furthermore, the magnitude of the discrepancy varies markedly among the different plants.

TABLE 36. — *Comparison of saps expressed from living and killed tissue* (DIXON, 1914) : —

PLANT	ORGAN	FREEZING POINT DEPRESSION °C.	
		Living	Killed
Ilex aquifolium	leaves	0.667	1.225*
Hedera helix	leaves	0.728	1.031**
Iris germanica	rhizome	0.450	0.829
Pyrus malus	fruit	1.507	1.919
Citrus limonum	fruit	1.033	0.588
Solanum tuberosum	tuber	0.523	0.588
Vitis vinifera	fruit	2.567	3.185
Chamaerops humilis	leaf	0.365	1.529
Beta vulgaris	root	1.473	1.761

* Heated.
** Desiccated, all others frozen.

According to THREN the more compactly the leaf tissues are arranged, the greater the difference expected between the two values. That is, *Buxus,* with compact leaves, showed the greatest deviation. But this would not seem to satisfy all of the results.

In this connection, the work of NEWTON (1924) is recalled; he found an inverse correlation between cold hardiness and volume of sap expressed from living wheat leaves. The difference was attributed to a greater amount of bound water and dry matter in the more hardy tissue. Unfortunately no osmotic pressure values were determined.

TABLE 37. — *Osmotic pressure of sap expressed from living vs. killed (heat) leaves* (data of THREN, 1934) : —

	LIVING	KILLED
	atm.	atm.
Buxus sempervirens	3.1	24.2
Vinca minor	5.1	14.4
Linaria cymbalaria	5.4	11.2
Sedum reflexum	7.9	11.3
Sedum album	6.2	6.2

Also pertinent to the problem are data reported by MEYER (1928), the result of sap expression studies on the leaves of *Pinus rigida,* with special reference to cold hardiness. The total water content of the leaves varied but little throughout the year, so that the development of cold resistance during the winter was not due to this factor. The proportion of sap expressible from living leaves was much less during the winter months than during the summer. This suggested, as did NEWTON's data, that the pressure method may be useful in estimating cold hardiness in plants. The explanation that the proportion of colloidally (gel) bound water was greater in winter was substantiated by the increased difficulty experienced in freezing the leaves. MEYER's results are shown in FIGURE 37.

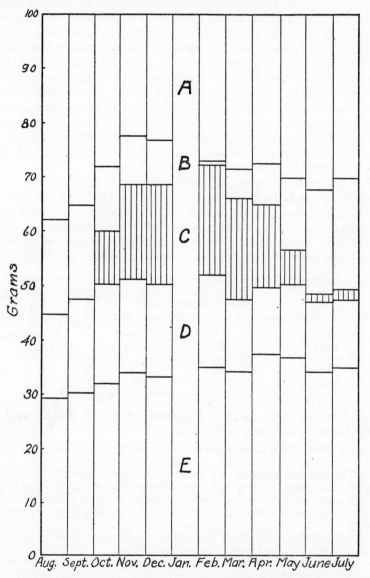

FIG. 37.—Seasonal variations in the dry matter content, inexpressible water, and water expressed as sap after different treatment of leaves of *Pinus rigida*. A, volume of sap expressed from unfrozen leaves; B, additional sap expressed from leaf samples frozen in an ice-salt bath; C, additional sap expressed from samples frozen in solid carbon dioxide; D, inexpressible water; E, dry matter content. Pressure, 5000 pounds per square inch. Data of MEYER (1928).

Later (1932) MEYER attempted to demonstrate a correlation between cold resistance in pine and the amount of bound water detectable by the calorimetric method. By this method there was a slightly greater amount of bound water in the summer leaves, attributed to a somewhat greater total water content. Nor could a clearly significant difference be shown by pressure-dehydration tests on living (ground) leaves in the summer as compared to the winter condition. Amounts of sap expressible were greater from summer leaves, but a part of this may be accounted for by the greater total hydration of those leaves. The disrupting effects of grinding should not be overlooked. Difficulties met in interpretation of bound water data obtained by such methods as the calorimetric are indicated in Chapter III (*see also* WEISMANN, 1938). LEVITT (1941) interprets such results as obtained by the pressure method, employed also by NEWTON (*loc. cit.*) and by MARTIN (1927), as a reflection of the degree of injury suffered by the protoplastic membranes from the application of pressure. Yet the behavior of living leaves in freezing and pressing studies must reflect properties other than a variable resistance of membranes. If in the hardened condition the permeability of the plasma membranes is increased, as indicated by studies in frost resistance, one should expect that expression of sap from living tissue should proceed more easily than from unhardened leaves. This is not true, as NEWTON and others have shown.

The difference in osmotic pressure between sap expressed from living and dead (frozen and thawed) beet root was found to be 0.1 atm. for tissue exhibiting a higher plasmolytic than cryoscopic value. For another beet root where the cryoscopic value was the higher, the difference was 3.1 atm. (TABLE 38). Sap in the first instance was believed to have been diluted by protoplasmic water to a greater extent than was true for the latter.

TABLE 38. — *Osmotic pressure of sap pressed from living as against dead (frozen) tissue, comparing two types of beets. Values in atmospheres at 22.5° C. (data of* CURRIER, 1943) : —

| PCD | EXPRESSED SAP | | DIFFERENCE |
	FRESH	KILLED	
5.8	8.4	8.5	0.1
0.7	13.2	16.3	3.1

Consideration of the data and discussion presented in this section brings out the following necessary conclusions:

1) No method that is above criticism has been devised for obtaining pure vacuolar sap.

2) The unknown quantities are filtration of solutes, especially by the semipermeable membranes of living cells; the diluting effect of colloidally held water, especially as may occur on freezing or otherwise killing the tissue followed by pressing; and other changes which might decrease or enhance the osmotic pressure, *e.g.*, enzymatic reactions.

3) It would appear that plants vary markedly with respect to differences in concentration of saps expressed from living and dead tissue.

4) The potential errors involved appear to be serious enough to throw doubt on much of the mass of osmotic pressure data obtained by the cryoscopic method.

Plasmolytic Behavior of Cells:— In conformity with the classical view of plant water relations, a cell in the condition of limiting plasmolysis immersed in a sap identical with that contained in its own vacuole would be expected to maintain a condition of limiting plasmolysis. In the case of a turgid cell such a result would not be expected for while the osmotic pressures may be equivalent within and without the cell, the diffusion pressure deficit is less within. Hence water would tend to move outward into the external solution, increasing the osmotic pressure of the vacuolar sap. At equilibrium there would be a balance with respect to DPD, but not to OP, and the cell will exhibit some turgor.

Experimentally, the vacuolar concentration of contiguous cells may be assumed equal to that in the cells under observation. Providing sap were expressed from the tissue in the condition of limiting plasmolysis, and providing the section to be immersed in the sap is also in this condition, fifty per cent of the cells should plasmolyze. It is necessary that the volume of external juice be large enough to preclude error due to dilution by water leaving the cells.

There are few reports in the literature of such a procedure. To show that sap expressed from living tissue is not isotonic with respect to living cells, DIXON (1914, p. 184) mounted sections of beet root and leaves of *Chamaerops humilis* in whole sap expressed from frozen tissue. Absence of plasmolysis under these conditions was taken to substantiate the claim that freezing had no concentrating effect on the cell sap. Sap from the living tissue gave a freezing point depression of 0.599° C., while that from frozen tissue was 1.517°.

BENNET-CLARK, GREENWOOD and BARKER (1936) made use of this procedure as an argument for water secretion. Cells of plants which displayed a marked discrepancy between plasmolytic and cryoscopic OP values, failed to plasmolyze in sap expressed from frozen contiguous tissue, while those in which the two measurements agreed well were approximately 50 per cent plasmolyzed.

That there may be different responses to this type of treatment in relation to the magnitude of the plasmolytic-cryoscopic discrepancy (PCD) was suggested by tests on red beet root (CURRIER, 1944a). It was shown that where the plasmolytic OP was the higher, fewer cells mounted in expressed sap became plasmolyzed than where the reverse was true (TABLE 39).

TABLE 39. — *Plasmolysis of beet cells in their own sap:* —

Beet number	Per cent plasmolysis	Beet number	Per cent plasmolysis
41	41	51	18
..	37	52	15
42	54	56	16
..	49	..	9
54	45	63	4
..	30	..	9
68	100	64	6

BEETS SHOWING NEGATIVE PCD (left); BEETS SHOWING POSITIVE PCD (right)

Although the above investigators make no mention of any injurious effect, this type of experiment may not be valid because of the alleged toxic action of expressed sap on living cells (PRÁT, 1927; ERNEST, 1935). Expressed beet root sap is reported to markedly increase the respiratory activity of discs of tissue immersed in it (BENNET-CLARK and BEXON, 1943). Diluting, boiling and filtering, and sterilizing the juice failed to significantly retard the effect. The active constituents present were found to be organic acids, malic especially. Just how an increased respiration would affect the plasmolytic response is not known. The malate effect resembles the ability of auxin to increase respiration (COMMONER and THIMANN, 1941), and water intake may be tied up with respiratory activity (VAN OVERBEEK, 1944). Further evidence relative to the effect of certain solutes on water balance in cells (BENNET-CLARK and BEXON, 1946) is discussed later under the subject of mechanisms.

One of the errors claimed to be inherent in any measurement of osmotic pressure is the response described as "stimulative" plasmolysis (cf. Chapter VII). Under certain conditions, and in certain tissues, cells plasmolyze in apparently hypotonic solutions, and even in distilled water. OSTERHOUT (1913) observed such phenomena in root tips of eel grass (Zostera marina). The effect was ascribed to an unbalanced ionic environment, which increased the permeability of the protoplasm, permitting osmotically active solutes and water to escape and resulting in the shrinking of the protoplast. WEBER (1929b) observed a similar behavior in fruit flesh cells of Polygonatum officinale that appeared to be perfectly normal. Plasmolysis occured when intact cells were mounted in a drop of tap or distilled water containing a small amount of macerated tissue. That the effect was not limited to these cells was shown by placing an Elodea leaf in the drop of water, whereupon plasmolysis also appeared. WEBER thought that an active substance might have been released by the addition of water or by slight mechanical pressure applied to the pulp, further suggesting that certain specialized cells contained the active material. No single explanation, however, could adequately account for the phenomenon.

GROSS (1940) concluded that the plankton diatom Ditylum brightwellii does not behave as an osmotic system, due to an anomalous plasmolytic behavior which he observed. Rapid shrinking and rounding up of the protoplast was found to occur in hypotonic sea water, in a fresh water medium, and even in distilled water. The response could be initiated by several treatments and conditions: (a) pressure applied to the organisms by means of a micro-needle, (b) change in the ionic environment—NaCl alone was effective, (c) the pH of the medium—at pH 8 the effect usually disappeared, and (d) light, prolonged absence of which caused plasmolysis. The process was described as similar to resting spore formation in every respect. The anomaly was such that less shrinking and plasmolysis occurred in molar sucrose solutions than in more dilute solutions. The fact that rounding up occurred upon transfer to dark conditions only after 16 to 24 hours, suggested to GROSS that the turgor mechanism involved osmotic work, and that reserve substances present in the cells were exhausted after this length of time.

Relatively pure water is generally believed to be withdrawn on plasmolysis of cells. GROSS states, however, that from this particular organism whole vacuolar sap is lost. No change in protoplasmic volume could be detected; evidently imbibitional forces are not responsible. GROSS favors a mechanism similar to the "water secretion" of BENNET-CLARK, et al. (1936).

Other examples of anomalous plasmolysis are known. KÜSTER (1929) and PRÁT (1934) may be consulted for literature. It is at the present state of our knowledge unprofitable to speculate as to the meaning of these so-called anomalies. Nor are generalizations permissible. Just as each plant has its peculiar physical and chemical architecture, so will it necessarily have its own particular variation of function. PRÁT states that "the only thing about which all the authors agree is the irregularity of the reaction."

He suggests a mechanism operative by a sudden increase in permeability, whereby water, and solutes, are permitted to leak out. This would not explain plasmolysis in distilled water. An active contraction of the protoplast seems to be a justified assumption in many instances.

The phenomenon to which the name "vacuolar contraction" has been given (KÜSTER, 1926), although differing fundamentally from plasmolysis, deserves discussion at this point. This is a marked swelling of the protoplasm with reduction in vacuolar size but with no essential change in cell volume nor separation of cytoplasm from the wall. It is not a simple osmotic process, since it can occur in a hypotonic environment as a result of some sort of stimulation. While onion scale epidermis and *Elodea* leaves have been preferred materials, the reaction may be observed in many types of cells (KÜSTER, 1940). ARENS and DE LAURO (1946) report that "hydropot" cells in the epidermis of *Sagittaria* leaves offer favorable material. Contraction may be experimentally induced by immersing sections or whole leaves in 1 : 1000 neutral red solutions (pH 7 to 10) for a short time. The vacuoles shrink often to a small fraction of their original size.

Apparently the increase in protoplasmic volume occurs at the expense of the vacuolar contents. ÅKERMAN (1917) was able to demonstrate an osmotic pressure increase of 5 atmospheres in vacuoles of *Drosera rotundifolia* tentacles, due to vacuolar contraction. ARENS and DE LAURO (*loc. cit.*) support the theory that water alone is absorbed by the cytoplasm, the tonoplast restraining the passage of solutes. This is based only on the retention, during the process, of neutral red or of anthocyanin in the vacuole. HARTMAIR (1937) found that in *Elodea* such a transfer of water from vacuole to cytoplasm occurred, but that in onion epidermis there was a decrease in plasmolytically determined osmotic pressure, hence the cause of contraction could have been a sudden increase in permeability of the tonoplast.

The underlying mechanism could well be an increase in the imbibition pressure of the protoplasm. ARENS and DE LAURO prefer to regard it as the result of oxidation-reduction processes, since many of the conditions leading to vacuolar contraction are associated with respiration—pH, wounding, age and activity of the cells, and the specific effect of neutral red.

The use of "cap" plasmolysis (page 88) as a device to study the effect of ions on protoplasmic hydration has been made by HÖFLER (1939) and his associates KAISERLEHNER (1939) and HOUSKA (1940). Swelling of the cytoplasm of onion epidermis to 5-10 times the original volume may be experimentally induced by the use of hypertonic solutions of K, Na, or Li salts. Ca, Sr, and Ba salts do not act in this way. Accompanying effects are an increased fluidity of the protoplasm and a cessation of streaming. It is of interest that the reaction is entirely reversible. According to HÖFLER the K salt might raise cytoplasmic hydration by becoming chemically bound to some protoplasmic building block, resulting in an enhanced attraction between this component and water. The cap plasmolysis method should prove valuable in other studies of this kind.

There is a great deal of physiological interest in both stimulative plasmolysis and vacuolar contraction, since they clearly demonstrate the contractile nature of the protoplasm and its wide variation in capacity to imbibe water. In certain instances the action might be interpreted as a defense mechanism where the cell is exposed to adverse conditions. The possibility should not be excluded that such variation may be associated with normal functioning of certain cells. The observations do suggest, however, that there are as yet too many unknown factors related to protoplasmic structure, permeability, and imbibition to allow a simple osmotic explanation of all cell water relations.

Cryoscopy of Tissues and their Equilibrium Bathing Solutions:— If cells at limiting plasmolysis possess in their vacuoles a sap equal in osmotic pressure to the external solution, the same should hold true where the external solution is hypertonic. Results of such tests utilizing beet root tissue (Currier, 1944a) indicated the expressed sap (after freezing) to be somewhat more dilute than an external "isotonic" solution for tissue exhibiting a $+$PCD ($Og > On \cdot Vn/Vg$). For $-$PCD tissue ($Og < On \cdot Vn/Vg$), the expressed sap was slightly more concentrated. Where the tissue cylinders were treated with weakly hyper- and hypotonic sucrose solutions, there was also evidence that the $\dfrac{\text{expressed sap O P}}{\text{equilibrium solution O P}}$ ratio was higher in the case of the $-$PCD beets. The data are shown in Table 40. Each value represents an average of five determinations.

Table 40. — *Osmotic pressure determinations of tissue cylinders and of their equilibrium bathing solutions. Atmospheres at 22.5° C.: —*

	Living tissue					
	PCD negative or zero			PCD positive		
	Iso-tonic	Hypo-tonic	Hyper-tonic	Iso-tonic	Hypo-tonic	Hyper-tonic
Limiting plasmolysis .	12.7	...	...	17.5	...	...
Expressed sap	13.1	12.1	15.5	16.4	14.8	19.4
External sol'n (initial)	12.7	8.3	16.9	17.5	13.6	22.4
External sol'n (final) .	12.8	8.8	16.8	17.5	13.7	21.5

	Dead tissue	
	PCD negative	PCD positive
Expressed sap	16.4	20.2
External solution	16.7	21.2
Difference	0.3	1.0

Eaton (1943) has suggested that the water secretion values of Bennet-Clark are invalidated by the questionable assumption that plasmolytic values measure the water retaining force of cells in the normal condition. He believes that solute accumulation during the immersion of sections in plasmolyzing solutions is a real possibility, and cryoscopy of tissues removed from such solutions, rather than of tissues of normal volume, would have led to different conclusions. The data in Table 40 do not bear this out with respect to one type of tissue. It is doubtful that sucrose would be absorbed from near-isotonic solutions sufficiently to be troublesome.

When equilibrium values were determined for dead tissues, there was no great difference between the two kinds of beets mentioned above. However, in seven out of a total of eight tests, the expressed sap was from 0.4 to 1.7 atm. more dilute than the external solution.

Some equilibrium studies on certain marine algae have been reported. For some materials, the expressed liquid may be considered almost pure vacuolar sap. Mosebach (1936) so views the sap obtained from the swim-bladder of *Sargassum linifolium,* where the expressed sap amounted to about 96 per cent of the fresh weight. For other materials, he believed that imbibed water in cell walls and protoplasm, released on pressing, could produce deviations much greater than purely methodical errors in technique. Hence, values obtained for several species (TABLE 41) are, if

TABLE 41. — *Cryoscopy of sap expressed from several marine algae and of the surrounding sea water. Atmospheres at 20° C. (data of* MOSEBACH, 1936) : —

| | EXPRESSED | | |
BROWN ALGAE	SAP	SEA WATER	DIFFERENCE
Cystosira barbata (shoots)	30.2	25.2	5
Sargassum linifolium ("leaves")	31.8	25.1	6.7
Sargassum linifolium (swimbladders) ...	31.7	25.1	6.6
RED ALGAE			
Rytiphlaea tinctora	29.6	25	4.6
Spyridia filamentosa	29	25.2	3.8

anything, too low. This table indicates that the osmotic pressure of these plants varies from 3.8 to 6.7 atm. above that of sea water. This infers that turgor pressures are also in this range of magnitude, but there is no proof that this is so. *Valonia macrophysa* and *V. utricularis* show a difference of only about an atmosphere between the surrounding sea water and sap, which can be obtained in an almost pure state.

Osmotic regulation in these forms must be largely one of accumulation of solutes, mostly salts. Osmotic adaptation by *Nitella translucens* to changing external concentration has been demonstrated (WILDERVANCK, 1932) ; a much greater regulative capacity is exhibited by many land plants (GASSER, 1942—*see* Chapter VII).

These results were interpreted to mean that imbibitional phenomena must be taken into account in measurements of osmotic pressure of expressed sap, although they do not preclude the possibility that water secretion forces may also be present. The differences demonstrated may actually be small compared to those which might obtain in other plants.

Auxin and Water Uptake:— The storage parenchyma of the tuber of *Solanum tuberosum* is a favorite experimental object for certain types of water relation studies, since it provides a large amount of homogeneous tissue. STILES and JORGENSEN (1917) observed that the swelling of potato tissue in tap and distilled water did not conform to current ideas of an osmotic system. A temperature coefficient (Q_{10}) of about 3 was indicated. This is not characteristic of purely physical systems, and has been interpreted by COMMONER, FOGEL, and MULLER (1943) as pointing to an enzymatic process associated with water absorption.

Several investigations have been undertaken to demonstrate the effect of auxin on water and salt uptake in potato. While the effect of auxin on growth processes has been a fertile field of research for many years, its role in the water relations of the plant cell has been recognized only recently. REINDERS (1938) found that potato tuber tissue showed an increased water uptake under the influence of auxin. In preliminary experiments, tissue discs 1 mm. thick and 17 mm. in diameter were permitted to remain in "stagnant" tap water for 24 hours, then were transferred to aerated distilled water, whereupon a considerable increase in wet weight occurred in the amount of from 18.6 to 30.5 per cent of initial weight after 8 days. Slight increases were noted even when the transfer was to non-aerated distilled water and to oxygen-free distilled water. A definite temperature effect was observed. As an example, the increase in fresh weight of discs kept in aerated water for two days at 21° C. amounted to 10.3 per cent, compared to 4.7 per cent for a temperature of 10-11° C. In another experiment, carried out at 21° C. and 1-2° C., the respective amounts were 11.3 and 1.6 per cent for the same period of time. Addition of heteroauxin produced a much greater increase in wet weight, and resulted in a greater loss of dry weight. Aeration of the bathing solution induced cell divisions and disappearance of starch from the surface region of the tissue disc. No cell divisions were observed in unaerated cultures. The conclusion of the author is that the auxin effect is on respiration itself, and that the additional energy released is somehow utilized in uptake of water.

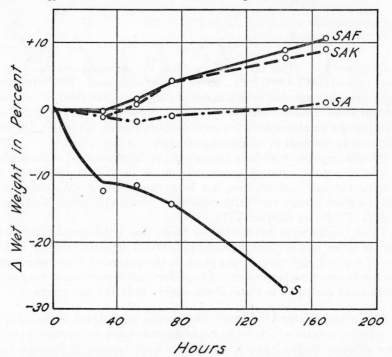

Fig. 38.—The effect of 0.2 M sucrose (S), 0.2 M sucrose plus 10 mgm. of indole-3-acetic acid per liter (SA), these concentrations of sucrose and auxin plus 10^{-3} M. KCl (SAK), these concentrations of sucrose and auxin plus 10^{-4} M. K fumarate (SAF) on changes in the wet weight of aerated potato slices. Data of Commoner, Fogel, and Muller (1943).

STEWARD, STOUT and PRESTON (1940) were unable to concur that Reinders' data proved water uptake to be an active process in potato tissue, because respiration was measured only by loss of dry weight. In their opinion the fact that auxin induces an influx of water into the tissue is no proof that the mechanism is not one of simple osmosis.

STEWARD and his collaborators however report data which do support the possibility of active water absorption by potato in the absence of added auxin. Discs placed in aerated 0.005 N solutions of KBr and KNO$_3$ showed increases in fresh weight surpassing those of discs in distilled water. A specific effect of the ions involved was suggested as a possible explanation. Whereas potassium increased water absorption, calcium acted as an inhibitor. The effect of potassium ion was increased when accompanied by nitrate ion.

These authors could not escape the conclusion that water absorption under the conditions of their experiments was in some manner linked to vital processes. Among these processes, respiration and protein synthesis appeared to proceed proportionately to water intake, even though the concentration of respirable reserves (sugars, amino acids) were depleted to a greater extent than in other cultures where protein synthesis and water absorption were less. The suggestion was offered "that actively metabolizing cells which can grow may absorb water in a manner which has but little relation to any conventional osmotic or suction pressure theory but may be more directly linked with metabolic processes (respiration and protein synthesis); processes which are determined by oxygen and affected by the nature of the salts present in the external solution."

In the view of REINDERS (1942), increased hydration of the protoplasm may possibly result from the formation of osmotically active solutes in the "so-called free water" of the protoplasm.

The problem was further investigated by COMMONER, FOGEL and MULLER (1943), who reported an "active absorption of water against an osmotic gradient." A decrease in wet weight by tissue immersed in aerated 0.2 M (hypertonic) sucrose solution could be prevented by the addition of auxin (indole-3-acetic acid). Where KCl or fumarate were also present, the tissue increased in wet weight. In the absence of auxin, water was lost. The authors postulated an active process, one closely associated with solutes, especially the four-carbon dicarboxylic acids, to be responsible. The suggestion that auxin controls absorption or accumulation of salt, thus affecting the intake of water, does not concur with the statement that water enters actively against an osmotic gradient. FIGURE 38 graphically represents some of the data of this investigation.

VAN OVERBEEK (1944) criticized the work of COMMONER, *et al.,* for two reasons. The lack of aseptic conditions during the tests prolonged for a week or more might introduce complicating factors. And since REINDERS observed marked absorption in distilled water, the suggestion that the auxin effect is on salt metabolism must be erroneous. The experiments were repeated under both aseptic and non-aseptic conditions, with the result that the effect of auxin on water absorption of potato was confirmed. Greater regularity, however, obtained under aseptic conditions (FIGURE 39). VAN OVERBEEK was unable to demonstrate an accelerating effect due to the addition of KCl or fumarate to distilled water, 0.2 M sucrose or 0.2 M mannitol solutions containing auxin. Naphthalene acetic acid acted similarly to indoleacetic acid. By means of cryoscopic determinations, sap expressed from the auxin treated discs was found to have a lower osmotic pressure than that from the control discs, so that on this basis the effect of auxin is not one of increasing the amount of osmotically active solutes. The decrease in OP was in line with the increased volume of the tissue so that probably there was no change in total solute.

We must conclude with VAN OVERBEEK that the effect of auxin must be either (*a*) one of decreasing the wall pressure or (*b*) an effect of "active" pressure. While the first is a definite possibility, there is also reason to believe that water absorption may be in some way associated with the increase in respiratory activity produced by auxin.

Active forces leading to retention of water against an apparent osmotic gradient would, on first consideration, be sought in rapidly growing tissue. The potato tuber is a dormant structure, yet potentially it is capable of growth. In this respect it differs from mature tissues, for example that of apple fruit parenchyma, where further growth is not normal.

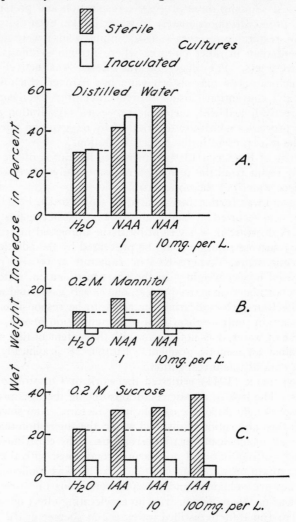

Fig. 39.—Effect of auxins on water uptake of potato tissue under sterile and non-sterile conditions. The height of the bars extending above the dotted line indicates the auxin-induced water uptake of the sterile cultures. A. Experiment in water and 1 and 10 mg per liter naphthaleneacetic acid. Duration of test, 4 days. B. Test carried out at same time and with same material as A; 0.2 M mannitol used as basic medium. C. Test similar to A and B, but made at a different time; 0.2 M sucrose used as basic medium, and 1, 10, and 100 mg per liter indoleacetic acid as auxin. Data of van Overbeek (1944).

It is evident that at least in some instances the phenomena are not due to solute accumulation. To say that auxin accelerates the respiratory rate carries little meaning without knowing how the extra energy output is related to water retention. If the auxin effect is one of increasing wall plasticity only, it is clear that no swelling could take place in hypertonic solution. The fact that expressed sap is slightly more dilute for the auxin-treated discs (van Overbeek) is still not conclusive evidence that the vacuolar OP did not increase, due to the possibility of active uptake of water by the protoplasm. Data on this point would be helpful.

Measurements of Diffusion Pressure Deficits:— Another manifestation of an "active" force has been observed in potato tuber tissue by LYON (1942), who used the simplified method (*cf.* Chapter VII). Comparison was made between the *observed* DPD value (OP of sucrose solution effecting no change in the volume of the tissue), and the calculated DPD value, derived as follows:

$$DPNn = On - TPn \tag{1}$$

$$\text{where } On = Og \cdot \frac{Vg}{Vn} \tag{2}$$

$$\text{and } TPn = TPs \cdot \frac{(Vn - Vg)}{(Vs - Vg)} \tag{3}$$

$$= Og \cdot \frac{Vg}{Vs} \cdot \frac{(Vn - Vg)}{(Vs - Vg)} \tag{4}$$

The results indicated that calculated DPDn values exceeded observed values by as much as 14 atm. for tubers in warm (70° F.) storage, or over half again as much as the observed DPDn. The average discrepancy was about 3 atm. for tubers which had been in storage at 42° F. and about 6 atm. for those at 70° F.

Certain trends are apparent in the data—the significantly higher discrepancy at the warmer storage temperatures; its absence at harvest time; apparent increase in turgor simultaneous with water loss. These observations are difficult to explain by means of the classical theory of osmotic pressure. The author suggests that while the water secretion hypothesis is a possibility, its proof is lacking, and that "the force could be one of pure chemistry, such as an effect of colloids on the diffusion pressure of water within the cells or a difference in electrical potentials, either of which could vary during storage through physiological changes."

LYON points out that the discrepancy could reasonably be due to: (*a*) underestimating the calculated normal wall pressure or (*b*) overestimation of the osmotic pressure at normal cell volume. As one limitation of the simplified method, there is the possibility of excessive Og values, for reasons stated on page 97 (Chapter VII). Such an error, if sufficiently great, would account for the discrepancy. It may be a matter of plasticity of cell walls, the degree varying under differing conditions. One might also question the validity of assuming a direct proportionality between volume and osmotic pressure at the three measurement states. The non-solvent fraction in potato tuber cells would seem to be significant. Regardless of these suggestions with respect to the method, there are indications here of some kind of active regulation. The wide variation in the calculated DPD value and the consistent trends are otherwise difficult to explain.

The water secretion theory of Bennet-Clark finds support in some investigations of BRAUNER and HASMAN (1946), who have proposed that an electrokinetic component is partly responsible for the DPD of cells. Using potato and carrot tissue in isotonic solutions of K_2SO_4, sucrose and $CaCl_2$, the DPD (gravimetric method) varied in a manner suggesting that the charge on cell membranes may exert a control on the movement of water. The differences were not attributable to permeability factors. Small amounts of $CaCl_2$ had a marked effect in lowering the DPD. In potato, about 10 per cent of the total DPD was ascribed to the electroosmotic factor. Somewhat higher values were subsequently (1947) demonstrated in beetroot and in carrot.

KERR and ANDERSON (1944) studied the osmotic quantities of cotton seeds in various stages of growth. In seeds less than 24 days old OP values exceeded the DPD, a relationship to be expected. But in older seeds the reverse was true to a marked degree (TABLE 42). Osmotic pressures were determined cryoscopically, using sap expressed from frozen tissue; DPD's were calculated by use of the change-in-weight method (Chapter VII). The authors considered two possible explanations: (*a*) some sort of active water absorption, and (*b*) imbibition. Use of respiratory inhibitors, as KCN and ethyl ether, indicated that respiratory activity was probably not directly related to the phenomenon. It was pointed out that the embryo remains very small during the first 24 days of its growth. The excessive DPD values appeared after this period, at a time when the embryo was rapidly developing and coincident with the breakdown of endosperm. The high colloid content of the embryo cells suggested the possibility that water liberated on freezing and pressing produced OP values which were too low. Imbibitional forces thus were believed to account for the difference between the two measurements, which is "more apparent than real."

TABLE 42. — *Osmotic pressures of cell sap from cotton seeds of three ages before and after immersion in sucrose solutions (data of KERR and ANDERSON, 1944) :* —

AGE OF SEEDS	OP OF SAP EXPRESSED FROM SEEDS	DPD OF SEEDS	CONC. OF SUCROSE SOLUTIONS	OP OF SUCROSE SOLUTIONS	OP OF SAP EXPRESSED FROM SEEDS AFTER IMMERSION IN SUCROSE
days	atm.	atm.	M	atm.	atm.
18	9.63	7.0	0.25	6.7	9.63
23	8.07	10.2	0.40	11.1	8.35
30	7.77	13.7	0.50	14.3	9.12

This work emphasizes the importance of colloidal hydration in the water relations of some plant tissues, a force which may be generally under-estimated.

Evidence from Studies of Frost and Drought Resistance:— The freezing point of living tissue has usually been found to be lower than that of dead tissue or its expressed sap. MÜLLER-THURGAU (1886) found —0.98 and —0.55° C. for living and dead potato tuber tissue respectively, and —0.8 compared to —0.4 for *Phaseolus* leaves. MAXIMOV (1914) reported —2.15° and —1.25° respectively for red beetroot, and —1.21° for the extracted sap. Similar data are reported by LEWIS and TUTTLE (1920), CARRICK (1930), CURTIS and SCOFIELD (1933), JACCARD and FREY-WYSSLING (1934), LUYET and GEHENIO (1937).

An adequate explanation of this behavior has not been offered, but there are several hypotheses which variously attribute the difference to *1*) capillary attraction of water in the intercellular spaces, *2*) the resistance offered by protoplasmic membranes to the movement of water out of the cells, *3*) non-solvent (bound) water in living cells liberated upon death, and *4*) errors in method. The reader is referred, for an adequate discussion of this subject, to reviews by WALTER and WEISMANN (1935), LUYET and GEHENIO (1939), and LEVITT (1941).

The display of a double freezing point by living tissue, confirmed by several workers, is a complicating feature in the interpretation of results.

After study and review of existing data, LUYET and GEHENIO (1937) favor the theory that the first freezing point represents the congelation of inter-cellular liquid; the second is due to freezing of the intracellular water. Also confusing the attempt to interpret freezing behavior of living tissue is the fact that variation of experimental conditions will produce different results. LUYET and GALOS (1940) studied the effect of rate of cooling on the freezing point of living and dead potato tuber tissue, concluding that the difference between the two values became less with decrease in cooling rate, and suggesting that at a velocity of about 0.1° C. per minute, the two should be approximately equal. Dead tissue did not behave in this manner. This confirmed earlier results of WALTER and WEISMANN (1935), who state that while the freezing point of living tissue invariably is lower than of dead tissue, no conclusions should be drawn from this as to the osmotic concentration of the cell sap in living and dead tissue. They attribute the discrepancy to the impossibility of stirring in such determinations, and to the varying speed at which ice is formed. The latter in turn depends on the permeability of the protoplasm to water, and on the DPD of the cells, since freezing first occurs in the intercellular spaces. They present data to show that under the same freezing conditions the same amount of ice formed in living as in dead tissues, and that the osmotic pressure of the cell sap is the same in both. This conclusion was necessitated by the ob-servation that when cooling curves indicated an equilibrium between the tissue and cooling bath, the areas under the two curves were the same. WALTER and WEISMANN's data are criticized by LEVITT (1941) as not conclusive, since it was not determined whether the tissue was alive at the end of the experiment, a doubtful assumption in his opinion.

Contrary to results obtained with tissues as experimental material, GEHENIO (1941) reported a higher freezing point for living myxomycete plasmodium than for dead. No adequate explanation seemed possible. One suggestion was that freezing caused the disintegration of protoplasm with the reduction in the size of particles and an increase in their number, thus augmenting the effective concentration. The phenomenon might also be explained by the preferential adsorption of water by the dead protoplasmic colloids.

There is better agreement between the freezing points of dead tissue and expressed sap, although the former yields lower values. This has been variously interpreted; according to some (*cf.* JACCARD and FREY-WYSSLING, 1934), it is due to the liberation of colloidally bound water, or to some other type of disintegration or disturbance such as ruptured xylem vessels. With this "dilution theory" WALTER and WEISMANN disagree, pointing out that cryoscopy of dead tissue, as of living tissue, is less accurate than of ex-pressed sap because of the impossibility of stirring, etc.; but when special precaution is taken the two values agree well. Their view, then, is that the concentration of cell sap remains constant throughout the living, dead, and expressed sap states.

In this connection tests carried out on beet root tissue may be of interest (CURRIER, 1944a). A mercury thermometer with a small (5 mm. diameter) bulb, and calibrated in fiftieths of a degree, was used. A small hole in a tissue cylinder accommodated the bulb. Freezing was initiated by inserting a small glass capillary filled with ice into the tissue. After the freezing point of the living tissue had been determined, the cylinder was frozen, and the freezing point of the dead tissue was ascertained in a similar manner.

Subsequently the sap was expressed and a third value obtained. From TABLE 43 it is clear that the living tissue froze in every instance at a lower temperature than did the dead tissue. The beet roots employed had previously been investigated with respect to plasmolytic and cryoscopic determination of OP. There was found to be considerable resistance to freezing in the case of +PCD beets, with particular difficulty in inoculation. The reverse was true of —PCD plants, where in some instances freezing was spontaneous, *i.e.*, required no inoculation. In line with other evidence, the differences were believed due to dilution and concentration effects as a result of freezing.

TABLE 43. — *Freezing points of living tissue, dead tissue, and expressed sap. Atmospheres at 22.5° C.:* —

PCD	LIVING	DEAD	SAP
Positive	26.4	22.8[a]	18.0
Positive	23.6	15.3	13.3
Zero	21.2	14.6	14.3
Negative	12.9	11.7	12.9
Negative	18.6	11.5	13.0

[a] Freezing not complete.

Recent reviews (LEVITT, 1941; SCARTH, 1944) on the subject of cold hardiness of plants have emphasized the fact that resistance to freezing temperatures by certain plants is due primarily to protoplasmic factors. While there has been shown to be some correlation with other characteristics accompanying the hardened condition, *e.g.*, small cells, lower moisture content, higher sap concentration, they are considered to be of only secondary importance. Considerable significance is attached to the physical state of the protoplasm in hardened as compared to unhardened cells. Associated with the former are (*a*) an increased permeability and (*b*) decreased consistency, both of which are attributed to (*c*) a greater hydrophily of the protoplasm. By means of this theory many of the observations on cold hardiness may be explained.

The experimental basis for this hypothesis is derived for the most part from application of micrurgical and plasmolytic methods applicable to living cells. Certain advantages are thus gained over the considerable number of chemical and physical procedures that have been employed with dead tissues and extracts. The following additional characteristics were found to be associated with the hardened condition of living plant cells: increased thickness of the cytoplasmic layer, high resistance to deplasmolysis injury, ability of the protoplast to round up on plasmolysis, greater density of protoplasmic strands, less rigidity of ectoplasm on dehydration, lower refractive index of ectoplasm, less clumping of plastids and granules on plasmolysis, greater non-solvent space (in some), less tendency of colloids to coagulate.

The literature of frost resistance is so extensive that only one phase of the problem will be considered here—the matter of *hydrophily* of the protoplasm. Frost resistance implies ability to withstand freezing temperatures. It means that the tissues are able to prevent formation of ice, or have an ability to withstand it. The term hydrophily, used in connection with protoplasm, refers to the total water content or hydration; it carries no implication as to the nature of the forces holding this water. The relationship between the degree of hydrophily developed by hardening cells and the amount of "bound" water in the protoplasm is in question. Levitt concludes from study of the literature that the reduced rate of water loss sometimes observed in hardy plants can usually be explained on the basis of some morphological character, rather than on bound water. It is well to emphasize again (Chapter VI) that knowledge concerning the water holding mechanisms in protoplasm is limited. While the evidence for water binding in dead systems such as expressed saps may be questioned, in protoplasm we are dealing with a system possessing active forces, a system that is able to perform osmotic work with regard to solutes, and probably also to water.

Several observations indicate that protoplasmic volume increases during hardening. LEVITT and SCARTH (1936) found this to be true for cortical cells of *Catalpa,* where the protoplasm occupied about 50 per cent of cell volume. In this amount it cannot help but exert a marked influence on water control. The work of KESSLER and RUHLAND (1938) indicated a greater volume of protoplasm in hardened tissues. The fact that smaller cells, with greater relative volume of protoplasm, are the more hardy, is of significance. On the other hand, SCARTH (1941), on the basis of an observed lower refractive index and a greater permeability of the ectoplasm, has suggested that the increased hydration on hardening may be limited to this outer protoplasmic layer.

LEVITT (1941) finds it difficult to reconcile the decreased water content of hardy plants with increased hydration of the protoplasm; he suggests that the walls may dry. A better explanation might picture the protoplasm as varying its hydrophily allowing reduction of water in vacuole and walls at the same time that its own water content increases. Such a process might involve unfolding of protein chains or opening of ring structures to present more points for hydration, the more active structure being maintained by metabolic energy.

Another explanation for increased hydrophily is possible. It has been reported that the respiration of hardened cells is of lower intensity than in non-hardened cells (*see* review by LEVITT, 1941, p. 124). This might suggest that respiratory energy is utilized in masking hydration points, and that a low rate would permit greater hydration. There seems to be no agreement however on the relation between respiratory rate and degree of hardiness. Regardless of the type of bonding involved the retention of water, as a part of protoplasmic structure, must be influenced by metabolic forces. The possibility must not be lost sight of that water may be held in living protoplasm by forces so intimately related to the living state that they cannot be studied in dead or injured cells, or in extracts.

In many respects drought resistance is similar to frost resistance. It has seemed logical to many investigators that a considerable amount of the water of true xerophytes must be bound to colloids. In spite of the numerous criticisms (*e.g.,* WEISMANN, 1938), methods for estimating bound water are still being employed in studies of drought resistance (WHITMAN, 1941, MIGAHID, 1945). The latter author has aptly stressed the point that where sap is expressed, bound water can be determined only when the press cake residue is also taken into account. He concludes that the bound water content of xerophytes is significantly higher than that of mesophytes. In several instances values in the order of 17 per cent of total leaf water was reported as bound.

The preceding discussion can lead to no definite conclusions as to the existence of active control of water in frost or drought resistance. The explanations listed above are highly speculative; they must await new methods for substantiation; only as the molecular structure of protoplasm in the living state is investigated and described may we hope to build a clear picture of the forces maintaining its structure and accounting for its remarkable properties.

Evidence from Animal Physiology:— Animal cells differ from plant cells in two distinct ways: they possess neither a semi-rigid wall, nor a large central vacuole. In many ways, however, they are functionally similar.

Lucké and McCutcheon (1932) consider plant and animal cells to behave as osmotic systems if experimental conditions are carefully controlled so that injury does not result in loss of semi-permeability, and if correction is made for osmotically inactive contents. For example, they found normal uninjured erythrocytes to swell and shrink in hypo- and hypertonic solutions to a lesser degree than would be expected of an ideal osmometer, but when a correction for osmotically inactive material was made approximate agreement obtained. Brooks and Brooks (1941) make the same general conclusion—that only osmotic forces are acting, but point out that some anomalous results are still unexplained.

Ponder (1944) discusses three possible explanations: a) the anomalies are due to varying amounts of bound water, b) the cells lose or gain solutes during the experiments, c) elastic structural forces residing in the protoplasm oppose uptake of water from hypotonic solutions as well as loss of water to hypertonic solutions. The last explanation was considered the most plausible.

Correction for non-solvent volume in marine invertebrate eggs did not produce the expected agreement in the pressure-volume relations of the cells (Leitch, 1934). For some cells the calculated amount of osmotically inactive material, based on the total protein and fat content, appeared to be too low; for others it was too high. He suggested that several factors might affect water exchanges; where volume changes were below expectation surface forces might prevent penetration of water. Brooks and Brooks (1941, p. 75) conclude that "most eggs do not behave as perfect osmometers even after allowance is made for the known amount of water and solids in them."

Differential behavior of animal cells and tissues toward water has been reported in many instances. Krogh (1939), in a monograph on osmoregulatory processes in aquatic animals, points out that most animal cells are in osmotic equilibrium with their bathing solutions; when the concentration is modified swelling or shrinking must occur. Some cells, however, are able to maintain hypo- or hypertonicity with their liquid environment. Since rigid walls are absent, neither turgor nor tension is great enough to be important in the attainment of a steady state with respect to water. Such a state can exist only because osmotic regulatory devices requiring energy are able to eliminate water or solutes as the case may be; these processes involve the utilization of metabolic energy.

Though the over-all evidence for active water regulation by the lower aquatic animals is inconclusive, several cases may be mentioned that are strongly suggestive. *Noctiluca miliaris,* a marine protozoan has a lower specific gravity than sea water, differing from most other members of the group. When mechanically or electrically stimulated its density increases, and this is accompanied by an excretion of acid. Thus there seemed to be some relation between the distribution of acid in the cell (around pH 3) and its ability to float or sink (GROSS, 1934). HARVEY (1917) found that cyanide treatment or absence of oxygen did not alter the density of the organisms, indicating that respiratory energy is not a factor.

The contractile vacuole of many fresh water protozoa is believed to function as an osmoregulatory device (review by KITCHING, 1938). Apparently it is able to control body volume by excreting water (or a very dilute solution) as fast as it enters by osmosis through the surface membrane much as water may be pumped from a leaky vessel. That cyanide slows the vacuolar rhythm and results in swelling may be taken to mean that osmotic work is involved. Transfer to hypertonic solution causes slowing or cessation of vacuolar activity.

BEADLE (1934) studied the water relations of *Gunda ulvae,* a small worm living in estuaries and adapted to existence both in fresh and sea water. He concluded that on change from sea water to fresh, water enters through the skin and the animal swells. The additional water is absorbed by cells of the gut and secreted into intercellular vacuoles by expenditure of energy. Following this original restoration of balance, the ectoderm is believed to inhibit further entry of water because of a reduced permeability. The latter is visualized as an "osmotic resistance" of the ectoderm cells similarly dependent on energy. The secretion of water into vacuoles seems to resemble that of plant cells postulated by BENNET-CLARK, et al. (1936).

Krogh states that in higher aquatic animals, most of the known osmoregulatory functions are confined to a more or less advanced type of kidney. In some organisms extra-renal excretion apparently occurs. One form of kidney characteristic of fresh water organisms produces a urine markedly hypotonic to the blood, sometimes nearly as dilute as the surrounding water; another type, as in mammals, is able to produce a concentrated urine hypertonic to the blood.

Other organisms adapted to changing environment are certain teleost fishes. Study of the eel *Anguilla vulgaris* (KEYS, 1932) revealed mechanisms by which the animal is able to maintain a fairly constant internal concentration when changed from fresh to sea water, and *vice versa.* Fresh water is hypotonic, sea water hypertonic. KEYS states that in the latter, water is swallowed and the excess sodium chloride is subsequently excreted by the gills. In fresh water the kidney is capable of filtration, and salt conservation.

According to ADOLPH (1930), a skinless frog may act more or less as a perfect osmometer. To the skin is assigned a role of active water transport, water passing inward more readily than outward.

In man the kidney is believed to perform a highly specialized type of osmotic work. According to common understanding the process involves filtration by the glomeruli and subsequent absorption of water by the tubules. The latter operate against an osmotic gradient. Other examples of active water transfer may be recognized in the function of the salivary glands and possibly the intestine.

The part played by hydrophilic colloids in the water balance of man has been stressed by some investigators (FISCHER, 1921; GORTNER, 1938). For example, in many instances transfer of water from one part of the body to another is explained by imbibitional phenomena. Since the ability of colloids to hold water varies greatly with changing environment such as salt concentration, etc., it is proposed that water may be taken up at one point and released at another.   In a strict sense this cannot be considered as active water transport.

PICKEN (1936) stated that the muscles of higher invertebrates appear to be "considerably less hydrated than would be the case if they were in simple equilibrium with the surrounding protein solution" and visualized some active regulation of hydration.   This suggests that energy is expended in decreasing the imbibition pressure of the protoplasm.   In a recent personal communication this author suggests that "regulation" may probably be achieved in the first place by the synthesis of structurally different proteins which differ in their affinity for water.

While ultimate explanations for the phenomena listed above are not at hand, it seems that active processes involving water are numerous in the animal organism.   For a thorough discussion of active transport of solutes and water in animals, *see* HÖBER (1945).

Relation to Solute Accumulation:— Though solute accumulation cannot receive detailed treatment in this volume, it seems appropriate to attempt a reconciliation of the processes of water and solute absorption since both may apparently be active processes.   Since solute accumulation implies absorption against a concentration gradient, the dynamic "steady state" maintained by the plant is usually characterized by a higher solute concentration within the cell than without.   The analogy between this and water secretion should be clear.

The known facts concerning solute accumulation by plant cells may be briefly stated:

1) Plants under the appropriate conditions retain within their cells higher concentrations of certain ions than exist externally (OSTERHOUT, 1922; HOAGLAND and DAVIS, 1923a).   Furthermore, the total ion concentration in the cell sap may exceed the external concentration by as much as 25 times (HOAGLAND and DAVIS, 1929).

2) The accumulation process has been demonstrated to depend on metabolic energy (STEWARD, 1932; HOAGLAND and BROYER, 1936).   This conclusion has resulted from tests utilizing cyanide, oxygen deficiency, temperature variation, and limited respirable food reserves.   Light was found by HOAGLAND and DAVIS (1923b) to be an important factor, probably through its relation to food synthesis.

3) Solute accumulation takes place in both aquatic and terrestrial plants.   Many investigators have used massive-celled algae such as *Nitella, Valonia, Chara,* and *Halocystis* since vacuolar sap in a fairly pure state may be obtained in sufficient quantities for analysis.   For a review of such studies, *see* OSTERHOUT (1936, 1947a).   Barley roots have been used with success, sap expressed from frozen and thawed roots being employed for analysis (HOAGLAND and BROYER, 1936).   Potato tuber tissue has been used in studies on salt uptake by Steward and his associates.

4) The preponderance of the ions determined in such studies are believed to exist within the vacuoles of the cells almost entirely in the free state (HOAGLAND and DAVIS, 1923a; OSTERHOUT, 1936).

5) The process appears to be limited to growing tissues or to those potentially able to grow.

6) While most investigations have dealt with electrolyte absorption, other solutes may be accumulated.

7) The underlying mechanism is not yet clear.   STEWARD and HARRISON (1939) distinguish between "primary" and "induced" absorption.   The first refers to an active process dominant in accumulation phenomena of living cells.   The second implies absorption due to the physical and chemical properties of the tissue with no dependence on metabolic energy.   Absorption of ions by dead tissues comes in this category.   The forces involved in induced absorption are those of diffusion, complex formation, colloidal adsorption, ionic exchange, and Donnan membrane potentials.

The mechanism underlying primary ion absorption is very complex and involves the little understood properties of living protoplasm. While the protoplasm must be the locus of the energy release, apparently a higher level of accumulation exists in the vacuole (HOAGLAND and BROYER, 1942). Though in the initial stages of accumulation by low salt plants, concentration in the protoplasm may greatly exceed that of the vacuole (BROOKS, 1938) in the steady or equilibrium state the vacuolar concentration is greater. Though this implies accumulation in the cytoplasm, followed possibly by passive release into the vacuole, the end result is equivalent to secretion. Intimately associated with the active process are problems of permeability, interionic relations, metabolic level, active water control, etc.

STEWARD, *et al.* (series of papers to 1943) concluded that ion accumulation is related to protein metabolism. The capacity to synthesize protein is considered essential to cells that accumulate and retain solutes in their cell sap.

Accumulation or active solute uptake by plants is an established fact. Until recently workers have directed little attention to the water relations of this process. From the similarity of ion uptake and water secretion one is prompted to ask, if ions are actively absorbed, cannot water also be accumulated by living cells? HOAGLAND has stressed the independence of ion and water uptake. Are these processes as independent as might appear? Or may they not be simply different aspects of a single process, the differences in rates being reflections of differences in availability or of transport away from absorbing organs?

STEWARD, STOUT, and PRESTON (1940), as previously noted, observed an anomalous water uptake in potato discs. The presence of potassium accelerated absorption whereas calcium had a depressing effect. Nitrate ions accentuated the acceleration due to potassium. The suggestion is made that in addition to solute accumulation, water absorption may also be related to respiration and protein synthesis. The results, they state "suggest that aerobic respiration, protein synthesis, water absorption, and salt accumulation are all mutually dependent processes which occur in all cells which are not subject to equilibrium conditions but the behavior of which, at constant temperature, is regulated by oxygen tension and the nature and concentration of the salt solution in which they are immersed."

The relation between water absorption (by roots) and active solute absorption becomes even more intimate in the theories of LUNDEGÅRDH (1946). Anions are pictured as actively absorbed by the protoplasm, energized by a special "anion respiration." Cations then move more or less passively from negative points on the surface to negative points in the protoplasm, being "dragged along" due to potential differences maintained by anion accumulation. The ions which move from the root hair across the cortex, K^+, NO_3^-, HCO_3^-, etc., carry with them spheres of water, the amount related inversely to the osmotic pressure of the cell sap. As the ions are permitted to "leak" into the vessels they carry this water along. They carry in addition what LUNDEGÅRDH terms "extra water," which includes metabolic water, some carried to the roots by sugars, and some due to changes in the swelling power of the protoplasm. In this manner, the bleeding sap (exudate) may be more dilute than the medium bathing the roots.

Relation to Other Plant Functions:— The possible role of active water control in other plant functions may be briefly indicated. Interrelations have been implied by various investigators with respect to the general processes of absorption by roots (VAN OVERBEEK, 1942; WHITE, 1942); to transpiration (DIXON and BARLEE, 1940); and to translocation (GOD-LEWSKI, 1884; JANSE, 1913; and BOSE, 1923). These will be considered in the two chapters that follow.

Some who have studied mechanisms of cell elongation, or cell growth, have been inclined to suggest processes involving active control of water. The theory that auxin acts to increase wall plasticity and promote active deposition of wall substance has many adherents, notably HEYN (1940). Evidence that plastic extensibility in potato tuber tissue is greater under aerobic conditions than where oxygen is excluded has been supplied by L. and M. BRAUNER (1943a). Others believe that auxin enhances the imbibition pressure of the protoplasm. STRUGGER (1934), for example, found by plasmolytic methods that an increase in protoplasmic viscosity accompanied cell enlargement, and concluded that an enhanced swelling pressure is directly involved. He suggested that acids resulting from respiratory activity might promote swelling. Other explanations of cell enlargement include an increase in solute concentration and the existence of electrical potentials across the cell membranes produced by auxin, either of which might bring about increased turgor, resulting in growth.

Growth is a complicated process. Perhaps several of the above mechanisms are operating simultaneously, all influenced by auxin directly or indirectly. The problem is one of the most difficult in physiology; nevertheless there has been much progress.

The striking movements exhibited by some plants have been of considerable interest to physiologists. The sudden drooping of leaflets and petioles of *Mimosa pudica* upon stimulation has caused much speculation as to the cellular mechanics involved. It is generally agreed that the response is the direct result of the loss of turgor by the cells comprising the lower region of the pulvinus. This may be due to an active contraction of the protoplast (BOSE, 1928; WEIDLICH, 1930) whereupon liquid is secreted into the intercellular spaces. Bose has been able to identify the contracting cells by staining methods, and claims to have found by actual measurement a decrease in cell diameter due to the contraction.

At the same time, the cells comprising the upper region of the pulvinus expand somewhat. This is due in part to stretching resulting from the force of gravity on the drooping leaf, and an attendant increased DPD, which causes an additional uptake of water (WEIDLICH, 1930). During the recovery process, which is of considerably longer duration than the initial response, the cells in the lower part of the pulvinus apparently reabsorb liquid and regain their normal turgor. That this liquid is relatively pure water, and that the contraction is not a result of changes in permeability which would permit whole cell sap to flow out, is the view of WEIDLICH (1930).

Glandular secretion is another process in plants poorly understood at the present time. According to BLACKMAN (1921), PFEFFER in 1877 proposed three hypotheses to account for the exudation of fluid from living cells:

1) An unequal osmotic pressure developed by the membrane in different parts of the cell,

2) Unequal distribution of osmotic material in different parts of the cell,

3) Presence of osmotic substances in cell wall outside of the membrane, causing water to move out of the cell.

BLACKMAN favored theory No. 2, where a steady concentration difference would be maintained by osmotic work requiring energy. Evidence supporting this view has been supplied by OSTERHOUT (1947b). By treating one end of a *Nitella* cell with an isotonic sucrose solution, the internal osmotic pressure at that end was apparently increased. On removal of the sugar solution, so that water completely surrounded the cell, water entered at the treated end and was expelled at the other.

Mechanisms:— Few mechanisms have been proposed to account for the active regulation of water in living organisms. There has been more speculation on active solute uptake than on water absorption, first, because of its relative importance in the nutrition of plants, and, second, due to the paucity of evidence on active water relations. Especially is this true in the plant field where there is little clear evidence for active water regulation. EATON (1943) thinks there are insufficient data to warrant postulating "uncertain physical and chemical forces" in such plant functions as bleeding and root pressure.

Some have attacked the concept of "vital" functions in physiology as unnecessary and even absurd. They imply a meaning different than the one used in this chapter. Although our usage of the term indicates the lack of a mechanical explanation at the present time, it presumes that an explanation may be forthcoming. To us, the term "active" implies a process involving the utilization of metabolic energy. In this sense salt accumulation and water secretion are both active processes.

ADOLPH (1943, p. 255) comments that, in addition to osmotic pressure, "other sorts of forces, both known and unknown to physicists, may be simultaneously present," and he is not optimistic that all of them are ever identified.

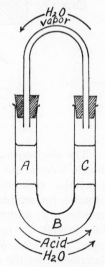

Anomalous osmosis might prove a starting point for an attack on active cell processes, for, in it, water moves in a direction contrary to that expected on the basis of concentration differences. Anomalous osmosis is a well-established phenomenon. It may be due to processes of the nature of electroosmosis or "anaphoresis" as described by OSTERHOUT and MURRAY (1939). They used the apparatus diagrammed in FIGURE 40 in which A represents an aqueous solution of trichloracetic acid separated from water, C, by a layer of guaiacol, B. As expected, acid moved to the right. Water, however, moved in the same direction at a greater rate so that its mol fraction in A decreased. The probable mechanism is that water of hydration is carried along with the solute. Calculations proved that over 25 mols of water would have to be transported by 1 mol of acid to account for some of the results obtained. Since hydration

FIG. 40. — Apparatus for demonstrating "anaphoresis." A, an aqueous solution of trichloracetic acid; B, a layer of guaiacol; C, a layer of water. From OSTERHOUT and MURRAY (1940).

did not remain constant, definite hydrates were probably not concerned.

Some have considered that electroosmosis may be a major factor in controlling the water balance of cells. It may act to implement osmotic pressure (positive anomalous osmosis), or to oppose it (negative anomalous osmosis). Under proper conditions a transport of water through a membrane from a concentrated to a more dilute salt solution may be demonstrated.

Electroosmosis may be defined as the movement of liquid along a charged solid surface (*e.g.,* pore walls in a membrane) due to a potential difference across a membrane exerted tangentially to the interface (that is, the pore walls). The difference in potential, termed membrane potential or liquid junction potential, is dependent on the presence of electrolytes in the solution; non-electrolytes are ineffective. Differential ion migration velocities and a heterogeneous pore system contribute to the production of the potential difference.

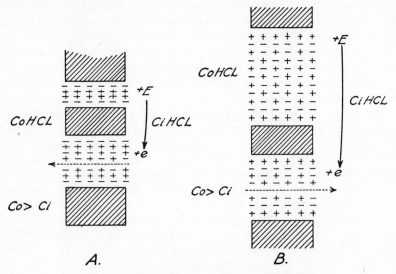

Fig. 41.—Diagrammatic representation of two membranes, (A) permeable to cations only, the other, (B) anion permeable. Each separates two HC1 solutions of concentrations C_o and C_1 where $C_o > C_1$. A diagrams positive anomalous osmosis and B, negative anomalous osmosis. The mechanisms are based on electroosmosis. From Höber (1945).

The electroosmotic flow is dependent on the production of an electrical double layer at the solid-liquid interface. On immersing the membrane in a solution containing electrolyte the surface assumes a charge (usually negative for natural membranes) which may result from ionization of the membrane or adsorption of ions from the solution. The liquid at the interface carries the opposite charge and becomes, at least in part, a mobile layer. The electrokinetic potential across the interface (double layer) is determined by the concentration and kind of electrolyte, the nature of the membrane, and other factors. FIGURE 42C diagrams the nature of this double layer within the pore of a membrane.

In order that electroosmosis may proceed, there must be a flow of current across the membrane; that is, there must be a closed circuit. BARTELL (1923) suggested that the return circuit occurs through the medium of the double layer. However, SOLLNER (1930) and SOLLNER and GROLLMAN (1932) pointed out that a heterogeneous system of different sized pores might account for return flow. FIGURE 41 helps to explain this mechanism.

FIGURES 41A and B represent membranes having pores of unequal size. Each separates two HCl solutions, those on the left being the more concentrated. In A the smaller pore is permeable to cations only; the wall is negatively charged; the movable liquid carries plus (H^+) ions. The membrane potential (E) across this pore is greater than that (e) across the larger pore setting up a driving force that produces a movement of the positively charged liquid toward the left. Since the normal flow is also in this direction, the residual flow is termed positive anomalous osmosis.

The membrane in B is positively charged. The smaller pore preferentially transports anions, therefore exhibits a smaller positive potential (e) than the larger (E). Movement of the vein of liquid in this pore is toward the more dilute solution, and is termed negative anomalous osmosis.

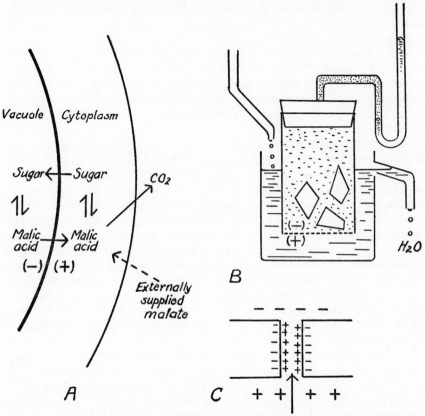

Fig. 42.—Electroosmotic flow according to BENNET-CLARK and BEXON (1943).

BENNET-CLARK and BEXON (1943) have introduced a theory of water movement by which they attempt to explain secretion across the tonoplast into the vacuole due to electrokinetic activity. Instead of the classical model

> solution | semipermeable membrane | water,

they prefer

> solution | permeable membrane | water

as being more characteristic of the cell. They propose that the excess turgor observed in their earlier work (BENNET-CLARK, et al., 1936) is due to continuous diffusion of solute. This might account for a potential difference across the tonoplast and provide the driving force for electroosmosis. Or the water might move as water of hydration with the solute, a process similar to OSTERHOUT and MURRAY's anaphoresis. Turgor in cells is pictured as resulting from such a continuous diffusion process rather than from a "static osmotic equilibrium which could only be attained with an ideal semipermeable protoplast." To organic acids such as malic is assigned an important role in this process.

FIGURE 42 from BENNET-CLARK and BEXON (1943) will aid in following the suggested series of events. In FIGURE 42A, malic acid diffuses from the vacuole into the protoplasm where it is enzymatically converted into carbohydrate. The latter moves into the vacuole, whereupon it is broken down to malic acid again. This completes a continuous diffusion cycle of non-electrolyte inward and electrolyte outward. In this way a potential difference might be maintained which in turn would account for an electroosmotic flow into the vacuole. FIGURE 42B represents a simple model used by BENNET-CLARK for illustrative purposes. A container, the bottom of which comprises a permeable ("oxidized collodion") membrane, contains a saturated salicylic acid solution with excess of solid. This is immersed in another vessel containing pure water. A hydrostatic pressure is developed as indicated by the manometer, which is greater than the osmotic pressure of the solution. This excess pressure is due to an electroosmotic flow through the pores of the membrane. One such pore is indicated as FIGURE 42C.

In a fourth paper on the water relations of plant cells, BENNET-CLARK and BEXON (1946) give further evidence that bioelectric forces exert an influence on water movement. Inner epidermis of onion bulb scale was mounted in a perfusion apparatus designed for rapid replacement of the bathing solution while the tissue was under microscopic observation. When tissue, which had been treated with KCl solution (27.9 atm.) long enough to cause complete plasmolysis (40 minutes), was exposed to a sucrose solution of the same osmotic pressure, a temporary swelling of the vacuole was observed. After 15 to 30 minutes the initial volume was reestablished. Transfer back to KCl produced the reverse effect—a shrinkage of the vacuole, followed by a return to the initial volume. That this result was not simply a diffusion effect on the OP of the solution between the wall and the protoplast was shown by the fact that isolated protoplasts behaved in the same way.

BENNET-CLARK and BEXON give the following explanation. Assuming a negative charge on the membrane, the permeability to K^+ is greater than to Cl^-. On transfer from sucrose to KCl, the greater penetration of K^+ produces a positive charge on the inner membrane surface. This potential difference effects an electroosmotic flow outward, and cell volume is reduced. When KCl is replaced by sucrose, preferential diffusion of KCl outward causes the inner surface to become negatively charged, and the electroosmotic flow is directed inwardly. Equilibrium obtains in both instances as the membrane potential drops to zero.

One point made insufficiently clear is whether the volume of protoplasm remains approximately constant during swelling and shrinkage of the vacuole. Vacuolar contraction, and its reversal, frequently reported in onion epidermis, could conceivably account for at least some of the volume changes observed.

BRAUNER and HASMAN, in a series of papers (*see* 1947) have defended the view that an electroosmotic flow of water is a significant component of DPD of plant cells. In their theory, bivalent cations should act to neutralize the electric potential in the pores of the double membrane (cell wall-cytoplasm). The difference between gravimetric determinations of DPD, one in sucrose solution, another in $CaCl_2$ or $MgCl_2$, in their view gives a measure of the electrokinetic component. As an example, for red beetroot the DPD in sugar solution was 7.90 atm.; in CaCl₂ it was 6.75 atm. Possibly one should inquire if at least some of the effect of the salt is not due to its penetration into the interior protoplasm, with a resulting change in capacity to hold water.

The suggestion that electroosmosis and related phenomena are operative in the control of water by plant cells is very plausible; their relative importance, however, is difficult to evaluate. The requirements for electroosmotic flow include: a permeable membrane with a heterogeneous pore system; electrolytes of suitable concentration on each side; and continuous diffusion of electrolyte demanding some device for maintaining concentration differences. It is this last that designates the process in living systems as an active one. If a mechanism suited to the maintenance of such concentration differences can be demonstrated, the above requirements can be met by living cells. HÖBER (1945), who has very adequately discussed mechanisms of electroosmosis, suggests, with reference to frog skin, that a continuous production and removal of hydrogen and bicarbonate ions would establish a permanent concentration gradient across the protoplasm and so produce the potential difference required for such flow.

Up to now our discussion of mechanisms has dealt with active transport of water across membranes. At the beginning of the chapter, we included in a definition of active water that water held within or outside the protoplasm due to the expenditure of energy.

The water retaining mechanisms in protoplasm are almost unknown. The views, however, of SPONSLER and FREY-WYSSLING, outlined in Chapter VI with respect to binding of water by protoplasm, aided by modern concepts of the structure of water and of proteins, are very suggestive. The ability of the protoplasm to vary its volume is known from many observations—stimulative plasmolysis, vacuolar contraction, frost hardening, etc. It is true that some of these responses could be the result of change in solute concentration but it is just as likely that water is actively moved, as revealed for example, by vacuolar contraction studies (*see* page 125, Chapter VIII). Perhaps a distinction is unnecessary in the light of recent suggestions of STEWARD and of LUNDEGÅRDH that water and solute uptake may be intimately related. Furthermore, salts can markedly affect the imbibitional properties of colloids.

NORTHERN (1942) found that stimulation decreased the structural viscosity of protoplasm, and concluded that this result was conditioned by dissociations of cellular proteins, at least in part. It was suggested that such dissociations produced a greater imbibition pressure in the protoplasm.

In their studies on foliar hydration, PHILLIS and MASON (1945) enter into this matter, with the thesis that the hydration of cotton leaves is largely controlled by protoplasmic imbibition. The latter is in turn controlled by the amount and kind of salts present. Sugars are ineffective in causing absorption of water. An imbibitional mechanism is favored in which microscopic vacuoles in the protoplasm are the proposed loci of accumulation of both water and salts. Since water in some instances was absorbed without an increase in the concentration of salt, an enhanced OP as the cause of water intake was ruled out. Following a suggestion of LLOYD and PLEASS (1927) the effect of salt was considered as weakening the protoplasmic framework.

REINDERS subsequently (1942) verified her earlier results and by extending the experiments to include six other storage tissues, concluded that water intake as observed in potato is a general phenomenon. Especially striking behavior was shown by tuber tissue of *Helianthus tuberosus*. While confirming the correlation with respiration, it seemed ". . . . most probable that water-intake is only a secondary phenomenon, a consequence of other metabolic processes, by which osmotically acting substances arise." These substances would more logically be formed in the protoplasm than in the vacuole, according to REINDERS.

Information relative to the hydration of protoplasmic proteins has been obtained by LEVITT (1946). Isolation of the proteins from potato tubers was apparently accomplished without denaturing them. The protein solutions were introduced into microcups where their osmotic pressures were determined manometrically. There was some indication that proteins from external tissues, allowed to form new periderm, exhibited greater hydration than those from internal tissues that were dormant. This is a new method of investigating the water relations of protoplasm; it should lead to other interesting results.

Movement of water from cell to cell could conceivably result from active processes causing inequalities in osmotic pressure within the cell, inequalities of membrane permeability, or changes in imbibition pressure. Reference is made to these possibilities in chapters which follow.

In conclusion, it seems evident that if active water movements, metabolically controlled and energized, are demonstrated beyond doubt in plants, it will be necessary to revise the basic concepts underlying many plant processes. Though momentarily seeming to confirm vitalistic ideas on water relations of plants, such a demonstration will require, in the long run, a deeper search into the physical and chemical mechanisms involved. And although certain classical views may seem already to be outmoded, it must be admitted that the evidence for active water movement is still far from complete as are many other aspects of protoplasmic activity.

Summary:— In the classical concept of cell water relations the protoplasm is passive with respect to the passage of water, and consequently water movement and retention are determined by forces of osmosis, imbibition, etc.

Recent work indicates that the protoplasm may play some vital role in water distribution.

There is a fairly consistent discrepancy between tissue osmotic pressures determined plasmolytically and cryoscopically. This has been interpreted by some as indicating that water may accumulate in vacuoles due to a secretory action of the protoplasm. Other explanations proposed for the discrepancy are: the presence of colloids in the vacuole; dilution of expressed sap by protoplasmic water, producing cryoscopic values which are too low; adhesion of the protoplasm to the wall, resulting in excessive plasmolytic values; and methodical errors in both procedures.

Refinement of sap expression technics has produced saps termed "protoplasmic" and "vacuolar" by some investigators. The results have been interpreted as supporting the secretion hypothesis. It seems questionable if any clear distinction of this type can be made on sap fractions obtained by pressure.

While plasmolytic methods by classical theory should provide an accurate picture of vacuolar concentration, many anomalous results have been obtained which may reflect some kind of active control of water by the protoplasm.

When expressed saps are compared with equilibrium bathing solutions by cryoscopic methods, discrepancies appear that indicate possible imbibitional or secretory activity of cells.

Auxin has been shown to increase water uptake by living cells. This has been considered as evidence for active secretion of water into the vacuole, but other explanations are possible.

The freezing point of living tissue is usually lower than that of dead tissue. The most plausible explanations are: difficulties exhibited by living tissue toward freezing point determinations, and protoplasmic factors. Forces regulating the state of water in protoplasm may constitute one of the latter.

Frost resistance in plants may be related to protoplasmic factors including increased permeability and decreased viscosity, both of which are attributed to a greater hydrophily of the protoplasm. Such a condition might involve a reversible increase in protoplasmic water at the expense of the vacuole brought about by unfolding of protein chains or opening of ring structures to expose more points for hydration, such structure being maintained by metabolic energy.

The evidence for active control of water by animal cells and tissues is such that water secretion, or active transport, appears likely in several instances.

A comparison of solute and water absorption has suggested that aerobic respiration, protein synthesis, water absorption, and salt accumulation are mutually dependent processes.

Active cell water relations may affect many other plant functions. Transpiration, translocation of salts and water, plant movements, and glandular secretion are a few.

Several mechanisms have been suggested to account for active water control by the protoplasm. Anomalous osmosis involving the carrying of water of hydration by ions during accumulation is one. Electroosmosis, the movement of liquid along a charged solid surface (pore wall) due to a potential difference across a membrane is another. Differential ion migration and a heterogeneous pore system contribute to such a potential difference. Continuous diffusion of solute may account for a potential difference and provide the driving force for electroosmosis. A continuous cycle involving enzymatic conversion of malic acid to carbohydrate in the protoplasm, diffusion of the latter into the vacuole and breakdown to malic acid again is one suggestion. Salts probably play an important role in any anomalous movement of water across membranes. The continuous production and removal of H^+ and HCO_3^- ions may be one source of solute for continuous diffusion from the cell.

Though the argument for active water regulation in plants is supported by an increasingly wide array of data, the overall evidence at present is inconclusive. One does, however, gain the impression that the classical views of cell water relations cannot account for many of the recent findings. There may be as yet too many unknown factors related to protoplasmic structure, permeability, and imbibition to allow a simple osmotic explanation of all cell water relations.

Chapter IX

UPTAKE AND MOVEMENT OF WATER IN PLANTS

Introduction:— The simple lower plants, having no specialized tissue for absorption and movement of water, are either limited in their habitat to a moist environment or they remain small in size and are adapted to periodic desiccation. Our common higher plants have developed specialized tissues and organs for the rapid uptake and transport of water; by means of these, and special protective layers that greatly restrict water loss, they are able to survive with a large portion of their surface exposed to the relatively dry environment whilst their living cells enjoy virtually an aqueous medium. In such plants there is a continuous but varying competition for water between the plant as a whole and the environment, and the struggle for water throughout the life of the plant is not confined to living cells but exists among dead cells and their aqueous contents, cell walls, vacuoles, protoplasm, and air spaces. When the absorption rate is high and transpiration low, competition is at a minimum. When uptake is reduced or water loss increased, competition for water increases and reaches a maximum during advanced stages of wilting if the water supply to the roots fails. Periods of stress occur diurnally in most plants due to excess transpiration during midday; seasonal trends are noted as annual plants pass through stages of maximum growth and maturation; annual trends take place in perennial plants during similar growth stages. Seedlings growing in moist soils and a moist atmosphere show low stress; in fact, they often have excess pressure in their xylem conductors as evidenced by the forcing of liquid drops out of hydathodes (guttation) or by exuding liquid from the xylem when excised. Plants in water culture may exhibit guttation even when fully grown, particularly during the night and early morning hours; stress in the xylem of such plants may be demonstrated during midday by the rapid inrush of dye when the stems are cut under a dye solution.   Plants growing in soil will guttate only if the soil is maintained near its field capacity and atmospheric humidity is high; as soil moisture is depleted stress mounts in the xylem, and throughout the plant. When the moisture content of the soil reaches the range known as the permanent wilting percentage, the plant is no longer able to absorb appreciable amounts of moisture; if more is not supplied it eventually dies.

Water Absorption:— Most plant physiology texts (*cf.* MILLER, 1938; MEYER and ANDERSON, 1939) describe the structure of roots and explain the relation of gross structure to the function of water absorption. KRAMER has reviewed the literature on soil moisture in relation to plant growth (1944) and on the absorption of water by plants (1945). MAGISTAD (1945) has covered the relations of salinity and alkalinity to plant growth. Water absorption will receive limited treatment here, emphasis being placed on recent experimental work on active absorption and the forces opposing absorption.

It has long been recognized that water uptake by roots may be active or passive (RENNER, 1915; KRAMER, 1945). Active absorption results from a metabolic functioning of the roots and is evidenced by root pressure, xylem exudation from excised roots and under some conditions, guttation. The term "active" as used here is not identical with that used in Chapter VIII because, in this case, a complex cellular mechanism is involved. The extent to which water secretion, etc., enters into the mechanism of active water absorption by roots has not been determined.

Passive absorption goes on when transpiration exceeds absorption and results from a DPD gradient developed in the leaves and transmitted to the roots through continuous columns of water under reduced pressure. Because conditions under which active absorption predominates occur only rarely in the life span of most plants, a large portion of the water used is taken up by passive forces. Nevertheless, active absorption has been stressed in physiological studies (WHITE, 1942) and it may play an important role in the growth of seedlings, lawn grasses, plants of the tropical rain forest, and by most crop plants during rainy spring weather.

Active Absorption:— PRIESTLEY (1920) was one of the first to give a comprehensive picture of a mechanism of active water absorption by the root in which structure and function were adequately related. According to this picture, water entering the root hairs passes inward across the cortex and endodermis and enters cells of the stele surrounding the non-living xylem vessels. This passage PRIESTLEY attributes to an osmotic gradient. Because the concentration of solutes in the xylem vessels may be less than in the surrounding parenchyma, and because, for continuous absorption, solutes must be supplied to the xylem, the cells surrounding the vessels are postulated to be more permeable to solutes on their inner surfaces and hence they would allow a "leakage" of solution into the xylem. The differential permeability might result from the fact that the cytoplasm of the xylem parenchyma cells is in contact through the outer walls via protoplasmic connections with living protoplasm; on the inner walls it faces a dead lignified layer. Furthermore, metabolism of the root cells might lead to oxidation of sugars to organic acids; osmotic activity would thus be enhanced because several acid molecules would result from splitting of a single sugar molecule; protoplasm is relatively permeable to organic acids and might release them in solution into the xylem elements.

If the above mechanism could provide solutes to the xylem in sufficient quantity to maintain a higher osmotic concentration than occurs in the soil solution, water should move in to satisfy the osmotic gradient, and higher osmotic concentrations within intervening tissues would not interfere because water movement is determined by gradients of diffusion pressure and not osmotic pressure.

CRAFTS and BROYER (1938) elaborated somewhat the above picture basing their theory on two essential assumptions (1) that the interconnected protoplasts of the living cells of the root form a continuous protoplasmic system (the symplast) extending from the root hairs to the xylem parenchyma; and (2) that the close relation of the cortex with its system of air-filled intercellular spaces with the soil atmosphere makes possible a higher metabolic status than occurs within the endodermis where intercellular spaces are lacking and where water movement would tend to sweep in CO_2 formed by respiration in the cortex. Since anatomical and physiological considerations seem to substantiate these conditions, functioning of the root mechanism is pictured as follows. When solutes are absorbed and accumulated in the root hairs a diffusion gradient is established across the symplast and movement inward occurs via the interconnected protoplasm, the tendency being to establish a uniform concentration. The metabolic gradient across the tissue on the other hand as determined by the $O_2 : CO_2$ relations would enhance accumulation of solutes to a concentration that could not be retained within the stele; leakage of solutes must take place and osmotic movement of water would tend to flush these along the cell walls and into the xylem vessels for these constitute the only avenue of escape at a pressure near atmospheric. This mechanism seems quite compatible with known root structure and it fits in fairly well with the gross picture of solute absorption by roots, xylem exudation by excised roots, and guttation from intact plants.

McDermott (1945) has shown that exudation from the roots of excised sunflower plants growing in soil is greatest when the soil moisture is near the moisture equivalent. At higher moisture contents exudation is lower, probably because of poor aeration. At lower moisture contents exudation is reduced until it stops. The exudation stream reverses as the wilting percentage is approached. The moisture equivalent mentioned by McDermott is a water content near field capacity, the amount of water a soil can hold against gravity. For an extensive report of experimental work on root pressures and exudation *see* Sabinin (1925).

A detailed study of the dynamics of xylem exudation indicates a more complex mechanism than the above discussion would indicate. Experiments by Grossenbacher (1938, 1939) prove that xylem exudation follows a fluctuating diurnal pattern that seems to be impressed upon it by the previous history of the plants. And auxin has been shown to greatly stimulate the flow of xylem exudate (Skoog, Broyer, and Grossenbacher, 1938). If it could be shown that the diurnal fluctuation in root pressure is caused by an auxin induced fluctuation in metabolic rate of the root cells, the above observations might still fit into the mechanism of Crafts and Broyer.

An even more serious departure from a strictly osmotic mechanism is indicated by results reported by van Overbeek (1942). Tomato plants growing in culture solution were decapitated and the excised roots placed in distilled water whereupon each plant was attached by rubber tubing to a small bore U-tube and two or more milliliters of xylem exudate collected. Then the U-tubes were replaced by potometer tubes and mannitol was mixed in the distilled water around the roots until flow in the potometer stopped. When flow had remained static for 15 minutes the mannitol solution was sampled and its osmotic pressure determined cryoscopically as was that of the exudate. Theoretically, if water movement into the roots were osmotic, these two solutions should be isotonic. In the experiments the concentration of mannitol required to stop flow was from twice to several times that of the exudate. However, the rate of exudation and concentration of the exudate were related to the concentration of mineral nutrients in the solution bathing the roots, the rate being lower and the concentration higher if culture solution were used in place of distilled water. van Overbeek concluded that the pressure with which tomato plants absorb water is composed of two fractions 1) an active pressure and 2) a pressure of osmotic origin. The nature of active water movement has been considered in a previous chapter; the above case is a good example of the way in which such active water movement may affect the water economy of plants.

In contrast to the above explanation of the differences in the concentrations of exudation sap and external solution, Lundegårdh (1946) suggests that the bleeding sap is frequently more dilute than the external solution as a result of the presence of "extra water." This is brought about by disappearance, through metabolic processes, of osmotically active substances in the stele.

Passive Absorption:— As emphasized in Chapter V, the diffusion pressure of water may be lowered in several ways *1*) by adding solute, *2*) by lowering temperature, *3*) by reducing hydrostatic pressure. When evaporational loss from leaves exceeds uptake by the roots, the diffusion pressure is lowered throughout the plant and particularly through the elongated tubes of the xylem is this pressure reduction equalized between leaves and roots. As tensions of a few atmospheres are developed in the xylem, the forces responsible for active absorption are exceeded and passive flow to satisfy the hydrostatic gradient becomes the dominant factor in water uptake.

Not only is the active mechanism no longer effective; experiments where living and dead root systems have been compared have led KRAMER (1933) to believe that the osmotic mechanism responsible for active water absorption actually constitutes a resistance for the more rapid passive uptake; dead roots allow more rapid flow than live ones.

These and other experiments of KRAMER (1932 to 1939, *see* 1945) and work by many others including the very practical process known as the acid-arsenical method for killing weeds (KENNEDY and CRAFTS, 1927, 1931; CRAFTS and KENNEDY, 1930; and CRAFTS, 1933*a, b,* 1937) all emphasize the fact that under most conditions in the field the movement of water into and through the plant as a result of transpiration is a reversible process, and that the water in the plant is in a state of tension stretched between the menisci in soil colloids and in hydrated cell walls of the mesophyll. The mechanics of water absorption and movement represent an adaptation on the part of the plant to the demands of transpiration and the limitations of the soil reservoir. The extent to which various plants have been able to meet these conditions determines to a considerable degree their distribution with respect to characteristics of the environment and their productivity within any circumscribed range.

Methods of Estimating the Availability of Water:— Moisture is retained in the soil by adsorptive and capillary forces. Its rapid absorption by plants is also hindered by the low permeability of living plant roots (KRAMER, 1933). RICHARDS (1941) has described a pressure-membrane apparatus for studying soil-moisture availability at tensions of one atmosphere or above. The method consists of enclosing a thin layer of air-dry soil in a cylinder on a permeable cellulose membrane that is supported by a brass screen. The soil is saturated with distilled water and then the excess moisture is forced out by gas pressure. The moisture retaining force at any given soil moisture content ("moisture tension" of RICHARDS and WEAVER, 1944) is measured by the gas pressure required to attain that content.

This method is weak in that it is useful only on laboratory prepared soil samples in which the natural structure has been destroyed in preparation; the pressure applied tends further to destroy structure; the effect of solutes on the diffusion pressure of water is not included in the measurement. The latter effect may be measured cryoscopically and the freezing point depression plus the moisture tension measure the DPD or total moisture stress of the soil.

Physiologically, soil moisture has been classified as *1*) that available for vegetative growth, *2*) that which may be used by certain plants to maintain life under conditions of low turgor, and *3*) that totally unavailable to plants (FURR and REEVE, 1945). The existence of a definite wilting coefficient or initial permanent wilting point has been contested since BRIGGS and SHANTZ (1912) first proposed the term. FURR and REEVE (1945) define the first permanent wilting point of the sunflower plant as permanent wilting of the basal leaves, a moisture status that practically marks the end of vegetative growth. For all useful purposes, this designates the point at which the soil must be irrigated if growth of a crop is to continue.

They designate ultimate wilting as the soil moisture content at which apical leaves wilt permanently. This stage is usually accompanied by irreversible wilting and, finally, death of the lower leaves. Between initial and ultimate permanent wilting lies a range of soil moisture contents for the study of which FURR and REEVE describe a standardized procedure. For light and medium textured soils this range is narrow and though it represents a significant shift in the DPD of soil moisture, the actual amount of water involved is relatively small. For heavy soils, because of lack of uniformity of soil moisture around absorbing roots, slow moisture movement, and strong adsorptive forces, this range may be significantly broad. Furthermore, cases are on record where crop yield has been reduced before any appreciable evidences of wilting could be detected, as will be mentioned later.

At field capacity (maximum moisture content in equilibrium with the force of gravity) the DPD of the soil moisture is between 0.1 and 1.0 atmospheres in most soils (usually less than 0.5 atm.). As water is taken from the soil, the total moisture stress mounts hyperbolically (*seè* Figure 9, Chapter III). Because of the rapid change of stress with decreasing water content, it has proved difficult to reach an agreement as to the significance of plant responses in the field, especially in the range between 5 and 10 atmospheres. Study of soil moisture in this range is difficult because of the rapid increase in DPD with small decreases in moisture content; also because it is impossible to maintain a constant water content within this range with plants growing in the soil; estimates of the absorbing power of plants at permanent wilting range from 4 atmospheres to 20 and higher.

Evidence regarding the availability of soil moisture for plant growth is conflicting. Apparently from the standpoint of crop production, in light and medium textured soils, moisture is equally available to plants throughout the range from field capacity to permanent wilting (VEIHMEYER, 1927; CONRAD and VEIHMEYER, 1929; HENDRICKSON and VEIHMEYER, 1942; and VEIHMEYER, EDLEFSEN, and HENDRICKSON, 1943). Much recent evidence has been advanced, however, to indicate that deep-rooted plants on heavy textured soils may show a marked response to water deficit before the soil mass has reached the permanent wilting percentage (PWP) (FURR and DEGMAN, 1932; FURR and TAYLOR, 1929; ALDRICH, LEWIS, WORK, RYALL, and REIMER, 1940; SCHNEIDER and CHILDERS, 1941; DAVIS, 1940; and WADLEIGH, GAUCH, and DAVIES, 1943).

Certain apparent differences in plant response to water deficits are to be expected; they probably result from inaccuracies in the interpretation of moisture determinations. The fact that, in light soils, water movement and root growth are rapid results in a fairly uniform depletion of moisture throughout the soil mass occupied by roots, and the bulk of the soil reaches the permanent wilting percentage at about the same time. In heavy soils where root growth and moisture movement are slow, the upper zone where the bulk of the roots occurs may become depleted (to or below the PWP) before the lower horizon reaches this point. As a result, most of the absorbing roots may occupy soil at or near the wilting range, whereas the deeper ones may penetrate to depths where there is ample available moisture; the root system may be somewhat restricted; and crop yield may be reduced before the average moisture content reaches a critical point. There may be no visible evidence of wilting on the part of the plant. Actually, one cannot measure the true PWP of the soil reservoir of a plant unless the whole soil mass is uniformly permeated with roots so that moisture is taken out evenly. Physiological responses have been observed, however, even though wilting was not visible. WADLEIGH and AYERS (1945) have reviewed some of this work.

ROSENE (1941) and HAYWARD and SPURR (1944) have investigated the influence of the DPD of the external medium upon the rate of water entry into roots of water culture plants. Although VEIHMEYER and HENDRICKSON (1934) have shown that sunflowers grown in sand cultures did not wilt when placed in sucrose solutions until DPD's of 16 to 20 atmospheres were reached (approximately equivalent to the DPD of the soil at PWP), absorption may be reduced at much lower tensions. The fact that such reduction in water uptake does not affect crop yields until forces from 16 to 20 atmospheres are involved indicates that plants normally absorb and transpire more water than they need for carrying on the various functions in which water takes part. The limits of deficit indicated by the results of VEIHMEYER and HENDRICKSON show that plants may endure high stress and still grow normally; somewhat higher values have even been found occasionally (RICHARDS and WEAVER, 1944).

Though growth of most plants is not markedly hindered at soil moisture contents above the PWP, plants vary with respect to root distribution, root hair formation, and other factors that affect their utilization of water. One plant that is commonly known to require frequent irrigation is onion; this is partially caused by limited root growth; ROSENE (1941), however, found that DPD's of 4.2 to 5.7 atmospheres represent the limits above which intact roots of onion were unable to absorb water. Isolated roots, dependent upon active absorption could only acquire water from solutions having DPD's below 1.8 to 3.3 atmospheres. An OP of 6.5 atmospheres limited absorption by intact roots of plants whose leaves were in an atmosphere of 50 per cent relative humidity and at a temperature of 25° C. HAYWARD and SPURR (1944) found that increasing the OP of the culture solution from 0.8 to 4.8 atm. caused an 80 per cent reduction in water absorption by corn roots. An OP of 6.8 atm. stopped absorption completely. The leaves of the plants were in an atmosphere having 70 per cent relative humidity and at 22° C. TAGAWA (1934), using beans in culture solutions, found that an OP of 1.94 atm. was sufficient to prevent absorption by excised roots (active absorption) whereas 14.68 atm. were required to prevent absorption by whole plants. The relative humidity was 60 per cent and the temperature 28° C.

In contrast to these findings with culture solution plants, RICHARDS and WEAVER (1944), with soils from Southern California, found plants to endure higher stress. At first permanent wilting, values (except for one soil) reached 7.5 to 16 atm., of which 1 to 9.8 atm. represented OP of the soil moisture. Total stress at the ultimate wilting point for 19 out of 24 of these soils ranged from 17.7 to 32.9 atm. (tension 16 to 28.9 atm., OP, 1.8 to 7.8 atm.). One soil showed a total moisture stress of 60 atm. at ultimate wilting, a value that seems unaccountably high.

Unfortunately, the above results can only be regarded as tentative because of excessive sampling of the soils and the use of approximate methods for determining osmotic pressure. Since the OP values usually found for fertile irrigated soils range from 1 to 2 atm., it is apparent that the soils reported above were actually saline. Crop production was poor in soils having OP values of 10 or more atmospheres at PWP; growth was completely inhibited where OP values reached 47 atm. (MAGISTAD and REITEMEIER, 1943).

Water Movement:— Experimental work has proved rather conclusively that the rapid longitudinal movement of water in plants takes place through the nonliving tracheal elements of the xylem. The forces involved in such movement are not as clearly understood. Both vitalistic and physical theories have been propounded. COPELAND's (1902) review presents the early concepts.

VESQUE (1883), STRASBURGER (1891), and DIXON and JOLY (1894) showed that plants could conduct water through dead tissues, and physiologists have generally discounted purely vitalistic interpretations of water movement; most, however, accept the view that living cells in some way condition the xylem tubes, keeping them free of gum and obstructions. MACDOUGAL and OVERTON (1927) have pointed out that living cells in contact with tracheal elements develop tyloses that plug them; anatomical investigations, however, indicate that tylose formation occurs only in xylem that is injured or that is approaching senility. The functioning of young active xylem and the provision of new xylem through cambial activity depend upon living cells; this does not prove that such cells are actively engaged in pumping water through tracheal elements.

BOSE (1923) has been the chief advocate in recent years of water transport by vital activity. He claims that by very delicate instruments he has been able to detect a pulsation of the protoplasm of living cells throughout the plant and proposes that this action of the cells promotes conduction by injecting liquid into the xylem thus setting up an intra-vascular pressure and producing a mechanical transport. MOLISCH (1928, 1929) supported this theory but the experimental evidence has not been generally accepted (DIXON, 1924; BENEDICT, 1927; MACDOUGAL and OVERTON, 1927).

It has been proposed (PRIESTLY, 1935) that water movement into the expanding leaves is associated with the processes of growth and differentiation and should be interpreted on an anatomical basis. The living xylem elements are assigned a major role in conduction; dead trachael elements are thought to act chiefly as storage tissue. That the living cells of the xylem are involved in the ascent of sap and that the dead elements are incidental and only function as reservoirs was suggested again in 1939 by HANDLEY.

Cohesion Theory:— Despite the objections cited, the cohesion theory of water movement in plants has gained almost universal acceptance by plant physiologists. This theory is based on the classical researches of DIXON and JOLY (1894), ASKENASY (1895), and DIXON (1914, 1924). As generally accepted the cohesion theory proposes that water is able to move through the xylem of plants, even to the tops of tall trees, by reason of its continuity and cohesion, and that such movement results from differences in diffusion pressure of water between the soil, the plant, and the aerial environment.

Cohesion and Adhesion:— Forces of cohesion between the water molecules and of adhesion between water and the cell walls permit the maintenance of continuity under conditions of greatly reduced pressure, and prevent, by the action of surface tension, the penetration of undissolved gas through the wet cellulose walls. Theoretical values for the cohesion force of water are very great (*cf.* TABLE 2, Chapter II, internal pressure).

HARKENS (1926) calculated the force of cohesion from the surface tension of water in the following manner. The surface tension of water at 20°C. = 72.8 dynes per cm. Assuming that a water column one square centimeter in cross section is ruptured to produce two new surfaces, each of one square centimeter, the energy required is equal to twice the free surface energy or 145.6 ergs per cm². The distance over which molecular attractive forces are effective approximates molecular dimensions, and force diminishes as a power of the distance. Assuming that the summation of molecular attractive forces acts as a constant force through a distance of 10^{-8} cm., then, since force $= \frac{work}{distance}$, the force required to rupture the water column would be $\frac{145.6}{10^{-8}} = 1.456 \times 10^{10}$ dynes or 1.48×10^7 grams per square cm. This is equivalent to about 14,000 atmospheres. The force of cohesion as calculated by van der Waals' equation is 11,000 atmospheres; by vaporization studies it is 10,500 atmospheres (SHULL, 1924); from internal pressure calculations it is approximately 17,000 atmospheres. All of these represent ideal values; practically the conditions necessary for obtaining such cohesions are impossible of attainment.

Experimental values for the cohesive force of plant sap obtained by measurement of the diffusion pressure deficit of water in the cells of fern sporangia are about 316 atmospheres, sufficient to support a static column around 10,000 feet in height, and entirely adequate to account for movement through xylem ducts to the top of the tallest tree (URSPRUNG, 1915; RENNER, 1915).

DIXON (1914) extracted sap from *Ilex aquifolium* and tested its tensile strength by sealing it in a capillary tube, warming until the sap just filled the tube and then cooling until the column was ruptured. From the thermal expansion of glass and water he was able to calculate the tension at the temperature of rupture; values determined were between 133 and 207 atmospheres.

In view of the fact that cellulose walls imbibe water and are thoroughly wet, the forces of adhesion must exceed those of cohesion. Many centers of hydration occur along the cellulose chains making up the walls. Consequently, in the immediate spheres of influence of these coordinating centers water must be held with such force that its molecules are oriented, the quasi-lattice structure assuming a closer packed and more stable condition than in the body of the liquid. At the same time, due to the rigidity of the walls, and the excess of transpiration over uptake, water in the centers of the lumina of conducting elements must be at times in a rarified or tensile condition. This would tend to expand the centers of abnormal coordination (holes) reducing viscosity and facilitating flow.

Liquid Continuity in the Xylem:— The cohesion mechanism, to function, depends upon continuous water columns. Evidence for and against such a condition is cited by COPELAND (1902), DIXON (1914, 1924, 1938a), MAXIMOV (1929a), MEYER (1938), and STRUGGER (1943).

When a gas bubble is present in a conducting element of the xylem, that element is eliminated, for the time, as a conductor of liquid water under tension. Many objections have been raised against the cohesion theory based on evidence that the tracheal elements of the xylem contain gas. COPELAND (1902), in his review of work on the rise of sap, concluded that the existence of chains of bubbles in the xylem (Jamin's chains) precludes the possibility of tensile columns. He postulated atmospheric pressure as the cause of the rise of sap. Much of the early work on this problem, which COPELAND reviewed, is invalidated by the fact that early workers did not realize the ease with which bubbles could be formed in a tensile water column by manipulation.

Four principal methods have been used in modern studies on the state of water in xylem ducts: (1) dye penetration; (2) freezing of the tissue; (3) transpiration measurements; and (4) direct observation of the xylem contents.

Dye Penetration:— On the basis of injection of dyes PRIESTLEY (1935) concluded that the mature wood of trees acts as a reservoir; only differentiating elements conduct water. He contended that water is drawn from the non-living vessels by the differentiating elements, and by some unexplained process is driven into the expanding tissues of the leaves. By isolating in early summer a branch from a tree having diffuse porous wood, PRIESTLEY found that upon removing the bark he could inject the tracheae all around the branch, the injections proceeding in rapid succession around the stem. At a loss to explain where the water originally present before injection went, he concluded that the tracheae had contained some gas at low pressure.

If the sap originally present in the branch was under tension, it would be surprising if during the process of isolating the branch the tensile columns had not broken. Probably much of the gas in the injected elements resulted from the isolation treatment. Where, due to excessive stress, bubbles are actually formed in stems, they may collapse during later periods when water is more abundant. If water remains wanting, then such elements are isolated by gum or tylose formation and new elements of smaller diameter may be formed as a result of cambial activity. In ring porous woods there is usually a direct correlation between the diameter of xylem elements and the availability of water. Whether this is merely a reflection of the effect of limiting water on turgor expansion during growth, or an adaptation on the part of the plant to greater tensions in the xylem, the result is the same, namely the production, as stress increases, of narrower and narrower elements that are less liable to bubble formation and more suitable for collapse of bubbles once they are formed.

MACDOUGAL, OVERTON, and SMITH (1929) studied the direction and path of dye movement in various woods and concluded that they were able to introduce the dye into the closed system of the conducting tubes. This was accomplished by forcing the dye under one or two atmospheres pressure into a hole in the stem, tightly fitted with a metal tube. The dye moved tangentially from the hole into elements of the xylem which had not been injured. From these experiments they concluded that since different species of trees showed different dye patterns, the patterns are determined by the relation of gas-filled to water-filled elements. Radial movement of the dye from one annual ring to another was not observed.

BAKER and JAMES (1933) criticized the results obtained by MAC-DOUGAL, OVERTON, and SMITH, and emphasized the fact that the introduction of a dye into the conducting system of a plant necessarily requires opening it at some point with an alteration of the original conditions of tension.

The long time periods between injection and observation by the above workers were believed by BAKER and JAMES to have led to error. Their own work resulted in radial transfer of dye from one annual ring to another. Because most dyes are poisonous to living plant cells, it seems possible that MacDOUGAL, OVERTON, and SMITH might have caused injury to their material, resulting in death of cells, invasion of air, and formation of tyloses.

It is commonly observed that when an intact stem of a transpiring plant is cut beneath a dye solution, the dye rushes in, going both up and down the stem. ARNDT (1929) interpreted the downward movement of eosin solution applied to cut ends of *Coffea arabica* stems as indicating that the descending sap in the xylem should provide an adequate mechanism for the downward transport of food. DIXON (1924) had similarly interpreted backward flow of eosin in potato shoots. Postulating that different xylem tracts might be isolated, he proposed that release of tension within a leaf might result in backward movement of foods in solution at the same time that water and salts were moving upward in other isolated tracts. DIXON later reversed his opinion concerning food movement (1933).

The immediate penetration of dye into a stem of an actively transpiring plant that has been cut beneath the solution may result from several actions:

1) If the liquid is under tension, a strain is developed in the conducting elements tending to reduce their diameter. BODE (1923) has shown by direct observation that this may amount to a reduction of several per cent in the total diameter, and MacDOUGAL (1925) proved by dendrographic measurements that a contraction of up to one per cent in the whole stem may be found during the day. Actual vessel contraction may greatly exceed this value since vessels make up only a fraction of the woody tissue and living parenchyma would probably shrink less. Immediately upon cutting a contracted vessel there occurs an elastic expansion which causes a rapid inward flow of dye at both cut surfaces.

2) Simultaneous with the rupture of a tensile water column in the xylem the diffusion pressure of water within that column increases and water moves out of the conducting elements into adjacent living cells which were under a saturation deficit, but in approximate equilibrium with the tensile water columns before cutting. Even root cells in which a saturation deficit occurred would contain water with a lower diffusion pressure than that in the xylem after cutting. Because of this dye may be drawn downward through a cut stem into the roots underground (KENNEDY and CRAFTS, 1927). In fact, this mechanism is employed for the destruction of deep-rooted perennial weeds by the acid-arsenical method (KENNEDY and CRAFTS, 1927; CRAFTS, 1933a, 1933b, 1937). In this method, instead of cutting, the foliage is sprayed with an acid solution containing arsenic. The acid kills the foliage and renders it permeable, whereupon the sap from the leaves and stems, plus the arsenic from the spray solution, is drawn down into the roots. Root systems of wild morning-glory (*Convolvulus arvensis*) and Russian knapweed (*Centaurea repens*) have been killed to depths of six feet in some instances and often as high as 95 per cent of a population may have its roots destroyed to a depth of four feet. Sodium chlorate, ammonium thiocyanate and other chemicals may be translocated by this same mechanism (CRAFTS, 1935; ROBBINS, CRAFTS, and RAYNOR, 1942). Individual plants may be treated by cutting off their tops under one of the above solutions, or by simply immersing them in a container of solution and allowing them to stand until the tops are killed and rendered permeable. This latter method is more effective when used on individual tops of plants that are interconnected underground. Here the undipped tops continue to transpire and thus draw solution through the dipped plant into all plants that are attached through the root system. A detailed discussion of the mechanics of this method, its limitations, and its advantages will be found in ROBBINS, CRAFTS, and RAYNOR (1942).

3) If the xylem elements contain gas under subatmospheric pressure, the dye solution is forced into them as the gas contracts under the pressure of the solution at atmospheric pressure. If the gas is water vapor, it will contract and condense completely at ordinary temperatures.

4) Air will be slowly forced into solution by the additional pressure resulting from capillary forces. Surface tension would cause water to be forced into a tube with a radius of 0.1 mm. with a pressure of about 0.015 atmosphere. This is equivalent to a rise of about 15 centimeters in an open tube. More important than the actual forcing of air into solution is the movement of liquid resulting from the shifting balance of capillary forces between tubes of different sizes. When a stem is cut vapor may be formed in a number of elements of varying diameters. If the gas is pure water vapor it will condense completely and dye will enter and move along all conducting elements. If air gets in through the cut or comes out of solution from the xylem sap, competition between capillaries will cause readjustment after the first influx of dye and bubbles may be seen to be moving in opposite directions in different elements as liquid from the larger ones flows into the smaller to satisfy capillary gradients.

5) A slight elastic expansion of the liquid itself occurs with the release of tension. This is of a minor magnitude.

PRESTON (1938) discussed the above possibilities and concluded that the last two are relatively unimportant. He developed equations expressing the rate at which dye would move into the xylem under the first three conditions basing these upon Poisouille's law. He assumed that resistance due to irregularities of the walls would not be appreciable. This contrasts with the view of DIXON and EWART, who considered that resistance in vessels would reduce flow to one-half the expected amount. Poisouille's law is based on streamline flow. When one considers the contour of vessel walls and visualizes the turbulence which the pits and thickenings might cause, he is forced to the conclusion that DIXON and EWART were probably nearer the truth than PRESTON.

By fitting his experimental data to his formula, PRESTON concluded that many vessels in the ash tree used were filled with gas under pressures ranging between 0.4 and 0.9 atmospheres. Other vessels may have become injected due to elastic expansion of vessels containing water under tension. Gas-filled vessels are located deeper in the trunk than water-filled ones.

PRESTON's conclusions were probably correct but they do not prove that the vessels contained gas in the intact trunk. The difficulty with this type of experiment, as may be easily confirmed under the dissecting microscope, is that when the columns are under high tension they may be disrupted by deformation of the walls before the vessels are actually severed. Hence, water vapor may occupy many vessels by the time the opening is made and the dye solution flows in. If the gas in the elements is pure water vapor, its pressure at 20° C. would be about 17.5 mm. of mercury or approximately 0.023 of an atmosphere. The pressure difference would be practically one atmosphere (actually 0.977) and inward flow should be rapid. The difference between this value and those quoted from PRESTON probably represents the role played by resistance due to turbulent flow along the tubes.

When tensions in the xylem are extremely high it seems doubtful if injection can ever be accomplished without some vapor bubble formation as the very inertia of the dye solution would resist the extremely rapid motion required to maintain liquid continuity as the elastic expansion throughout the length of a stem caused recession of the sap from the cut. To be convinced of this one has only to watch the formation of vapor in the elements of a woody stem of a plant in a state of permanent wilting as the bark is removed under a dissecting binocular. Although the stem will undergo considerable bending and twisting, as soon as the tensile columns are subjected to deformation by jarring, squeezing, or cutting the tubes, they break and vapor occupies the vessels as the water columns recede from the point of rupture. Many, often most, of the elements have vapor in them before the dye can flow in and make contact with the sap columns.

BAKER and JAMES (1933) report that in the majority of cases investigated the upward movement of dye approximately equaled the downward movement, and the ratio was independent of the saturation deficit in the plant if the measurements were made very quickly after the injection. This led to the conclusion that the first equal injections were the result of released tension. Long time measurements of dye penetration show the amount of movement as a function of the amount of water deficit in the plant parts toward which the dye is flowing.

KENNEDY and CRAFTS (1927) and CRAFTS and KENNEDY (1930) studied the rate of movement of eosin solution into the stems of wild morning-glory plants growing under varying conditions of temperature, humidity, and soil moisture and which were cut under the solution. They concluded that if the rate of transpiration exceeded absorption (causing tension in the xylem) dye penetration was influenced chiefly by the amount of transpiration before cutting, *i.e.,* the saturation deficit. When transpiration was low it varied directly with the amount of transpiration and inversely with soil moisture. BRETT (1943) has confirmed these results.

Plant injection has become a standard practice in the treatment of mineral deficiency diseases including chlorosis, zinc deficiency, etc. A variety of methods have been developed depending upon the nature of the chemicals to be supplied and the reaction of the tissues to them. Some applications are made as liquid through cut branches and bore holes at the base of the tree; others involve use of pure chemicals in bore holes or slits in the bark, and some chemicals are readily absorbed through the leaves so the injection is not required.

Because ROACH (1938, 1939) reviews much early work on this topic and describes detailed methods used by him and his collaborators for diagnosing and curing mineral deficiencies, only a few of the recent publications will be mentioned. BENNETT (1931), using solutions and dry salts, developed methods for treating lime-induced chlorosis of pears and the adoption of his dry-salt method has resulted in salvaging a large acreage of fruit trees that were destined for removal. Over 75,000 trees had been treated by 1931 and the method has been widely used since.

ROACH (1938) and ROACH and ROBERTS (1945) stress the use of injection for diagnosing mineral deficiencies. In the latter paper the test solutions used in detecting deficiency of N, P, K, Ca, Mg, Fe, Mn, Zn, Cu, Ni, and B are described and all necessary equipment is pictured. Injection methods for curative purposes for both liquids and dry salts are mentioned and apparatus is illustrated. These methods are finding wide use in treating fruit trees. Their success depends largely upon a thorough knowledge of the physiology of sap movement as the transpiration stream is largely responsible for distributing the chemicals.

Much effort has been expended in attempts to inject insecticidal, fungicidal, and bacteriocidal agents to better the welfare of plants. However, at present, less success has attended this work than that on mineral deficiencies.

Freezing of Stems:— PEIRCE (1936a, 1936 b) froze portions of intact buckeye and castor bean stems with liquid air under various environmental conditions, and, after detaching, tested the conductivity of the frozen portion to gas by blowing through it. Under conditions of water deficit there seemed to be evidence that some of the elements were not filled with ice. Such a procedure might be faulty, however, because contractions and expansions must occur in a stem subjected to such rapid cooling. Expansion during the formation of ice in the outer part of a stem would cause local strains on the vessels nearer the center causing rupture in the liquid. Furthermore, disturbance of forces of cohesion at the liquid: crystal interface as ice is formed might result in rupture.

Transpiration Experiments:— In 1914 BAKKE performed a series of experiments on sunflower plants that were lifted from the soil and brought into the laboratory to wilt. He made continuous transpiration experiments using cobalt chloride indicator paper and found a sharp rise in transpiration rate just beyond the permanent wilting condition. He interpreted his results as indicating that wilting occurs at a definite point and permanent wilting represents the most advanced stage of wilting possible without serious rupture of the water columns in the xylem. Continuing the work in 1918, BAKKE found the stomatal movements not to be important during advanced wilting. During progressive wilting there was a gradual drop in transpiration, followed by a plateau of no change and then an abrupt rise in rate. The plateau was considered to represent a state of equilibrium between the plant and its environment representing the maximum tension that the plant could develop. The rise at the end of the permanent wilting range represented serious rupture of the water columns. When this rupture was complete the plant could not be expected to recover when moisture was added to the soil.

From *a priori* reasoning KNIGHT (1922) decided that as a plant passes from a state of turgor to a wilted condition, there is no reason to expect that at any particular stage in the wilting process the water columns would suddenly rupture. He pictured replacement of water by gas as a gradual process during wilting, the water columns being severed one by one until enough are broken to bring about failure in the supply to the leaves. Working with detached shoots in potometers, KNIGHT made simultaneous measurements of stomatal opening and transpiration during progressive wilting. Wilting was induced by closing the stopcock of the potometer, thus stopping the water supply. There was a sharp increase in stomatal opening accompanied by an increase in transpiration during early wilting; this was followed by a gradual drop. The increase however did not correspond with that observed by BAKKE, as it occurred early in the wilting process. Objection could be made to the use of detached shoots in such experiments for reasons mentioned earlier.

Direct Observation of Xylem:— Numerous direct observations have been made on the xylem of plants to determine the presence or absence of gas in the conducting tracts. Among the first to use this method were VESQUE (1883) and his student CAPUS (1883). Unfortunately their method of preparing their material by cutting and peeling undoubtedly caused formation of vapor phase in every element whose water was under tension. Their observations were largely responsible for the persistence of the idea that there were liquid-gas chains (Jaminian chains) in xylem conductors.

HOLLE (1915) and BODE (1923) made critical observations on the state of water in the xylem of plants. They concluded that even under conditions of extreme wilting there were continuous intact columns of water in the xylem. Conclusions of earlier workers that gas was present were found to be the result of faulty preparation and observation. BODE used a horizontal microscope to observe the vessel contents of rooted shoots of *Cucurbita, Tradescantia, Impatiens,* and *Elatostemma.* In some instances the xylem could be observed directly through the transparent overlying tissues. Removal of the outer collenchyma before observation was found not to affect the state of water in the underlying xylem, if care was taken to avoid jarring or destroying the ducts. The water threads remained continuous in spite of wilting that greatly increased the tension. Any slight local disturbance was found to cause a rupture when a high state of tension existed.

Wilting and drying of leaves of sunflower and squash plants begin with the most basal leaves and progresses upward. Under these conditions there is found a progressively increasing number of xylem elements which contain gas, either as a result of penetration from the outside through hydathodes or drying areas or due to a rupture of columns caused by the strains placed upon them as a result of changes in tissue form and tensions, which accompany shrivelling of the leaves (STOCKING, 1943). Nevertheless, intact water-filled elements are found even in severely wilted leaves.

HAINS (1935) combined direct observation with a dye penetration method to study the state of water in the xylem of trees. By carefully peeling off the bark and exposing the xylem he was able to detect gas in the vessels, due to differences in the refraction of light by gas- and water-filled elements. If no difference in appearance was noted the elements contained all gas or all water. Puncturing the stem he could determine whether gas or water was present and injection of dye indicated the existence of subatmospheric gas pressure or of tensions in the water columns.

Experiments were carried out on *Alnus, Acer, Aesculus, Sambucus,* and *Fraxinus.* Gas was not present in the stems during early spring but appeared at the onset of hot dry weather; it disappeared during the wet fall in *Sambucus* and *Fraxinus.* All outer wood of *Alnus, Acer,* and *Aesculus* contained gas in the fall and Hains considered this to be chiefly in nonconducting fibres.

From these observations, plus many that have been made on the maple tree (*Acer*) which is noted for its bleeding in the spring, it seems that during the hot, dry period of summer when water becomes deficient gas may form in most of the larger xylem vessels. These may therefore serve as reservoirs during the summer as well as conductors during the spring when water is abundant and the flush of growth is on. During winter and early spring many of these probably regain their liquid contents, but in some trees gas apparently continues to occupy a fair portion of the wood for it is the gas pressure formed upon warming of the trunk that causes the rapid bleeding observed in maple. The original source of this bleeding sap is the roots that actively absorb water as spring growth commences; the sugar results from hydrolysis of starch present in the wood parenchyma. Detailed studies on this hydrostatic-pneumatic system in trees have been made by MacDOUGAL and his associates.

CRAFTS (1939*d*), studying *Ribes inerme* plants that were in a state of permanent wilting, found that the bark could be removed without rupturing the water columns in the outer xylem vessels. However, a slight jarring of the exposed vessels, as by tapping with a dull instrument (the back of a scalpel) caused formation of vapor, and recession of the water columns took place so rapidly that it could not be followed; change in appearance from the translucent water-filled to the glistening gas-filled condition appeared to be instantaneous. Working with plants having lower deficits and observing xylem elements of different sizes, it was possible to produce bubbles that expanded rapidly or slowly and, using plants with little or no water deficit, bubbles could be formed that gradually contracted and disappeared. These experiments parallel those of Bode and illustrate the role played by capillarity in the healing of broken water columns under conditions of reduced stress in the xylem. The simple fact that vapor bubbles may be formed in uncut xylem vessels and that these continue to expand after being formed is proof that tension exists, for the vapor phase would not continue to expand if the pressure were above that of saturated water vapor at the temperature of the experiment, that is around 17.5 mm. of mercury. The extremely rapid expansion observed in vessels of plants that are permanently wilted proves that the tension is high for in so expanding the water originally present, except for the small amount involved in formation of vapor, must move out at high rates, overcoming inertia and the resistance to flow through capillaries.

Tensions Developed in the Xylem; Direct Measurements:— Difficulties in technique have thus far prevented the direct measurement of tensions that occur in the xylem sap. Use of manometers attached directly to cut branches, stumps, and stems entails severing of the conducting tracts. Tensions greater than one atmosphere cannot be developed within a system containing gas for the gas will expand indefinitely under subatmospheric pressure. The attachment of manometers to bulk tissue rather than to individual vessels permits the drawing of air into the system through the intercellular spaces with the result that only pressures above the zero atmosphere level can be measured.

Boehm (1892) and Thut (1932a) were able to demonstrate that if branches were carefully prepared a rise of mercury above the 76 cm. level could be obtained. The use of conifers that possess tightly packed tissue, few intercellular spaces, and short elements of the tracheid type tends to prevent the occurrence of gas movement out of the wood and into the manometer. Boehm was able to obtain a height of 90.6 cm. and Thut recorded a maximum rise of mercury of 101.8 cm. in one experiment with *Juniperus.* To obtain such a rise the base of the stem was boiled to remove air. Such experiments, while clearly demonstrating the ability of the leafy shoot to lift mercury above the barometric level, do not pretend to measure the actual tensions that exist within the conducting tracts of intact plants.

Calculations by Dixon (1914) on the resistance to flow through xylem conductors indicate that a force at least twice that represented by the weight of the transpiration columns would be required to move water through stems at a normal rate of flow. If this approximation is valid there should exist tensions of 20 to 24 atmospheres or more in the uppermost parts of tall trees during periods of rapid transpiration.

Potometer Experiments:— Renner (1912) used the potometer to study tensions in the xylem of a plant. Uninjured branches, tops of shoots, or twigs were installed in simple potometers. Freshly cut surfaces provided for water uptake, and the resistance of the stem was increased by the use of a clamp, or by double notching. After the rate of water uptake was observed the branch above the potometer was cut. The stump still in the potometer was taken into the laboratory and the rate of water uptake under a known pressure difference was observed by attaching a suction pump to the stem. On the assumption that the resistance in the stump remained constant and that the rate of water movement into the stem was proportional to the pressure drop across the resistance, RENNER calculated that tensions of 1.0 to 1.5 atmospheres were customary in herbaceous plants. He found an extreme tension of 5 atmospheres in one experiment with *Forsythia*. The soil around all of the experimental plants was well watered, which probably explains the low tensions in the plants.

Earlier (1911*a*) RENNER had used potometer methods to determine tensions in rooted bean plants as well as in leafy shoots. He recorded pressure deficits of wilted leaves of 10 to 20 atmospheres, while tensions of culture solution plants were found to be about 1 atmosphere. RENNER believed that the maximum tension was limited by the osmotic pressure of the leaves.

NORDHAUSEN (1916, 1917, 1921) was skeptical of RENNER's results, feeling that important changes occurred in the resistance of the stem causing a reduced flow under the force of the pump. This would result in the tension values being too high. He modified RENNER's method by introducing a porous clay disk of known resistance at the base of the cut stem. By comparison of the rates of flow through this resistance under the action of the stem, with the rates obtained with a known pressure drop, he calculated tensions of 3 to 4 atmospheres in trees and 7 to 8 atmospheres in cut shoots. The higher values in the cut shoots he explained as arising from increased water deficits from restricted supply caused by cutting and applying the clay resistance.

DIXON (1924) believed that NORDHAUSEN's values represented minimum tensions as the clay resistance would cause some plugging of the stem and air would be introduced during the preparation of the experiment.

HOLLE (1915) pointed out that the vessels in wilted leaves of *Alliaria officinalis* are full of water as shown by direct observation. Under this condition the diffusion pressure deficit of water in the vessels should equal the osmotic pressure of the mesophyll cells (since turgor equals zero). The osmotic pressure of the xylem sap due to solutes would reduce this value slightly.

A modification of RENNER's method was used by EATON (1941) in calculating the overall tension in the xylem. A water culture plant was placed with half of its roots growing in a high salt solution and the other half growing in a low salt solution. The roots were alternated between the solutions so that for a given time period there was an equal area of absorbing surface in each solution. Measurement was made of the amount of water absorbed from each solution for a given length of time. It was assumed that the flow of solution into the roots was proportional to the pressure head and that the resistance was the same in both cases. An average value for the tension at the base of the shoot which satisfied both sets of water uptake and osmotic values was found to be 3.55 atmospheres.

No consideration was given to the effect of the different solutions on the permeability of the roots, and the influence of time and temperature on the osmotic pressure of the solutions was neglected. As EATON points out, such a calculation represents at best only an overall figure, and a fluctuation from perhaps positive pressures at night to relatively high tensions during the periods of rapid transpiration is probably undergone by water in the xylem.

As previously mentioned PRESTON (1938) studied the rate at which dyes were injected into cut ash stems. He calculated the tensions which must have existed at zero time, to cause the rate of injection observed, to be in two instances of the order of 3 atmospheres. This value represented very approximately in his estimation the tension present in the vessels immediately after cutting. It is questionable whether this can be taken to represent the tension in the vessel system before cutting since, as PRESTON points out, the equations which he used are not valid at zero time.

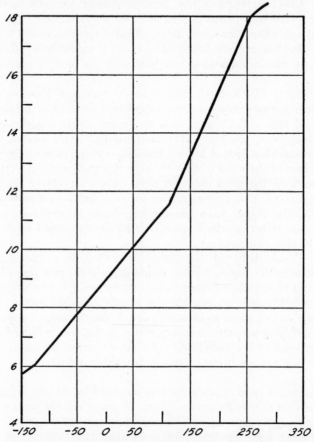

Fig. 43.—DPD gradient from the root up the stem of *Arthrophytum haloxylon*. The vertical axis is DPD gradient in atmospheres per meter, the horizontal axis centimeters. The zero point represents the crown and all negative values are measured downward along the root. From ARCICHOVSKIJ and OSSIPOV (1931b).

"Suction Tension" Measurements:— If there is a direct water contact between the liquid in the xylem and that of the neighboring cells, the diffusion pressure of water in the cells should approach quite closely the diffusion pressure of water in the nonliving xylem conductors. Calculation of the tension in the xylem should be possible from a knowledge of the diffusion pressure deficit of water in the living cells and the osmotic pressure of the tracheal contents.

A large amount of work has been done in measuring the DPD (suction tensions) of plant cells and tissues. URSPRUNG (1935) and BECK (1928) have reviewed the results; Molz (1926) has made many determinations. The method has been described in Chapter VII.

Ernest (1931, 1934b) and Oppenheimer (1930a) have severely criticised the plasmolytic methods for determining DPD. Some of these criticisms are given in Chapter VII. Though many of them may be valid, the method has provided an approximate picture of the water balance in cells and tissues that is extremely useful in explaining the behavior of plants.

Newer Methods of Estimating Tensions in Xylem:— Arcichovskij and associates (1931), in a series of five papers, discuss the results of investigations on suction pressure measurements in plants. Six methods are considered, *i.e.,* gravimetric, potometric, "Schlieren," optical, mechanical, and electrical methods. Fundamentally all of these methods are based on determining the concentration of a solution which has a DPD equal to that of the test material.

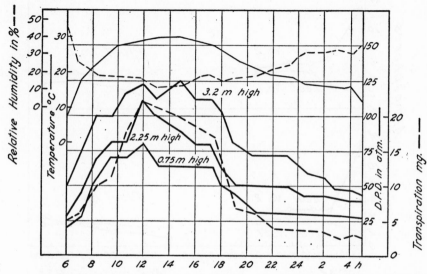

Fig. 44.—Diurnal fluctuation in transpiration and in DPD at different heights on the stem of *Arthrophytum haloxylon*. The heavy dashes represent transpiration, the heavy lines DPD, the light dashes relative humidity and the light line temperature. From Arcichovskij and Ossipov (1931b).

The "Schlieren" method appears to be the most useful. When a twig with a ring of exposed xylem is immersed in a sugar solution, water will move into or out of the cells, depending on whether the immersion solution has a lower or higher DPD than that of the tissue. This water movement will be apparent in the solution due to the differences in the refractive indices. If the solution has a lower DPD water will move into the stem and will be indicated by concentration currents falling away from the twig. Conversely, water moving out of the twig into a solution of higher DPD will be detected by the rising of the diluted solution. If the experimental twig is horizontal and the test area is in a glass chamber containing a sugar solution, the streaking of the density currents in the solution can be observed and a solution having an equivalent DPD determined.

Certain objections to this method immediately come to mind. Such an exposure of xylem caused by removing the bark must expose much ruptured phloem tissue, and phloem exudation into the test solution would set up complicating density currents. Furthermore, such a method is dependent on a differentially permeable membrane and the walls of dead xylem elements are not differentially permeable although it is possible that a careful removal of bark would leave a layer of living xylem cells which could act like such a membrane.

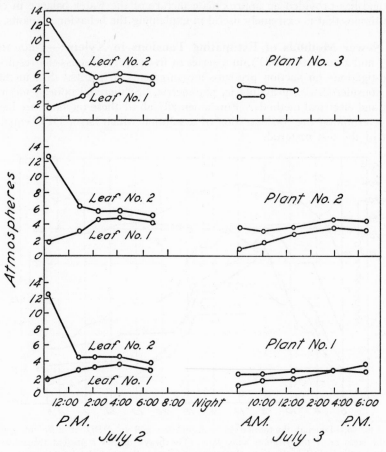

Fig. 45.—DPD measurements on the petioles of squash plants. Solutions injected into the petioles tend to assume a concentration having the same DPD as the tissue. DPD values in atmospheres are shown on the vertical axis. (From Stocking, 1945).

Arcichovskij and Ossipov (1931b) used this method to determine the suction pressure of the Central Asia desert shrub *Arthrophytum haloxylon* Litiv. DPD's up to 142.9 atmospheres were recorded for this plant and a DPD gradient of as much as 44 atmospheres per meter was observed. The specific gravity of sap flowing from cut twigs was very low in relation to that of the external sugar solution, indicating that the moisture deficit of the tissue was due to high tension rather than osmotic pressure. Figure 43 shows the increasing gradient in DPD from the roots up the stem of such a plant as measured by Arcichovskij and Ossipov (1931b). Figure 44 shows the diurnal fluctuation in transpiration and DPD of *Arthrophytum* with data on temperature and relative humidity.

Plants with hollow petioles such as those of squash or pumpkin are convenient material to use in testing the DPD of the tissue (Stocking, 1945).

Standard sucrose solutions of known OP can be injected directly into the petioles with little injury to the leaf and at periodic intervals one or two drops can be withdrawn with a micropipette and analyzed by use of a refractometer. When such a technique is used it is found there is a very rapid initial change in concentration of the injected solution because there is a tendency for the DPD of the tissue to approach that of the solution. Subsequent to this initial change there is a diurnal fluctuation in the OP of the injected solution following the normal trend of the DPD of the tissue when the plants are growing in the field on a normal day. FIGURE 45 gives some evidence for such a diurnal fluctuation representing changes in the tissue of from less than 1 atmosphere DPD at night to more than 5 atmospheres during the period of greatest water deficit in the day. Culture solution plants also exhibit the same general trends.

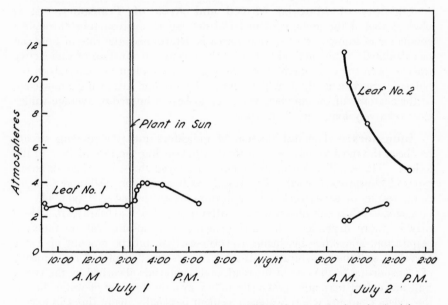

FIG. 46.—DPD values of solutions in the petioles of a squash plant in the laboratory. Placing the plant in the sun caused a rapid rise in DPD. Reinjection on the second day indicated a DPD of about 3 atmospheres.

A graphic reflection of the influence of the environment on the DPD of water in the intact plant is illustrated in the case of a plant growing in culture solution in the moderate atmosphere of the laboratory. FIGURE 46 shows the OP of sugar solutions injected into the petioles. As a result of being placed in the sun for 20 minutes at 2:10 p.m. an immediate jump in the OP of the injected solution was observed which gradually returned to the lower steady state upon return of the plant to the laboratory. In this case leaf 1 was originally injected at 9:00 a.m. on July 1 with a solution having an OP of 2.4 atmospheres. On the following morning leaf 1 was reinjected with a sugar solution of OP 1.8 and leaf 2 with a solution of OP 11.5. There was a very rapid drop in concentration of the solution in leaf 2 and only a slow increase in solution 1, indicating a DPD of less than 3 atmospheres in the tissue.

Rate of Water Movement Through Plants:— Although our knowledge of the movement of water in the xylem dates back, as does much of our insight into plant physiological processes, to the time of STEPHEN HALES (1738), nevertheless the rate at which materials are moved through the tissues of transport in the plant has been an elusive problem. Confronted, in higher plants, by an organism which possesses in contrast to the higher animals no specialized pumping organ nor large, easily recognized conducting tubes, the plant physiologist has been slow to understand the mechanisms of transport in the plant.

The rate of movement of the ascending "transpiration stream" has been studied in three ways: 1) observation of quantity of material moved and cross sectional area of the tissue of transport, 2) by the use of indicators, and 3) by direct observation (*see* discussion above). Attempts have been made using these methods to study the movement of the "assimilation stream" as well.

Quantity of Material Moved and Area of Transport:— It is obvious that if the amount of material moving in a given time through a conductor of known cross sectional area is determined, the rate of flow can be calculated. This method has, until the recent introduction of radioactive tracers, been the chief method of studying the movement of materials in the phloem. Such a method, while improved with our increasing knowledge of the anatomy of the conducting tissues, at best is limited to average values over relatively long periods of time.

Indicators:— The introduction of indicators into the moving stream has been the most widely used method of measuring the rate of flow in the xylem. These indicating methods have employed the use of four different types of indicators: 1) salts, 2) dyes, 3) radioactive material, and 4) heat. Some results of early work with indicators are presented in TABLE 44.

Salts.—While salt absorption, as often pointed out (HOAGLAND, 1944), may be more dependent on climatic factors determining carbon fixation, respiration, and other biochemical processes than on the amount of water absorbed, still the transpiration stream provides an efficient and rapid means of transporting to the rest of the plant body materials absorbed by the roots. Salt movement may not necessarily follow exactly the flow of water, but in the xylem elements where water movement is usually many times in excess of diffusion rates, salt movement may approximate that of the water.

SACHS early pointed out the fallacy in using cut branches or plants with injured roots in experiments on sap movement in plants, criticizing the results of early workers (McNAB, 1871; and PFITZER, 1878). His determinations were made by use of lithium salts applied directly to the roots in solution or to soil. The rate of movement of the lithium through the plant was tested by means of the typical lithium flame test.

Dyes.—While the use of dyes facilitated the detection of the tracer materials, the possibility of adsorption and consequent reduced rate of movement made such determinations open to criticism, particularly if strongly adsorbed dyes were used. STRUGGER (1943) and others have used fluorescent materials in studying the movement of the transpiration stream. Special emphasis was placed by STRUGGER on the movement of the fluorescent material via the cell walls from the vascular bundles through the intervening tissue to the evaporating surface. While stressing the fallacy of SACHS' imbibitional theory in respect to intravascular movement of water, he places great emphasis on imbibition as a factor in the extravascular movement. Materials passed rapidly through the walls of the mesophyll and palisade tissue without entering the living cells.

TABLE 44.—*Summary of investigations on rate of sap movement in plants.* (after HUBER, 1932):—

METHOD	DATE	INVESTIGATOR	POINT OF ENTRY	HOW DETECTED	EXPERIMENTAL PLANTS	RATE IN METERS PER HOUR
1. Salts						
Lithium citrate 1871		MacNab	Cut surface	Flame color	....	2.7-3.3 ......
Lithium nitrate 1878		Pfitzer	Cut surface	Flame color	5 plants chiefly herbs	
Lithium nitrate 1-3% 1878		Sachs	Roots in soil	Flame color	10 experimental plants	0.19-2.06
Iron sulfate 1890		Bokorny	Roots in H_2O Whole and cut plants	Berlin blue reaction	Tobacco and others	1.33
2. Dye						
Indigo Carmine 0.4% 1878		Pfitzer	Cut surface	Direct observations of veins	*Phaseolus Vicia faba*	1.44-4.66
Eosin in H_2O 1891		Strasburger	Cut surface	Dye on sections	Deciduous and lianas	0.6-6.0
Eosin in H_2O 1905		Ewart	Cut surface	Dye on sections	European deciduous evergreen	0.92-2.05 0.16-0.23
Eosin in H_2O		Ewart and Rees	Cut surface	Dye on sections	Australian wood (*Eucalyptus*)	to 12.3
Eosin in H_2O 0.2% 1929		Arndt	Supplied to main *topped stem, lateral branches	Dye on sections	*Coffea*	Upwards about 0.1 somewhat less downwards 0.02-0.15
Acid Fuchsin 1925-26		MacDougal	Cut surface or hole	Dye on sections	*Conifers*	
Methylene Blue 0.25%...1931		Coster	Cut surface ¼-1 minute	Dye on sections	32 tropical lianas, herbs, trees	5.4-150
3. Radioactive Indicators						
Thorium B 1932		Huber and Seith	Cut surface	Radiations of Ash. Electroscope Photoplate	Conifers *Sanchezia*	0.16-0.3 4.80
Thorium B 1934		Baumgartner			*Sanchezia*	1.3-2.5

More recently ZIEGENSPECK (1945) using fluorescent materials confirmed STRUGGER's results on water migration in the walls of parenchymatous cells.

Radioactive tracers.— While radioactive indicators have proven extremely useful in clarifying the path of mineral transport (STOUT and HOAGLAND, 1939), and while such tracers are being extensively used in investigations on food manufacture and transport in plants, relatively few experimenters have employed them in the study of the velocity of water movement in the xylem. HUBER (1932), together with his student BAUMGARTNER (1934) used Thorium B in studying the movement of the xylem contents in some conifers and in *Sanchezia*. Their results are given in

TABLE 44. In this early work the electroscope and photoplates were used as analytical tools. Apparently analyses with the Geiger counter of the movement of radioactive phosphorus in the phloem and xylem of an intact plant are useful only when there are large concentrations of radioactive material in a given portion of the plant (COLWELL, 1942).

Heat.—The ingenious thermoelectric method first used by REIN (1928, 1929) for determining the rate of flow of blood and developed by HUBER (1932) for measuring plant stream velocities, allows determinations to be made on intact plants with a minimum of injury. Repeated and localized measurements are possible on the same plant; this is a distinct advantage over any method previously used. The method consists essentially of the brief local application of moderate heat and of measurement by means of thermocouples of the rate of transfer upward or downward. In rapidly moving streams the thermocouples are placed at a distance sufficient to prevent interference by radiation or conduction. This is from 4 to 25 cm. from the heating element.

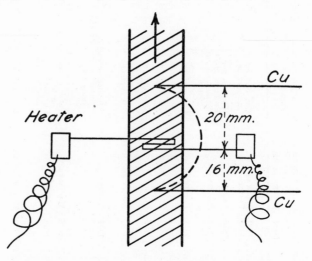

FIG. 47.—Arrangement of heating element and thermocouples used by HUBER and SCHMIDT (1937) for measuring slow rates of movement of sap streams. Cu—Cu represents the thermocouple points.

Measurement of velocities in more slowly moving streams, *i.e.*, in conifers or in the phloem, is more difficult. DIXON (1937) modified the thermoelectric method by placing the thermoindicators 1 cm. apart and the near junction 1 cm. from the heater. Both the junctions and the heater were placed on the undisturbed bark. Determinations took from one-half to a whole hour. HUBER and SCHMIDT (1937) modified the thermoelectric method by bringing the thermocouples closer to the source of heat. They placed one thermocouple on either side of the heat source with the lower element somewhat closer than the upper, *i.e.*, 16 and 20 mm. By measuring the rate of heat transfer both in a normally transpiring plant, and a control in which, due to very humid conditions, there was supposedly no movement of the transpiration stream, they were able to measure rates of sap movement in the neighborhood of 5 cm. per hour. FIGURE 47 shows the arrangement of the heating element and thermocouples used by HUBER and SCHMIDT.

Variations in the Rate of Sap Flow:— Use of the thermoelectric method permitted the measurement of velocity of sap flow in roots, stem bases, and tips. A striking lessening of velocity was observed by HUBER and SCHMIDT (1936) in going from base to tip of trees. This is explained on the relationship of number of conducting elements to number of leaves drawing water through these elements. BAUMGARTNER (1934) found that the slender branches of birch exhibited the opposite state, *i.e.*, the rate increased rapidly toward the tip. In this case the sum of the effective cross section of the branches must be less than that in the stem. Roots are especially adapted to rapid flow of material in the xylem as pointed out by RIEDL (1937).

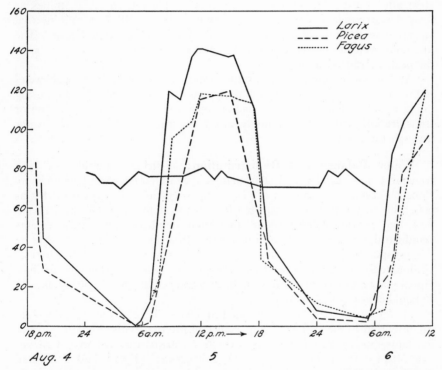

FIG. 48.—Diurnal variation in rate of sap movement in *Larix, Picea,* and *Fagus.* The vertical axis is rate in centimeters per hour. The solid line through the center represents the null point readings on an excised shoot. From HUBER and SCHMIDT (1937).

HUBER and SCHMIDT (1937) investigated the velocity of the transpiration stream in a number of trees and classified them into three groups: *1*) oak-type, in which the velocity diminishes toward the tip, being greatest at the base of thick limbs; *2*) birch-type, where the velocity increases toward the tip and from stem to bough to twig; *3*) the normal type, where the differences in velocity between different parts of the tree were absent. This last type, according to these authors, was postulated by the Leonardo-Jaccard theory of constant water conductivity as being a normal situation. The majority of the trees investigated fell into the oak-type.

Ring porous trees such as oak, ash, and locust have their xylem-conductive area confined in general to a relatively small portion of the outer part of the annual rings. According to HUBER and SCHMIDT, this is a result of air entering the wide vessels during the course of vegetative development. Consequently the rate of sap movement is in this case high (up to 43.6 meters per hour), being about ten times that found in diffuse porous trees such as beech, maple, linden, etc., where a greater conducting area is available.

In the case of conifers, the velocity of sap movement is usually less than half a meter per hour.

Diurnal variations in rate of flow, as would be expected, follow fairly closely the transpirational fluctuations. From a relatively quiet transpiration stream at night, movement is initiated in the morning in the upper branches and gradually reaches the lower parts of the stem and lastly the roots. At night the reverse takes place as water moves into the roots and stem after the tip has ceased to transpire. This movement continues as long as water deficits exist within the plant. FIGURE 48 shows the diurnal variation in the rate of sap movement in *Larix, Picea, and Fagus*. The maximum velocity of the transpiration stream is reached several hours after the peak of transpiration.

Annual variations in transpiration rates are reflected in annual cycles in the movement of water through the plant. BAUMGARTNER (1934), using birch, found such a trend. Any factor causing a reduction in absorption or transpiration will correspondingly affect the rate of movement of water through the plant.

Water Balance and Redistribution:— During conditions of high transpiration a shrinkage of stem diameter is a characteristic phenomenon. BODE observed an expansion of vessels upon cutting and explained this as being due to the release of high tensions in the stem. MacDOUGAL, OVERTON, and SMITH (1929) report that their dendrographic measurements "confirm the contention of several investigators that the tensions set up by the transpiring leaves may amount to as much as two hundred atmospheres." Undoubtedly the greatest strain on the cohesive water columns in an individual plant must occur during the most advanced stages of wilting as long as liquid continuity is maintained.

MESCHAZEFF (1882) is mentioned by DELF (1912) as being the first to call attention to the ecological importance of internal redistribution of water in plants during periods of water deficits. PRINGSHEIM (1906), CHANDLER (1914), BARTHOLOMEW (1926), SAVASTANO (1934), and FURR and TAYLOR (1935) have emphasized that certain plant organs may act as reservoirs from which others may draw water. Young leaves of some plants are able to draw water from older leaves and remain turgid longer during progressive wilting. Fruits may act as reservoirs from which leaves can draw water during wilting.

PRINGSHEIM (1906) and CHANDLER (1914) found a correlation between the osmotic pressure of the sap expressed from an organ and its ability to absorb water. BECK (1928), however, repeated some of PRINGSHEIM's work and reported that water did not move along an osmotic gradient but along a "suction tension" gradient which was maintained by reason of differences in the elasticity of the cell walls of young and old leaves.

While it is obvious that if direct water contact exists between two organs the water will flow along a gradient in diffusion pressure of water, it is not necessarily true that such a gradient is maintained only by differences in osmotic pressures and wall pressures of the various cells. Imbibitional forces as well as osmotic forces influence the diffusion pressure of water, and as has been discussed earlier, certain recent evidence has been presented to support the theory that the vital activity of the plant cells also influences the diffusion pressure of water (*cf.* Chapter VIII). Although the amount of colloid in a highly vacuolated parenchyma cell may be small and perhaps can be neglected in studying the water relations of the individual cell, imbibitional forces associated with the colloids in less vacuolated cells may be very important.

STOCKING (1943) was unable to find a correlation between the osmotic pressure of the expressed saps of squash leaves and the sequence of wilting except in the case of shaded leaves where the osmotic pressure falls to an extremely low value. Wilting in this case occurs first in the shaded leaves. In squash the tip leaves may continue to grow and expand even when the plant is removed from the culture solution and allowed to wilt in a moderately shaded condition. The flower buds may continue to open and bloom while the basal leaves are dying. It seems probable that the greater imbibitional pressures of the slightly vacuolated, highly protoplasmic, expanding cells of the young leaves could account for the lowered diffusion pressure of the water in their sap. Thus imbibition enables them to maintain their turgidity in the presence of the wilted lower leaves; otherwise these cells must actively secrete water into their vacuoles. KERR and ANDERSON (1944) have recently come to this conclusion in regard to the ability of young cotton seeds to absorb water.

The water reserves of plants in general are not equally distributed among the different organs but the lower leaves and shade leaves are usually richer in water and lower in osmotically active solutes than the upper or sun leaves (MARSH, 1941; MAXIMOV and K. MAXIMOV, 1924). During the wilting of sunflower this difference disappears as a result of withdrawal of water from lower leaves by the upper. When such wilted plants were watered, MAXIMOV and K. MAXIMOV found that the older leaves were unable to recover but continued to dry out. However, if these leaves were cut and placed in water they were able to again recover their turgor. The MAXIMOVS explain this as being due to the greater absorbing power of the young leaves and hence their ability to deprive the older leaves of water even after the wilted plant was well watered.

Direct observation of the xylem contents led STOCKING (1943) to conclude that the lower leaves of severely wilted sunflower plants contain many air filled xylem elements. Such a discontinuity of the water in the xylem would lead to a high resistance to water movement. He believed that whereas the young leaves were able to obtain water during the wilting of the plant at the expense of the older leaves, the application of water to the soil should cause the upper leaves to regain their turgor and failure of any leaves to recover could in part be traced to a disruption of the xylem contents so that the rate of water absorption could not reach that of water loss. The recovery of the basal wilted leaves when placed with cut petioles directly into water as found by MAXIMOV tends to substantiate this conclusion.

CHANDLER (1914) felt that the internal redistribution of water in the plants which he investigated occurred at such slow rates that movement would not have to occur through the non-living xylem conductors but could occur through the living cells of the stem.

The effects of drought upon the various functions of plants are important in agriculture and forestry. Work in this field is considered in Chapter X.

Translocation of Solutes:— Work by MASKELL and MASON (1929) and CLEMENTS and ENGARD (1938) on inorganic solute movement, and by STOUT and HOAGLAND (1939), and BENNETT and SNELL (1939) using radioactive indicators shows that the major primary movement and distribution of mineral nutrients in plants takes place in the xylem in conjunction with the transpiration stream. HOAGLAND (1944) has emphasized that absorption of water and salts are largely independent, and the selective uptake of nutrient ions by living cells during their upward passage through the xylem further indicates their independent behavior. However, while they occur together to make up the xylem sap there seems to be no reason for assuming an independence of movement; once started on their way through the xylem tubes, water and salts move along together, and, with the exception of those absorbed along the route they reach their final destination in the leaves where the bulk of the water is lost by transpiration.

Much of the salt absorbed by roots is used in the building of leaves. However, when these have accumulated sufficient to meet their needs for growth and the osmotic retention of water, there is evidence (MASON and MASKELL, 1931) that the surplus is moved out via the phloem in conjunction with carbohydrates.

Concerning food movement in plants, there is general agreement that gradients in concentration are intimately involved (MASON and MASKELL, 1928a, 1928b; CURTIS, 1935; LOOMIS, 1935, 1945; ENGARD, 1939a; HUBER, SCHMIDT, and JAHNEL, 1937). On the mechanism of movement there are many theories; these may be grouped into two categories: 1) those postulating movement of solute molecules in, through, or upon the surface of the sieve-tube protoplasm. By this mechanism solutes are pictured as moving along gradients but independently of each other and of the solvent water; 2) the mass-flow or convectional-flow theory that visualizes a flow of solution through the phloem along positive gradients of hydrostatic pressure developed osmotically. The first category includes several mechanisms including diffusion accelerated by protoplasmic streaming (CURTIS, 1935), "activated diffusion" a term implying an accelerated diffusion carried on by the protoplasm with the utilization of metabolic energy (MASON and MASKELL, 1937), and diffusion or some analogous process accounting for rapid attainment of equilibrium by molecules adsorbed on the surface of the sieve-tube protoplasm (LOOMIS, 1935, 1945; CLEMENTS, 1934a, 1940). All these call upon the active protoplasm for the required energy and their advocates picture the functioning sieve tube as an active element, rich in protoplasm, and capable of expending metabolic energy at a high rate.

The second category includes only one mechanism but presents two views of the sieve-tube function. That of MÜNCH (1930), introducing the symplast concept, visualizes the interconnected protoplasts of the plant as constituting a continuous system, relatively impermeable on its outer surface but highly permeable throughout its mass. The sieve tubes are pictured as making up a specialized mechanism of the symplast where water, absorbed osmotically, brings about high turgor in the regions of synthesis. This turgor promotes a rapid mass-flow of solution through tubular connections that traverse the sieve plates to regions of utilization where assimilation, respiration, and condensation for storage reduce the osmotic activity of the solutes allowing the water to return to the xylem. CRAFTS (1938, 1939a), on the basis of anatomical studies, contends that the mature, functioning sieve tubes become permeable, allowing a ready passage of solutes in solution from cell to cell. Leakage to the outside is prevented by a limiting layer of living cells around each sieve-tube strand. Movement from mesophyll to sieve tube is by diffusion, accelerated by protoplasmic streaming via the symplast. Removal of assimilates from the sieve tubes is pictured as an active absorption by living parenchyma cells of the phloem followed by symplastic movement to points of utilization or storage. The mass-flow mechanism involves a recirculation of water; MÜNCH calculates that around 5 per cent of the total water used by the plant is involved in this recirculation. He performed experiments wherein this water as it flowed from the cambium of trees was collected and measured.

The protoplasmic theories are supported by evidence that under certain conditions solutes appear to move independently in the phloem, that the sieve tubes are rich in proteinaceous materials indicating a high protoplasmic content, and that radioactive phosphorus absorbed into the phloem of leaves moves both upward and downward in the stem whereas mass flow should be predominantly in one or the other direction. The greatest weakness of these theories is that no exact physical mechanism is known or has been pictured that will account for rapid transport of the quantities of material found to move either along the protoplasm or through the lumen independent of the water. From the pictures that have been presented in the preceding chapters of the molecular structure of water, carbohydrates, amino acids, and proteins, it seems that the mutual attraction of these substances, as indicated by the various points available for coordination through hydrogen bonds, would resist the movement of food substances either along the surface of the protoplasm or through static water. Those molecules that were held in the protoplasm would be removed only with difficulty. Those in the solution occupying the lumina of sieve tubes would diffuse independently over short distances to satisfy local gradients; their rapid movement over great distances independent of the solvent is not possible by any known physical mechanism.

Although the rapid migration of hydrogen and hydroxyl ions has been pictured as involving a proton jump along chains of coordinated water molecules, a similar movement of large molecules seems improbable.

The mass-flow mechanism is supported by evidence for a permeable condition of the functioning sieve tube, the presence of a concentration gradient of osmotically active materials in the phloem and the phenomenon of phloem exudation that seems, at least in some instances, to account for normal rates of flow. It receives substantiation from studies on the movement of virus, auxin, and radioactive indicators that depict a simultaneous transport of foods and indicators, depending largely upon the establishment of source and sink by regulating assimilation or hydrolysis at the source and utilization or storage at the sink. Weaknesses of the mass-flow theories include a lack of knowledge relative to the resistance offered by cross walls in the phloem, need for more convincing evidence for the passive function of sieve tubes, a fundamental discrepancy in the composition of phloem exudate from cucurbits as contrasted with composition of their fruits, and a general lack of analytical data on the sieve-tube contents of a variety of plants. Cucurbits which have been employed so much have proved atypic (CRAFTS and LORENZ, 1944b) and should be used with caution. Future work, to be of value, should make use of viruses, auxin, and radioactive isotopes that can be injected with little or no injury and detected by very delicate and accurate methods.

Reviews on translocation cover the literature quite thoroughly up to about 1940; CURTIS (1935) and MASON and PHILLIS (1937) emphasize the viewpoint of the protoplasmic theories; CRAFTS (1938, 1939b) supports the mass-flow hypothesis. More recent publications on the relation of the structure of the sieve tubes to their function (CRAFTS, 1939a, c) extends the view that these elements become permeable at maturity allowing ready flow of nutrients in solution through the phloem. Observations on phloem exudation are extended. CLEMENTS (1940) and COOIL (1941) question the evidence for the lowered activity of mature sieve tubes and the attendant high permeability. CRAFTS and LORENZ (1944a, b) found translocation into the fruits of cucurbits to be very rapid but concluded that phloem exudation in these plants could not be accepted as a manifestation of normal phloem transport. The carbon: nitrogen ratio of the exudate was not compatible with that of the fruits.

Analyses of the stems and leaves of raspberry by ENGARD (1939a, b) support the view that transport of organic materials follows a diffusion pattern, gradients being present where translocation occurs. Major carbohydrate movement is in the form of sucrose and occurs in the phloem. Nitrogen absorbed by the roots moves upward freely in the xylem and is available for reduction and elaboration to amino acids and protein in all living cells of the plant.

LOOMIS (1945) from many studies on carbohydrate metabolism in maize concludes that sucrose is the principal compound involved in translocation. He considers that neither the protoplasmic nor mass-flow mechanism can explain carbohydrate transport in maize and proposes a mechanism involving polarized movement, a secretory type of movement that commonly takes places against gradients in concentration. WENT and CARTER (1945) show that injury of the petioles of tomato plants hinders sugar transport through the adjacent stem.

Indicators of various types have been employed in translocation studies. ROUSCHAL (1941) used fluorescein and found that it tends to accumulate in young active cells and in the protoplasm of mature sieve tubes but not in their lumina. The dye streams along with assimilates in the phloem and this flow can be reversed, hence he pictures a mass-flow mechanism. He found that whereas the main flow of the assimilate stream from a leaf occurred in the large sieve tubes of the petiole, independent and opposed streaming may take place in extrafascicular sieve tubes. Thus movement both in and out of a given leaf might occur by mass flow. Such movement might also take place in opposite directions in the stem in different vascular bundles.

Radiophosphorus has been used as an indicator. BIDDULPH (1940) found this element to be rapidly absorbed by bean roots and carried upward in the transpiration stream. In further experiments (1941) he found radiosposphorus injected into bean leaves to migrate out, the initial movement being predominately downward, a fair portion reaching the roots during the evening following injection. A small amount moved upward. Such movement might take place by the mechanism mentioned by ROUSCHAL.

COLWELL (1942) used radiophosphorus for translocation studies on squash plants. His results emphasize the care needed to restrict movement to the phloem. When the tracer is so restricted, its movement is correlated with food movement in the plant.

BIDDULPH and MARKLE (1944) studied the distribution of radiophosphorus in cotton plants following injection into leaves. They found movement out of the leaf and down the stem to occur at a rate of better than 21 cm. per hour. Though movement followed a diffusion pattern, rates indicated an active mechanism. Upward movement in the stem was variable. Movement from the phloem into the xylem occurred, resulting in a recirculation within the plant. RABIDEAU and BURR (1945) used radiocarbon as a tracer for transport studies. Exposing leaves to CO_2 containing C^{13}, photosynthesis resulted in formation of carbohydrates that moved both upward and downward in the plants. Radiophosphorus applied to roots moved readily past killed areas of the stem but photosynthate containing radioactive carbon failed to pass such regions. They conclude that the latter materials move exclusively through the phloem.

Studies on translocation of the reproductive stimulus in plants have shown that flower induction is caused by a definite substance that may act locally or may be moved. LOEHWING (1938) using a slit panel, so that the tops and bases of soybean plants could be subjected to different photoperiods, showed that whereas flower induction is normally localized in these plants, defoliation brought about transfer from donor to receptor regions. He concluded that flower initiation was not caused by photosynthates but by some hormone-like substance. Flower initiation on a receptor region subject to long-day treatment could be brought about by defoliation if a donor region consisting of another portion of the plant was given short-day treatment.

HAMNER and BONNER (1938), using *Xanthium pennsylvanicum,* found that though the initial perception of the floral stimulus is by mature leaves subject to a short photoperiod, the stimulus may be transported from these to other portions of the same plant or that it might move through a graft or across a diffusion contact to another receptor plant. Defoliation is not required in *Xanthium* as the stimulus moves normally both up and down the stem to donor regions that have not received induction. They attribute floral initiation to a definite hormone-like substance.

WITHROW and WITHROW (1943) studied floral induction in the same plant and found translocation between an induced donor plant and a receptor only when tissue union was established as a result of uninterrupted tissue contact for four days or more. The floral stimulus failed to translocate downward through a killed petiole or through functional xylem. It also failed to cross a ring. They concluded that it moved only in the bark, a result in harmony with those of MOSHKOV (1939). STOUT (1945), studying translocation of the floral stimulus in sugar beet, found that it would move down a donor shoot and into a darkened shoot but not into an illuminated shoot where all three shoots came from the same beetroot. This substantiates the defoliation results of LOEHWING and indicates that the flower-inducing substance like curly-top virus (BENNETT, 1937, 1940a, b) is translocated along with food material.

Further studies on virus movement (BENNETT, 1940a, b; HILDEBRAND, 1942; HILDEBRAND and CURTIS, 1942; BENNETT, CARSNER, COONS, and BRANDES, 1946) confirm BENNETT's *earlier convictions* (CRAFTS, 1939b) that rapid transport of virus takes place in the phloem and is correlated with food movement. If this is true, and much evidence now indicates that it is, there seem to be only two interpretations: first, that virus particles are bonded to food molecules and that they move together along concentration gradients of food, or, second, that they all move together by mass flow of the assimilate stream. The first possibility seems doubtful in view of the accumulation of curly-top virus in the seed coats of sugar beet seed during storage of carbohydrates in the seeds. There seems to be no logical reason for their separation at this point if they are really tightly bonded. That BENNETT favors the second alternative is indicated in his review article (BENNETT, 1940b).

Studies on transport of thiamin in tomato by BONNER (1942) show that this material is synthesized in mature leaves and transported to the young developing leaves, where it concentrates to a high level, and to the roots. It accumulated above a girdle at the second node of the plants and below one made by steaming the stem in a region between the mature leaves and the young expanding ones. These tests indicate a movement in the direction which food materials might be expected to move. Studies on pantothenic acid and riboflavin (BONNER and DORLAND, 1943) indicated that distribution of these compounds follows a pattern similar to that of thiamin. Pantothenic acid accumulated at girdles in the same way as thiamin; riboflavin failed to accumulate.

In a third series, BONNER (1944) tested large lots of tomato plants by girdling some and leaving others ungirdled and measuring concentrations initially and finally present in both girdled and ungirdled plants. He found that thiamin, pyridoxine, pantothenic acid, riboflavin, sucrose, total nitrogen, and non-protein nitrogen all accumulated above the girdle. The extents and rates of accumulation varied and BONNER questions the value of such evidence as it relates to the mechanism of mass flow. In view of the possible differences in rate of synthesis, rate of transport, degree of accumulation, utilization in growth, destruction, and possibly leakage into the xylem, it seems unlikely that uniform rates and ratios of accumulation could be expected. The evidence, such as it is, indicates a simultaneous movement of these various materials in the tomato, and such movement can best be explained by mass flow.

Recent work on translocation of plant hormones has concerned the effects of dichlorophenoxyacetic acid on weeds. In 1944, BEAL found that the roots of sweet pea produced nodule-like swellings and that the stems bent and grew abnormally following application of 4-chlorophenoxyacetic acid to the stem or leaflets. Evidently this material moved within the plant.

FERRI (1945), studying translocation of synthetic growth substances, showed that they could be absorbed by roots from the soil and moved upward through the xylem. Such movement was independent of living cells. Similar experiments were performed by SKOOG in 1938.

Recent work on absorption and translocation of 2,4-dichlorophenoxyacetic acid by MITCHELL and BROWN (1946) shows that movement of the stimulus resulting from treatment is correlated with movement of organic foods in bean plants. When the 2,4-D was applied to roots the resulting stimulus was translocated through non-living cells of the stem, indicating that it traveled in the transpiration stream in the xylem. WEAVER and DE ROSE (1946) obtained similar results with bean plants. In alfalfa, basipetal movement was most rapid in young active tissues. Figures 1 and 2 of their paper give excellent evidence for upward movement in the xylem past a killed region and subsequent accumulation in the phloem. This is reminiscent of the results of MASKELL and MASON for nitrogen and of SKOOG for auxin.

From this review it is evident that the tendency is toward use of non-toxic and naturally occurring indicators in translocation studies. The more recent work supports the view that such indicators, when in the phloem, accompany any food materials in their movement through the plant. The simplest and most compatible mechanism to account for such flow would seem to be mass flow along hydrostatic gradients developed osmotically. Such a mechanism involves a recirculation of water and entails a close correlation between the functioning of xylem and phloem. A thorough consideration of this mechanism in all of its ramifications brings out the fact that practically every plant function is in some way tied in with processes of solute and water movement. Water is absolutely essential to the welfare of higher plants and as such plants have left their moist habitats and invaded the valleys, the mountains, and the deserts, they have developed intricate absorption and translocation mechanisms and marvelous protective coatings. By means of these they have maintained their aqueous surroundings to a remarkable degree; that is, they have taken their environment with them. And if we, as agriculturists, wish to further their welfare and so protect ourselves, we must, to the limit of our abilities, improve the environments of our crop plants. We must do to a greater degree what the plant has so largely done for itself, that is, we must simulate the perfect environment for plant growth and production by supplying, along with minerals and a favorable soil, an adequate and unfailing supply of water.

Summary:— Simple plants having no vascular tissue are limited to moist habitats; higher plants have developed tissues for rapid uptake and transport of water; protective layers restrict water loss; these plants survive dry habitats whilst their living cells have an aqueous medium. The soil acts as a reservoir from which the plant can absorb so much water.

Water may be absorbed actively from soils near their field capacity. In a saturated atmosphere such absorption causes guttation. Under conditions of high transpiration water loss exceeds uptake and a passive absorption by the roots takes place.

Water movement takes place in the non-living xylem elements along a hydrostatic gradient developed by transpiration pull. The water columns are in a state of tension much of the time, a state made possible by the forces of cohesion (internal pressure) between the water molecules and adhesion between water and the cellulose walls. When such columns break, bubbles of water vapor form and the elements occupied by them are rendered ineffective in water transport. When tension is reduced, such bubbles may shrink and collapse, mending the columns.

Studies on the xylem have been made using dyes, freezing, transpiration measurements, and direct microscopic observation. These studies largely confirm the cohesion mechanism. Many methods have been used to estimate tensions in the xylem; potometer methods, measurement of "suction tension", and observation of differences in refractive indices have proved useful. Periodic measurement of the concentration of solutions injected into the petioles of squash leaves has given a view of changes in water status of the plants.

Many methods have been used to study rates of water movement in plants; comparison of the weight of water lost with the transverse area of conducting elements gives an over-all average rate. Indicators, including salts, dyes, radioactive materials, and heat have proved valuable; rates up to several meters per hour have been measured. Rates of flow vary with water supply, transpiration, and with structural variations in the plant.

Water balance in plants varies and with it water distribution. Redistribution between leaves, fruits, trunk, and roots takes place under fluctuating stress. Young leaves usually exceed old in their ability to absorb and hold water; sun leaves exceed shade leaves.

Translocation of water and solutes in the plant are correlated. Minerals absorbed from the soil travel upward in the xylem with the transpiration stream. Foods synthesized in the leaves move downward to the roots and upward to growing parts and to developing fruits through the phloem. Excess minerals, with the possible exception of calcium, may move out of leaves via the phloem.

Two main theories on the mechanism of food movement are *1*) the protoplasmic theories postulating movement in, on, or along the surface of the sieve-tube protoplasm independent of water and accelerated by metabolic energy; *2*) mass flow, picturing a simultaneous movement of foods and water in solution through the lumina of the sieve tubes along a gradient of hydrostatic pressure developed osmotically. Sieve tube elements are assumed to have a ready permeability for such flow and the solution under pressure is maintained in phloem strands by sheaths of living parenchyma cells.

Current research on translocation indicates that sugars, nitrogen compounds, fluorescein, radiophosphorus, the flower-inducing hormone, phloem-limited viruses, thiamin, pyridoxine, pantothenic acid, riboflavin, auxin, and 2,4-dichlorophenoxyacetic acid may all be transported in the phloem and some experiments indicate that two or more are commonly carried along together. The simplest explanation for such movement is the mass-flow mechanism which involves a recirculation of water and entails a close correlation between the functioning of the xylem and phloem.

Chapter X

WATER LOSS AND WATER RETENTION

Introduction:— The maintenance of a favorable balance between water loss and water absorption is essential in the economy of a plant, for growth and development depend upon an adequate water supply. Favorable, as used here, does not imply a positive hydrostatic pressure within the xylem conductors, nor does it necessarily mean a positive supply in the soil. It has been shown that a plant may absorb water from the soil against a diffusion pressure deficit variously estimated to be 4 to 16 atmospheres, and it is obvious that tensions within the xylem may attain much higher values in plants that are developing normally. The inference is that there are definite limits of DPD for water in the soil, and water in the plant, above which the plant cannot operate normally. And because of these limits, water loss must be eventually counterbalanced by an equal uptake if the plant is to grow and develop and maintain life throughout a normal span. Because the larger vessels of the xylem, and many parenchyma cells of xylem, phloem, and cortex may act temporarily as reservoirs, the plant may survive diurnal periods when loss exceeds uptake. However, such deficits must be replenished, at least during periods of active growth, if the plant is to thrive. And because of the interrelation between the various processes of absorption, movement, and loss, an effect on one will cause a correlated effect on the others. The term water balance is commonly used by plant physiologists to describe these processes as they relate to the water economy of plants.

Transpiration, that is, loss of water from plants in the vapor form, has been termed both beneficial (CLEMENTS, 1934*b*) and a necessary evil (BARNES, 1902; CURTIS, 1926). Probably both viewpoints have some justification. Certainly the maintenance of moist wall surfaces within the stomatal chambers of leaves, for absorption of CO_2 during rapid photosynthesis, results inevitably in loss of water by evaporation, and much evidence is at hand to prove that such evaporation is usually far in excess of any requirement, because plant growth in tropical regions where the air approaches water saturation is very luxuriant.

Although the work of HASSELBRING (1914), KIESSELBACH (1916), MUENSCHER (1922), and MENDIOLA (1922) indicates that different rates of transpiration may occur without materially affecting mineral salt absorption, experiments on translocation of minerals within the xylem by CLEMENTS and ENGARD (1938), WRIGHT (1939), and STOUT and HOAGLAND (1939) prove that transpiration facilitates the distribution of minerals within the plant. More recent studies by HOAGLAND (1944) show that the previous salt status of the plant is extremely important in such studies. It seems therefore that some loss of water by transpiration is necessary; on the other hand, transpiration in most terrestrial environments is far in excess of requirements for purposes of translocation. Hence, conservation of water by the plant is important both economically, where the supply may fail and so limit growth, and essentially for xerophytes, where the water supply may determine survival.

Most studies on transpiration emphasize water loss and the relation of the various physical mechanisms and physiological processes to it. From the ecological viewpoint water retention or the prevention of loss is of the greatest importance. From this viewpoint it becomes obvious that the primary function of the above mechanisms and processes in the plant is water conservation. Opening of stomata is necessary for the gaseous exchange essential to photosynthesis; stomatal closure is just as necessary for the conservation of water, particularly in arid regions. While stomatal opening is of general occurrence and most plants photosynthesize, differences in time and extent of stomatal closure are extreme. Many important ecological relations of plants are related to this process as it functions in water conservation and the adaptation of plants to the supply of water in their environments.

Under conditions of rapid absorption and low transpiration, water may be lost from plants by guttation. These conditions may prevail in fields of young grain and in lawns (CURTIS, 1944) during the night and early morning hours in the spring; they have been observed in vegetable and forage crops and they are prevalent under the humid environment of the tropics. They are favored by warm soils, cool saturated atmosphere and adequate but not excessive soil moisture.

In contrast to the above situation, it is widely recognized that most plants live the greater part of their lives in a state of negative water balance; that is, transpiration often exceeds absorption and pressure in the xylem is subatmospheric. Transpiration is termed stomatal, cuticular, or lenticular, depending upon the structures through which the water vapor passes, and all three types may occur at the same time.

Stomatal transpiration is normally the predominant form in leafy plants and it consists of *1*) evaporation of water from wet cell walls of the stomatal chambers, *2*) diffusion from the humid atmosphere of these chambers through the stomata into the external atmosphere, and *3*) movement of the vapor from the surface of the leaf where under still conditions it tends to form a molecular cloud.

Laws of Evaporation:— Although many publications describe the loss of water from plants, soils, and free water surfaces (LEICK, 1939), few formulae have been presented that express the nature of this loss in measurable terms. Such formulae as exist apply only to relatively simple systems and they prescribe the most rigid experimental conditions.

Even the simplest case—the evaporation of water from a free water surface—is sufficiently complex so that only a few conditions governing the loss can be exactly expressed mathematically. Nevertheless, certain general principles of evaporation are demonstrable, and apply not only to loss from free water surfaces but, with modification, to transpiration as well.

Because of the kinetic movement of liquid molecules and the statistical rules governing energy distribution among them, there is a certain escape of high energy individuals from any gas-liquid interface. Since this escape represents a loss of kinetic energy from the liquid cooling occurs, and, if the evaporation rate is to be maintained, heat must flow into it.

Molecules entering the gas phase partake of the nature of gas molecules—that is, they have unordered motion. Consequently, molecular movement at the interface is omnidirectional and condensation as well as evaporation is taking place. When the gas and liquid are at the same temperature and in a restricted space, an equilibrium attains; the gas is saturated and the net loss or gain of water by the liquid is zero. Although evaporation and condensation under these conditions have real and equal values, in the more general use of the term meaning net loss, evaporation would be considered as having a value of zero. Because of the ease of measuring net water loss, the term is more conveniently used in this sense.

Evaporation from a Free Water Surface:— DALTON in 1801 made several important observations on evaporation; he has been credited with a formula for calculating the rate of evaporation from extensive areas of water. HUMPHREYS (1940) doubts the authenticity of the formula attributed to DALTON. The following statements by DALTON indicate the state of knowledge of the subject up to DALTON's time.

"Some fluids evaporate more quickly than others. The quantity evaporated is in direct proportion to the surface exposed, all other circumstances alike. An increase of temperature in the liquid is attended with an increase of evaporation, not directly proportional. Evaporation is greater where there is a stream of air than where the air is stagnant. Evaporation from water is greater the less the humidity previously existing in the atmosphere, all other circumstances the same."

DALTON's observations lead him to conclude that ". . . . the evaporating force must be universally equal to that of the temperature of the water [vapor pressure of water at saturation at surface temperature] diminished by that already existing in the atmosphere [vapor pressure of water in air]." He further concluded that, "The quantity of any liquid evaporated in the open air is directly as the force of steam from such liquid [vapor pressure] at its temperature, all other circumstances being the same."

Since, in studying transpiration, we are dealing with evaporation from relatively small areas, STEFAN's (1881) analysis of the rate of evaporation from flush circular areas is of interest. STEFAN found that such evaporation into still air could be expressed mathematically by the formula

$$V = 4\ a\ k\ \log\ \frac{P - p^0}{P - p^1}, \text{ where} \tag{1}$$

V = amount of water evaporated per unit area.
a = radius of the evaporational area.
k = the diffusion coefficient.
P = atmospheric pressure.
p^0 = the vapor pressure of the liquid in air.
p^1 = the vapor pressure of the liquid at saturation at the surface temperature.

The coefficient of diffusion of water vapor into air has the dimensions of mass diffused per unit area per unit time for a unit vapor-pressure gradient.

If p^0 and p^1 are small in comparison with P, the equation becomes approximately

$$V = 4\ a\ k\ \frac{(p^1 - p^0)}{P} \tag{2}$$

The importance of STEFAN's relation is that evaporation from small areas is shown to be proportional to the linear dimensions of the evaporating surface and not to the area as is suggested by DALTON for large areas.

Evaporation from Tubes:— When water evaporates from a surface that is not flush with the edge of the container molecules escaping near the periphery of the liquid cannot diffuse laterally but are confined to the tube immediately above the fluid and hence contribute to the total vapor pressure above the liquid. Evaporation under these conditions is reduced. STEFAN (1873) calculated the rate of evaporation in this case to be

$$V = \frac{kA}{h} \log \frac{P-p''}{P-p'}, \text{ where} \qquad (3)$$

V = rate of total evaporation.
A = area of the tube.
h = height of the tube from the liquid surface to the free air space.
p'' = partial pressure of vapor at the free end of the tube.
p' = partial pressure of vapor at the evaporating surface.

The equation becomes $V = \frac{kA}{h} \frac{p'-p''}{P}$ $\qquad (4)$

when p' p'' are small in comparison to P.

Factors Affecting Evaporation from Free Water Surfaces of Uniform Shape and Area:— Since evaporation involves the escape of molecules from a body of fluid against internal forces of attraction and forces resident in the surface film as well, many factors relating to intermolecular forces in the liquid affect evaporation rates. The more important factors will be discussed.

a) *Solutes.* — Any solute dissolved in a liquid reduces the diffusion pressure and hence the rate of evaporation of the liquid. Because they dissociate, salts in aqueous solution are particularly effective in lowering the evaporation rate of water. For example sea water evaporates about 5 per cent less rapidly than fresh water under similar conditions.

b) *Temperature.* — Evaporation of a liquid increases with increased temperature in approximately the same ratio as the vapor pressure at saturation increases with temperature. When air temperature is above that of water the latter will cease to evaporate before the air is saturated; if the temperature relations are reversed, evaporation will continue into the saturated atmosphere and dew may be deposited.

c) *Dryness of the air.* — The evaporation rate of a liquid depends on the concentration of liquid molecules in the vapor layer in contact with the liquid surface, and it is the gradient of concentration above, that determines diffusion away. In still air evaporation is approximately equal to the differences in absolute dryness of the air rather than to relative humidity as is shown by equations (2) and (4). That is,

$$V = k \frac{p^1 - p^0}{P}, \text{ where} \qquad (5)$$

V = amount of water evaporated per unit area, the area being large and the water flush with the surface.
k = the diffusion coefficient.
p^1 = the vapor pressure of the liquid at saturation at the surface temperature.
p^0 = the vapor pressure of the liquid in air.
P = atmospheric pressure.

Vapor pressure deficit is defined as the difference between the actual vapor pressure at a given temperature and the maximum possible vapor pressure (saturated) at the same temperature. It should be understood that the above equation holds only where the temperatures of the evaporating surface and the air are the same. LEIGHLY (1937) discusses vapor pressure deficits stressing the fact that the temperature equality mentioned above represents a special case seldom attained.

d) *Atmospheric pressure.* — Evaporation rate changes approximately in inverse proportion to the total barometric pressure (equation 5). This follows from the kinetic law of gases.

e) *Wind velocity.* — Evaporation increases with wind velocity due to eddy diffusion of vapor near the liquid surface (JEFFREYS, 1918; VAN

ORSTRAND and DEWEY, 1915). According to LEIGHLY (1937), air moving over an evaporating surface has two effects: *1*) a turbulence or eddy diffusion at some small distance from the surface and *2*) a laminar movement of air very near the surface in which region the velocity decreases to zero at the surface layer. In this boundary layer the gradients of vapor concentration, air velocity, and temperature are linear.

The thickness of this boundary layer of even simple evaporimeters is a function of at least five factors, namely: *1*) wind velocity in free air, *2*) length of evaporating surface in the direction of the wind, *3*) density of the air, *4*) molecular viscosity of the air, and *5*) length of evaporating surface at right angles to the wind (MARTIN, 1943). In the case of evaporation from leaves the qualitative character of the surface must be added. Corrugation, creasing, occurrence of hairs, and close proximity of adjacent leaves all tend to increase the thickness of the boundary layer.

LEIGHLY's formula for evaporation into moving air, modified by MARTIN to include the length of the evaporating surface at right angles to the direction of wind flow is as follows,

$$V = c\,k\,(p' - p'')\,R^{-0.2}\,L^{-0.3}\,W^{+0.5} \qquad \text{where} \qquad (6)$$

V = amount of water evaporated per unit area.
c = a proportionality constant.
k = the diffusion coefficient.
p' = vapor pressure at the surface.
p'' = vapor pressure at the edge of the boundary layer.
R = length of the evaporating surface at right angles to the wind direction.
L = length of the evaporating surface parallel to the wind direction.
W = wind velocity.

The exponents for the factors R, L, and W were determined experimentally using blotting-paper evaporimeters and are in good agreement with data reported by RENNER (1910, 1911*b*), THOMAS and FERGUSON (1917*a*, *b*), JEFFREYS (1918), GALLENKAMP (1919), SIERP and SEYBOLD (1927), and SEYBOLD (1929).

The above equation may be summarized by stating that evaporation from small areas varies as the square root of the wind velocity and inversely as the 0.3 and 0.2 powers of the length and breadth of the area. Certain presumed variations of this law are, according to MARTIN, probably due to failure to determine the actual temperature of the evaporating surface (*see* WALTER, 1925).

It should be noted that this expression of the rate of evaporation into moving air is very different from the formula given above expressing the rate of evaporation into still air where diffusion is molecular and "eddy diffusion" is not involved. The first holds approximately where a steady horizontal wind is present and cannot be reduced to the second which applies only in the absence of air movement.

Transpiration:— Because of the complex nature of the process of evaporation and the added complexities of leaf structure, transpiration is an intricate process that presents many experimental difficulties. On the other hand gross measurements of the rate and volume of water loss by plants may be readily made and many methods for studying water relations of plants both in the greenhouse and in the field have been devised. But having made measurements on water loss, the experimenter often meets his most difficult task in attempting to interpret their meaning, and unless a rigid control has been exercised over most or all of the external factors, their explanation may be difficult or even impossible. Of the immense literature on transpiration it is obvious that only a small portion can be treated here.

Methods of Measuring Transpiration:— The methods which have been extensively utilized in determining the rate of water loss by a transpiring plant logically fall into three groups: determinations of *1*) the loss of weight by whole plants or plant parts, *2*) the amount of water vapor given off, and *3*) the rate of water absorption. Detailed considerations of the various techniques employed with descriptions of the types of apparatus used and the numerous modifications suggested are given by BURGERSTEIN (1920), GRAFE (1924), MAXIMOV (1929*a*), and LEICK (1939).

While it has the advantage that the transpiring organs need not be enclosed in an artificial atmosphere which would modify the rate of water loss, the unwieldiness of the loss in weight method has somewhat restricted its use particularly when ecological experiments with numerous large plants have been desired.

If the surfaces of the culture vessel in which a plant is growing are sealed in a way such that water loss is restricted to the plant itself, changes in weight are brought about by transpiration (lenticular, cuticular, and stomatal) combined with the processes of metabolism (catabolic and anabolic). Under normal conditions of even moderate or reduced transpiration, the loss of water vapor completely overshadows any changes due to other physiological processes in the plant. Periodic weighings coupled with accurate determinations of leaf area, or green or dry weight enables the investigator to express the rate of transpiration per unit of plant area or weight.

Several problems arise, however, which make the analysis difficult. These are chiefly concerned with abnormalities in response of culture plants compared with those growing undisturbed in the field. Obviously, injury to the root system of the experimental plant through transplanting to a culture vessel immediately before making observations on transpiration rate is to be avoided. Not so apparent, however, are the modifications which may arise in plants grown continually in pots or large containers. Control of nutrition, water supply, soil pH, and air supply to the roots are among the most troublesome problems. These may be appreciated when one realizes the volume of soil which the roots of single herbaceous plants may permeate under natural conditions. Not only may the water supply be abnormal in potted plants but stomatal response (because of variation in water supply or due to some other cause) may be different in potted as compared with field grown plants. Obviously the transpiration rate from such an experimental plant would be far from comparable with that of its field grown complement.

Nevertheless, the loss in weight method when employed critically has been one of the most useful, particularly for laboratory and greenhouse experiments, as well as for certain ecological and irrigation studies such as those carried out by BRIGGS and SHANTZ (1913, 1916), KIESSELBACH (1916), VEIHMEYER (1927), and VEIHMEYER and HENDRICKSON (1927). Various automatic recording devices have been developed to obtain continuous records of weight loss (BRIGGS and SHANTZ, 1915; BRAUNER, 1931; SCHRATZ, 1931; and others).

The unwieldiness of using whole plants in the weight method has been circumvented by modifications whereby plant parts are removed and their loss in weight while standing in water recorded. Such a drastic treatment may so alter the water supply (either by increasing the resistance due to plugging of the tracheae with air, latex, or mucilage, or by decreasing the resistance through the removal of the roots and much of the conduction resistance) that completely abnormal results may be obtained (TABLE 45). Cutting under water at a time of day when little or no tension exists should avoid the plugging of xylem conductors with air and hence provide experimental plant material most like that of the normal plant. A dramatic illustration of the plugging action of latex can easily be observed on *Poinsettia*. The flowers of this plant, when cut and placed in water, often begin to wilt within a few hours. If the shoots are removed from the water and immediately held with the lower 1 to 2 inches of their bases in a flame, the heat and generated steam cause the latex plugs in the xylem to be blown out. If then the ends, while still hot, are placed in water, a very rapid recovery from wilting is often observed. The recovery may be so rapid, if wilting has not progressed too far, that the leaves will move visibly, and the drooping tip becomes erect within a few minutes. A similar effect upon a wilted shoot plugged with air may be shown by sealing its base in a bottle of water and aspirating it (STOCKING, 1948).

TABLE 45. — *Transpiration of Solidago virga aurea in milligrams per gram fresh weight per minute. Cut surface renewed hourly (data of* LEICK, *1939) : —*

TIME OF DAY	ROOTED PLANT RICHLY WATERED	ADJACENT CUT PLANT STANDING IN WATER	DIFFERENCE IN PER CENT
10 : 30 A.M.	61.5	35.8	42
11 : 00 A.M.	50.7	41.2	19
11 : 30 A.M.	53.7	46.5	13
12 : 00 M.	54.3	53.2	2
1 : 00 P.M.	63.1	54.7	13
2 : 00 P.M.	60.4	50.0	17
3 : 00 P.M.	49.4	45.3	12

A further modification of the loss in weight method is one in which the cut part is immediately weighed without placing in water and rapid subsequent weighings made. Under favorable conditions the initial loss in weight of the cut piece approaches that from the piece before cutting. Studies have been made by this method which has proven fairly successful for plants that transpire slowly (HUBER, 1923; IVANOV, 1924, 1928) but not for rapidly transpiring plants (MAXIMOV, 1929a).

Recently WEINMANN and LE ROUX (1945) have made a critical analysis of the rates of transpiration of barley, maize, oats, wheat, and tall fescue plants before and after cutting. The transpiration of the intact plant was measured in each case by weighing on a torsion balance and immediately afterwards under identical atmospheric conditions the transpiration of the cut shoot was determined. These experiments were carried out on relatively young plants and agreement in the rate of water loss for three minutes before and after cutting was poor. The average discrepancies ranged from 49 per cent in maize to 106 per cent in barley. In only approximately 35 per cent of the experiments with wheat and only 10 per cent of those with the other plants did the transpiration rates agree within 20 per cent. This further emphasizes the fact that extreme caution must be used in interpreting the results of transpiration experiments on detached plant parts.

Quantitatively the amount of water transpired by a known leaf area may be most accurately determined by drawing air of known moisture content over the leaf and subsequently through an absorbent such as anhydrous calcium chloride or magnesium perchlorate. The increased gain in weight of the absorbent over the gain found when an equal volume of air of the same original humidity is drawn through the absorbent gives the weight of water transpired. Such a method used by FREEMAN (1908) is a modification of the methods of E. and J. VERSCHAFFELT (1890) and GENEAU DE LAMARLIÈRE (1892) and has been further modified by MINCKLER (1936) and HIESEY (1940). The latter investigators used a vacuum pump to draw air over the plant part and flow meters to determine the volume of air moving. The main objection to this method is that an artificial atmosphere exists around the experimental part.

Qualitative and semi-quantitative investigations have been carried out using cobalt chloride paper, hygrometers (of horn, cellophane, and *Yucca*), and calcium chloride-containing vessels attached directly to the transpiring leaf. Of these only the cobalt chloride method has been used extensively and it has been standardized as a quantitative method. LIVINGSTON and his students have been especially responsible for the development of this method (LIVINGSTON, 1913; and LIVINGSTON and SHREVE, 1916).

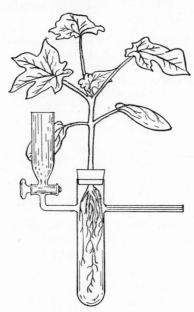

Indirectly the amount of water absorbed can be used as an indicator of water lost by the plant. Potometers for cut and intact plants are especially good for class demonstrations and, when combined with the weight method, yield valuable data on the lag between water loss by transpiration and water absorption. In this way the fluctuation in the water content of a plant can be studied. Such an apparatus is shown in FIGURE 49. The artificial environment surrounding the absorbing area is again a source of error.

FIG. 49.—Potometer with growing plant for study of water absorption and loss. Redrawn from MEYER and ANDERSON (1939).

In summary, it may be said that extreme difficulty has been encountered in devising a method of studying transpiration which is accurate but does not significantly affect the environment of the experimental plant. The gravimetric and potometric methods on whole plants are most likely to alter the action of absorbing organs and indirectly the stomata while the volumetric method may alter the environment of the leaves. Any method utilizing cut parts must be employed with extreme caution and only after adequately checking the various possible effects of cutting. Choice among the methods available must be made after carefully considering and, if possible, measuring the effects that the method will have on the plant itself.

Expression of Results:— In order to express the amount of water transpired on an area basis exact measurement of leaves is important. The numerous methods include weighing of cut out leaf tracings on paper of known weight per unit area, calculating area by photoelectric means, leaf matching, and other methods. MILLER (1938) discusses these various techniques at some length.

Three general methods of recording water loss have been used: *1*) by expressing the weight of water lost per unit time per plant unit, such as unit of area, green weight, or dry weight, *2*) by comparing the water lost by unit plant area with that lost from a similar area of water, and *3*) by expressing the total amount of water lost over an extended period of time per unit weight of dry substance produced by the plant for the same time period. These three means of expressing transpiration have been termed respectively: *1*) intensity of transpiration, rate of transpiration, absolute transpiration, *2*) relative transpiration, transpiration capacity, transpiring power, transpiration resistance, and *3*) water requirement, efficiency of transpiration, coefficient of transpiration.

Cuticular Transpiration:— Not only the thickness but also the composition of the cuticle on the surface of epidermal cells varies considerably with species, age, position, and condition of the plant organ. An example of the influence of the environment on cuticle formation may be found in seedlings of citrus grown under humid conditions. Such plants were subject to sun scorch due to the little cuticular protection afforded and to poor stomatal response (NIGAM, 1934). In fruit the cutin may so completely permeate the epidermal and hypodermal layer as to completely imbed the epidermal cells. Cuticular transpiration though a function of the permeability may not be directly correlated with cuticular thickness. Cutin is a heterogeneous substance composed of several wax-and-oil-like fractions. MARKLEY and SANDO (1931) studying the wax-like coating on the surface of apples separated the petroleum ether soluble fraction from the one that was petroleum ether insoluble. The former was composed chiefly of the hydrocarbon triacontane ($C_{30}H_{62}$) with small amounts of heptacosanol ($C_{27}H_{56}O$) and traces of true oils, while the latter was identified as ursolic acid $C_{30}H_{48}O_3$. These two fractions increased with age and development of the fruit but not uniformly. The oily petroleum ether soluble fraction increased faster rendering the layer more impervious to water.

PIENIAZEK (1944) found that when lenticular transpiration, which amounted to from 8 to 25 per cent of the total water loss, was excluded, by covering each lentical with paraffin, the rate of transpiration from several varieties of apples was not directly related to thickness of the cuticle itself but that varieties with a large wax deposit on the surface of the cuticle lost water most slowly. This wax deposit on apples has different chemical and physical characteristics from the cuticle (MARKLEY and SANDO, 1931).

Diurnal fluctuations have been observed in the physical properties of leaf cuticle. By measuring the contact angle of water drops on leaves of *Brassica sinapis* and *Triticum vulgare,* FOGG (1944) studied the wettability of the cuticle. A diurnal change in the contact angle was observed (FIGURE 50). This would imply that there is a diurnal fluctuation in cuticular transpiration in normal plants. Wilting caused a marked reversible rise in contact angle which was not, according to FOGG, a mechanical stretching effect.

Cuticular transpiration is most conveniently studied in hypostomatal leaves where the stomata can be covered by vaseline or other water impervious coatings, thus limiting water loss to that which passes through the cuticle of the upper leaf surface. Using this method and comparing transpiration from wilted leaves and leaves with the stomata sealed, AGAMOV (1927) showed that even with wilted leaves having apparently completely closed stomata, cuticular transpiration was slightly augmented by stomatal transpiration.

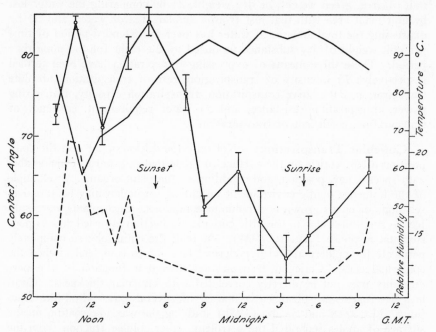

FIG. 50.—Diurnal fluctuation in the wettability of leaf cuticle as shown by change in contact angle of water drops. The solid line with circles represents contact angle; the vertical bars show significant differences for the points. The dashed line represents temperature; the light solid line, relative humidity. Data of FOGG (1944).

Under certain abnormal conditions such as wilting, or with age, the cuticle of leaves may develop fine cracks through which water loss is increased. HOLLE (1915) describes such cuticular fissures in wilted leaves of *Rochea falcata,* and KAMP (1930) found that the cuticle of old leaves split into fine fissures. Although no observation of such cuticular cracks were made by MENDEL (1945), he felt that such cracking of the normally very slightly permeable cuticle of citrus (BARTHOLOMEW, 1931; OPPENHEIMER and MENDEL, 1939) might explain an observed anomolous transpiration rate following irrigation of certain trees which had suffered from low soil moisture. The transpiration rate from these trees failed to reflect stomatal movement.

That cuticular transpiration may reach appreciable values is shown by the work of RUDOLPH (1925), who found that cuticle on the leaves of many plants permits a considerable water loss. As much as 30 per cent of the total water loss was found to be cuticular. In contrast, desert succulents may survive for months and even years with no water uptake, because cuticular transpiration is reduced to a negligible value.

An extensive discussion of the effects of environmental factors on the rate of cuticular transpiration has been presented by GÄUMANN (1942) with a theoretical consideration of the possible effects of the structural resistance of the cuticle, protoplasmic resistance, self-generated convection currents, air humidity, leaf cooling, and wind velocity.

Fluctuations in the Rate of Transpiration:— The rate at which water escapes from the colloidal walls of the mesophyll is a function of the complex interaction of internal and external forces and their influence upon the DPD of the water in the wall and in the intercellular spaces. Under conditions of adequate water supply the normal daily fluctuations in meteorological conditions are reflected in the daily march of transpiration.

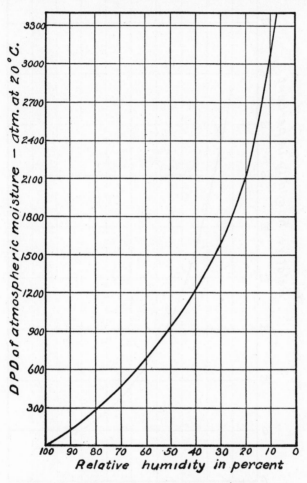

Fig. 51.—DPD of the atmosphere at 20° C as related to relative humidity. Data of table 18, Chapter V.

For, although equilibrium is never attained, the movement of water into, through, and out of the plant responds to the tendency to establish equilibrium of water in the soil, plant, and atmosphere. In the final analysis, it is the diffusion pressure deficit of the water vapor in the atmosphere which most profoundly affects this movement. In TABLE 18 of Chapter V, figures are given for the DPD of the atmosphere at constant temperature and changing relative humidity. FIGURE 51 shows a graph of this relation. SHULL (1939) has pointed out that the influence of temperature at constant relative humidity is very small. He did not, however, point out that the capacity of a given volume of air to hold water is greatly affected by the temperature. For example, as shown in FIGURE 52, a change in temperature from 40° F. to 50° F. may cause a change in relative humidity of from 76 to 54 per cent, or a change in DPD of from 350 to 810 atmospheres when the air contains 0.004 pound of water per pound of dry air.

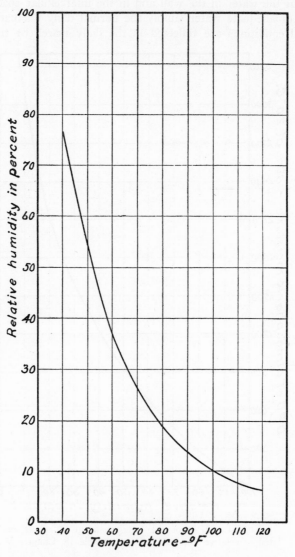

FIG. 52.—Relation between atmospheric temperature and relative humidity for an atmosphere containing .004 pounds of water per pound of dry air.

As a result of humidity and temperature changes there is a diurnal fluctuation in DPD of the atmosphere, as shown in FIGURE 53. Coupled with this fluctuation is the influence of light upon transpiration. This may act either directly to increase the temperature of the leaves above that of the atmosphere or physiologically to alter the permeability of the protoplasm or the movement of stomata. Diurnal fluctuations in transpiration rates have often been measured (BRIGGS and SHANTZ, 1916; SAYRE, 1920; MAXIMOV, 1929a; CHUNG, 1935; MILLER, 1938; and others). A more critical analysis of the individual effects of various factors on the rate of transpiration has been made through use of control cabinets where temperature, humidity, light, and air flow are rigidly controlled (DAVIS and HOAGLAND, 1928; ARTHUR and STEWART, 1933; BIALE, 1941; MONTERMOSO and DAVIS, 1942; and MARTIN, 1943).

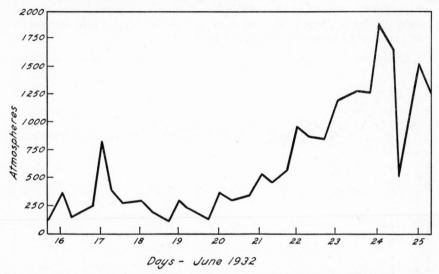

FIG. 53.—Diurnal fluctuations in DPD of the atmosphere at a station in Washington, D. C., during a 10-day period in June 1932. Data of SHULL (1939).

Rhythmic fluctuations in transpiration independent of environmental conditions have been known for a long time (KOHL, 1886; CURTIS, 1902; LLOYD, 1908). Experimenting with *Fouquieria splendens* in a dark room and as near constant temperature as possible, LLOYD found a variation in transpiration rate. He felt that stomatal opening after midnight might explain a rise observed in the transpiration at that time but that such stomatal movement could not cause a lowering in transpiration rate after the maximum was reached. The occurrence of an early morning maximum in plants kept in total darkness was observed. The potometer method, using cut shoots, was employed, hence the fluctuations appear to be independent of root pressure rhythm which HOFMEISTER (1862), and GROSSENBACHER (1938) found.

Using lemon cuttings and working in control cabinets with constant darkness, temperature, and humidity, BIALE (1941) verified the existence of a rhythmic fluctuation in transpiration. Similarly, MONTERMOSO and DAVIS (1942) found such a rhythm in rooted *Coleus* leaves grown under controlled conditions (FIGURE 54). The rigid control used in the chambers permits no doubt as to the existence of this rhythm. By altering the light and dark periods before placing the experimental material under constant dark conditions, these authors were able to invert the maximum and minimum points on the curve as shown in the figure.

The work of MONTERMOSO and DAVIS has not been carried to such a point that a complete explanation of the phenomenon may be made. Unfortunately, no data on stomatal movement were presented. Two possible explanations appear. The most obvious would involve a rhythmic fluctuation in stomatal movement in the dark, such as has been observed in some plants. SAYRE (1926) found a diurnal opening of stomata in the dark for two days. After this length of time the degree of opening was reduced. The curves presented by MONTERMOSO and DAVIS appear to show a decline after about this same period of time. TAGAWA (1936) observed continued stomatal movements in beans for several days when kept in constant darkness or when exposed to constant light. The second possible explanation would involve a diurnal fluctuation in root resistance. Such changes in root pressure have been discussed in Chapter IX.

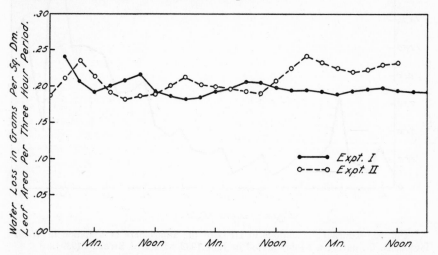

FIG. 54.—Diurnal fluctuations in water loss from rooted Coleus leaves under controlled conditions. The leaves were in the dark during the above tests and temperature and humidity were constant. The solid line represents plants preconditioned under normal light-dark conditions, the dashed line plants preconditioned under reversed light-dark cycle. From MONTERMOSO and DAVIS (1942).

Internal Factors Affecting Transpiration:— The anatomical and physico-chemical differences among species, and between individuals of a single species causing variation in transpiration rate are difficult to differentiate and evaluate. However, they have received considerable study. It is convenient to group them into two sets (a) those affecting the diffusion pressure of water in the walls directly, and (b) those influencing the rate of removal of water from the sub-stomatal chambers. In the first group are 1) wall structure, 2) physical resistance to water movement (friction), and 3) osmotic properties of cells. In the second group are 1) internal exposed surface, 2) stomatal aperture, 3) cuticle, and 4) morphological modifications.

Wall Structure:— The cell walls of plants are made up largely of carbohydrates and polyuronides. The organic portions of these compounds have the generalized approximate formula $C_n H_{[2n-2]} O_{[n-1]}$ where n has a value of 5 or 6 or some simple multiple thereof. From this formula it is evident that, of the organic portion of the molecules, around 25 per cent of the atoms are oxygen. And whereas each of these oxygens has a covalence of 2 that is ordinarily satisfied in the molecular constitution of the compound, an equal number of secondary or residual valences exist, each of which is capable of holding one water molecule through a hydrogen bond. Furthermore, the cellulose and uronide chains making up the walls are so spaced in the micelles or fibrils that they form a microcapillary matrix capable of holding much water by microcapillary forces.

When the hydrostatic pressure of the water in the xylem approaches atmospheric pressure in value, all walls are highly hydrated and it has been assumed that the outer surfaces constitute virtually free water surfaces. Little energy is required to move water up to and through cell walls under these conditions for movement is simply a process of exchange. When the water balance shifts far to the negative side some water is withdrawn from the walls, the constituent molecules come closer together, and the capillary structure becomes more dense. The walls perform two essential functions in relation to transpiration by leaves in addition to their usual structural service; by virtue of their colloidal and microcapillary nature they act as conductors; because of their imbibitional properties they store water during periods of abundance against deficits that develop during rapid water loss.

BANGHAM and LEWIS (1937), using cut strips of *Ficus elastica* leaves, found that water did not readily enter the intercellular passages by capillarity. Less polar compounds (paraffin oil, benzene, chloroform, ether, and essential oil) did enter. The writers concluded that transpiration does not take place from a liquid film of water on the cell walls of the mesophyll.

LEWIS (1945) has performed experiments indicating that the mesophyll walls in leaves are hydrophobic in nature: that is, they are not readily wet, the interfacial tension between walls and water being low. The effect of such a condition would be that water would remain deep within the walls and that the surfaces would remain relatively dry. LEWIS' experiments indicate this to be true. Earlier HÄUSERMANN (1944) had demonstrated that such a lyophilic liquid as butyl alcohol which has some hydrophilic properties best wets the inter-cellular surfaces of *Dianthus barbatus* leaves. From this observation he proposed that such surfaces are composed of cutin.

Transpiration from such surfaces could not approach that from free water surfaces of equal area. This may explain the low ratio of transpiration to evaporation from free water surfaces found by TURRELL in experiments to be described. Release of fatty substances by living cells has been postulated to explain deposition of cutin and suberin in the endodermis and cuticle of plants. Possibly this same type of material may escape from mesophyll cells in minute quantities and impregnate the outer exposed wall surfaces rendering them hydrophobic.

Another characteristic of the cell wall which may greatly influence the water holding capacity of the cell is the degree of elasticity which it possesses. The cell walls of some xerophytes exhibit little or no elasticity. In this connection, it has been pointed out (PRINGSHEIM, 1931; ERNEST, 1934c) that there is essentially no change in volume from the water-saturated state to limiting plasmolysis. Hence, the DPD can increase rapidly and considerably with the loss of a very small amount of water. This is believed to enable plants with inelastic walls to adapt themselves to drought conditions. These cells may rapidly change from a condition of complete turgor to zero turgor and hence from zero DPD to a DPD equal to the OP of the cell sap with little corresponding change in the volume of water lost. Such a condition would greatly enhance the plant's resistance to water loss.

Physical Resistance to Water Movement:— As mentioned above the volume of the cell walls varies with water balance and as the walls become thin during periods of high deficits resistance to longitudinal movement parallel to the cell surface must be appreciably increased. Covalent forces that space the carbohydrate molecules along the chains, however, are little affected by water content and so lateral movements across walls as occur in movement from cell to cell are not greatly changed. Hence dehydration of cell walls probably does not become a major factor of resistance to transpiration until a point is reached where air begins to replace water in the capillary structure. This does not occur until other disturbances have severely affected the cells. Study of the walls of living mesophyll by means of the microscope shows that they remain plastic, elastic, and normal in appearance throughout the normal stages of wilting and in fact until the cells are almost completely collapsed. Probably cell wall structure has little direct effect upon water movement and loss in leaves, at least until they reach a stage of permanent wilting.

Nevertheless, the resistance offered by even the minor veins of the leaves is extremely small compared to that offered by the cell (WYLIE,

1938; MER, 1940). Root pruning and stem incisions have shown that over 50 per cent of the cross section of the root as well as of the stem may be prevented from functioning without severe injury to young citrus trees, and ready lateral transfer of water may be observed (ELAZARI-VOLCANI, 1936). The protoplast particularly exhibits a high resistance to rapid water movement which may be increased or decreased by the presence of specific ions, by changes in temperature, or by light intensity, as will be discussed in a subsequent section.

Osmotic Properties:— Just as imbibitional forces enable cell walls to maintain their form and water content, so do osmotic forces through the development of turgor make possible the normal unwilted stature of plants. And in proportion to the effect of such form upon evaporation from leaves does osmosis affect transpiration. The direct effects of solute concentration upon vapor pressure of water are shown by TABLE 18 to be almost negligible at concentrations that occur in plants. Furthermore, as explained in Chapter V, turgor increases the vapor pressure of water in the cell so that at full turgor the water-vapor pressure of the cell sap is equal to that of free water of the same temperature and pressure.

SHREVE (1931) found that free cell sap with osmotic pressures of 4.9, 11.7, and 20.0 atmospheres respectively evaporated in the ratios 1.011:-1.005:1.000. This reflects the relatively minor influence of small additions of osmotically active solutes upon vapor pressure. When sugar solutions were allowed to evaporate through semi-permeable membranes the reduction in rate was much greater, but in this case the solutes were probably able to accumulate in the solution immediately in contact with the membrane or actually within the pores of the membrane, a phenomenon that does not occur in leaves.

BOON-LONG (1941) similarly found that the presence of a collodion membrane reduced by 10 per cent the rate of evaporation of a sucrose solution over that brought about by osmotic concentration alone. Increase in osmotic pressure of leaf cell sap by exposure to light, scalding of petioles, or direct introduction of glucose caused a decrease in the permeability of the tissues to water as determined by the plasmolytic method. According to BOON-LONG this lowering of permeability is chiefly responsible for reduction in the transpiration rates which he found in plant organs subjected to these treatments. However, the hardening of cabbage tissues during exposure for seven days to 5° C. caused an increase in permeability which more than counterbalanced a simultaneous increase in osmotic pressure. Consequently the transpiration was greater for the hardened than for the non-hardened plants.

Internal Surface:— Because evaporation is a function of surface it follows that, when transpiration is high, the exposed intercellular surface of the leaf might become a limiting factor. Most investigators have followed the development of air spaces in leaves by determining their volume by infiltration methods. In the leaves of vascular plants the volume of space differs not only among plants but also as a response to environmental conditions.

SIFTON (1945) in a review of the subject reports that UNGER (1854) found in 41 species a minimum air space of 77 parts per 1000 in leaves of *Camphora officinalis* and a maximum of 713 parts per 1000 in *Pistia texeris*. Shade leaves with more spongy parenchyma have a greater volume of air space than sun leaves. Air space varies with water supply but not uniformly among plants, and evergreens have a smaller volume than deciduous plants.

TURRELL (1936) attempted to determine the area of internally exposed cell walls and to compare this with total leaf area. A wide variation was found in different species, and a comparison of leaves in high and low light showed differences within a species. In general the palisade parenchyma exposes much more surface per unit volume than does spongy tissue. Ratios of internally exposed tissue to external surface are given in TABLE 46.

TABLE 46. — *Ratios between internally exposed cell walls and external leaf surface* (*data of* TURRELL, 1936) : —

PLANT	TYPE	RATIO OF INTERNAL TO EXTERNAL SURFACE
Bryophyllum calicynum	succulent sun	7.9
Syringa vulgaris	mesomorphic shade	6.8
Syringa vulgaris	mesomorphic sun	13.2
Ricinus communis	mesomorphic shade	12.7
Vitis vulpina	mesomorphic sun	11.6
Catalpa speciosa	mesomorphic sun	19.2
Gaultheria shallon	xeromorphic shade	8.2
Berberis nervosa	xeromorphic shade	9.9
Citrus grandis	xeromorphic sun	17.2
Eucalyptus globulus	xeromorphic sun	31.3

TURRELL (1944) concluded that leaves having the largest internal exposed surface should also have the highest transpiration rate, other conditions being similar. To test this assumption he studied *Nerium oleander* and *Vinca rosea* (periwinkle) grown under conditions of low and high light intensity. These two genera with different stomatal distributions were chosen in order to minimize the effects of stomatal control over transpiration. Stomata of periwinkle were considered 2.5 times too close together for maximum diffusion into still air; those of oleander 1.49 times considering each stomatal pit as a unit and 5.7 times for the stomata within a pit. The stomatal pits of oleander occur only on the dorsal surface, whereas the stomata of periwinkle occupy both leaf surfaces.

The xeromorphic leaves of both species, grown under high light intensity, had greater internal: external surface ratios than the mesomorphic ones developed in lower light. In spite of the fact that the internal transpiring leaf surface averaged 8.1 times the external for periwinkle, and 15.6 times for oleander, the ratio of transpiration per unit internal leaf surface to evaporation from a unit free water surface was only 0.012 for periwinkle and 0.027 for oleander. These figures indicate that factors other than internal evaporating surface are concerned in controlling the rate of transpiration from xeromorphic leaves.

Stomatal Number and Distribution:— In spite of conflicting opinions (*see* MILLER, 1938), the weight of evidence indicates that a genetic factor is involved in determining the numbers and distribution of stomata in leaves. Any factor that limits the expansion of a leaf increases the ratio of stomatal number to leaf area and also the pore space per unit area (SALISBURY, 1927).

MAXIMOV (1929a) gives a detailed consideration of ZALENSKI's (1904) investigations on the anatomical differences of leaves of the same plant. ZALENSKI, working on the relation of structure to position of leaves, found that small apical leaves, having numerous stomata and thick cuticle, were more xerophytic than broad basal ones. SMITH (1941) found a similar condition in bean. Stomatal frequency increased from base to apex of the lamina, and from base to top of the plant. SALISBURY (1927) found that variations in stomatal number on an area basis depended upon the size of the epidermal cells according to the formula:

$$I = \frac{S}{E + S} \times 100 \qquad \text{where} \qquad (7)$$

I = the stomatal index that is constant for any species.
S = number of stomata per unit area.
E = number of epidermal cells in the same unit area.

Leaves or portions of leaves which, because of position on the plant or because of xerophytic condition, are reduced in size, show high stomatal frequencies (number of stomata per unit area). A similar condition is shown by exposed upper leaves, sun leaves, apices and margins of leaves, and by leaves of woody as compared with herbaceous plants, and leaves of marginal vegetation as compared with shade species. All of these differences, however, are due chiefly to variations in growth of the epidermal cells, that is, to the spacing of the stomata and not the number developed. Under conditions of high humidity there does, however, appear to be a reduction in the proportion of stomata to epidermal cells formed. Aquatics have lower stomatal indices than land plants. Poor nutritional conditions appear in some instances to reduce the stomatal index.

Methods of Measuring Stomatal Openings:— Both direct and indirect methods have been utilized in studying the degree of stomatal opening. These methods have been discussed by STÅLFELT (1929) and NADEL (1938). The latter author critically examined the alcohol fixation method of LLOYD which has been used extensively and at times without due caution.

It is obvious that where the conditions of the experiment and the nature of the leaf permit, the direct microscopical observation of intact, untreated leaves is the most reliable means of determining the degree of stomatal opening. Often, however, conditions are such that this is not possible and resort must be taken to the microscopical examination of treated material or to one of the more indirect methods such as porometry, infiltration, or measurement of transpiration.

Of the various treatments which have been used to prepare the epidermis for microscopical observation (drying, placing in water, and chemical treatment to prevent stomatal change) only the alcohol fixation method proposed by LLOYD (1908) has been used extensively. This method consists of stripping the epidermis from the leaf and quickly immersing it in absolute alcohol. There is an immediate, rapid dehydration and hardening of the cellulose walls before the alcohol penetrates the cells appreciably. Obviously, any turgor changes which might occur during the stripping and immersion would tend to invalidate the method. LOFTFIELD (1921) used the alcohol method in studying some sixty different species of plants. He checked the method against direct observation of undisturbed leaves of alfalfa and several other species, finding good agreement between the two methods. Rapid stripping and transfer of the epidermis into the alcohol was found, however, to be essential to prevent dimensional changes.

A more critical analysis of the method (NADEL, 1938) showed it to be valid only for plants with easily detachable epidermis while plants with adhering or partially adhering epidermis were not found suitable. Even in the first group, if mesophyll cells are left attached to the epidermis, changes in stomatal opening may take place in alcohol.

ASHBY (1931) has compared the porometer method with LLOYD's alcohol fixation method with good agreement in *Geranium* and *Verbena*. The well known porometer method first introduced by DARWIN and PERTZ (1911) measures the rate at which air can be drawn through the leaf. Thus it gives an average or statistical value for the diffusion capacity rather than an absolute measure of pore size. This measure is a function of mesophyll resistance, viscosity of the air, pressure difference employed, as well as being subject to the mechanical difficulties of attaching the porometer cup to the leaf by lightly clamping the leaf between a glass plate and a greased (beeswax-vaseline) washer. Nevertheless the method has been used with apparent success (OPPENHEIMER, 1926; HARTSUIJKER, 1935).

Few attempts have been made to calculate the actual aperture of the stomata from figures obtained by use of the porometer. These have usually been of an empirical nature where porometer figures have been plotted against observed stomatal areas obtained either directly by use of a microscope on the living leaf or indirectly by LLOYD's alcohol fixation method. The most recent attempt to calibrate the porometer is that of HEATH (1941) using the resistance porometer described by GREGORY and PEARSE (1934). This instrument employs standard capillaries in series with leaf resistance. In contrast to the older flow porometers, it can be used to calculate independently of the pressure drop the resistance or conductance of the leaf area through which the air flows. The conditions for the valid use of methods of calculating flow resistance and the theoretical limitations involved can be found in HEATH's paper.

It has been observed (WILLIAMS, 1947) that the behavior of stomata under a porometer cup cannot be regarded as normal at least so far as shock response is concerned and consequently doubt is thrown upon observations made by use of the porometer on stomatal response to light-dark stimuli. Further clarification of this problem is needed.

A very simple and rapid semiquantitative method which is well adapted to use in the field where rough determinations are to be made is found in the infiltration method (MOLISCH, 1912; STEIN, 1912). If a drop of liquid of low surface tension and viscosity is placed on a leaf with open stomata, it will penetrate through the stomata, filling the intercellular spaces and giving a water-logged appearance. If a series of liquids of differing surface tensions and viscosities is used, an approximate estimation of the degree of stomatal opening can be made. In place of the series of liquids proposed by Molisch (absolute alcohol, benzol, and xylol), other authors have used different liquids. STAHL (1894) used paraffin oil, petroleum, and petroleum ether; DIETRICH (1925), xylol, petroleum, castor oil plus turpentine, and paraffin oil; SCHORN (1929), varying proportions of isobutyl alcohol and ethylene glycol. WEBER (1923) employed ammonium vapors which penetrate the leaf killing the cells and turning them brown.

Certain other gross qualitative methods have been used to determine the opening of stomata such as the use of cobalt chloride paper as a measure of transpiration, and techniques in which the curling of strips of cellophane are used as a measure of humidity. These methods are, however, of little value in studies of stomatal opening.

Genetic Factors:— SHAFER (1942), experimenting with excised leaves of several inbred and hybrid corn seedlings was unable to demonstrate any differences in water loss between the various strains. GYÖRFFY (1941) concluded from a comparative study of the osmotic values of a number of plants that polyploids are more variable in osmotic pressure and hence more adaptable to dry conditions than diploids. In grafts an advantageous increase of osmotic value beyond the 2n level was observed in tetraploids. CLARK, HECHT, CURTIS, and SHAFER (1941) found that the stomata of high yielding varieties of inbred and hybrid corn open earlier and close later than those of low yielding strains.

Stomatal Regulation of Transpiration:— The role of stomatal closure in the control of transpiration has proved difficult to determine. Early concepts following the demonstration of stomatal movement pictured stomatal control as being complete except for cuticular transpiration. LLOYD's (1908) work indicated that stomatal movement and transpiration are not closely related. LOFTFIELD (1921) claims these results to be invalid because of faulty technic. In work on alfalfa and several other plants, Loftfield showed that stomatal movement and transpiration from cut shoots paralleled each other quite closely. Stomatal movement in cut shoots differed markedly from that in intact plants, hence Lloyd's comparison of stomatal opening on intact plants with transpiration of cut shoots was hardly valid (*see also* LLOYD, 1912, 1913). RENNER (1910) also criticised LLOYD's conclusions.

According to current opinion, it seems that when stomata are wide open, transpiration rate depends upon factors governing evaporation. Among these the diffusion pressure deficit of water as determined by tension in the xylem and frictional resistance to rapid flow plays a major role. These factors continue to be dominant until the stomata are at least half closed; from then on, stomatal opening apparently determines water loss quite accurately.

Effect of Mineral Nutrients on Transpiration:— The presence of osmotically active solutes reduces the diffusion pressure of water; other things being equal, evaporation from a solution is a function of solute concentration. Some effects of the presence of salt in the soil solution are: osmotic influences upon water uptake; increased equilibrium concentration within plant cells; and secondary effects, specific for the particular salt, upon permeability, guard cell movement, leaf abscission, etc.

The immediate effect of adding a salt to a soil of low salt content is to increase the diffusion pressure deficit of soil water, reducing the gradient between the soil solution and the root cells (MAGISTAD, 1945). This reduces water absorption, less water is available to the leaves, and transpiration is lowered. If, however, the added salt concentration is low and the soil used is of low salt content, certain ions may act specifically causing an increase or decrease in transpiration depending upon the nature of the ion and not on its colligative properties (HARTER, 1908; REED, 1910; BOUYOUCOUS, 1911). Similar results were obtained with the use of single salt solutions (HANSTEEN-CRANNER, 1914; KISSER, 1927).

In short time studies on the addition of salt to low salt soils, MEYER (1931) found a reduction in transpiration for all concentrations used. The specific effects of low salt concentrations were not noted; apparently the slight increases in the transpiration of plants in solutions of very low concentration were obscured by the concentration of salts naturally present in the soil employed. The differences in retarding effect between different salts could in this case be explained on the basis of their colligative properties.

Secondary effects of salts were observed by ILJIN (1922a), who found sodium and potassium to stimulate opening of guard cells; calcium checked the opening. Sodium and calcium in high concentrations induced leaf abscission. The water requirement decreased rapidly with increase in salt concentration (MEYER, 1931), while $CaCl_2$ caused, first, an increase, and then a decrease. There was an increased succulence of tops where NaCl and $CaCl_2$ were added to the soil.

Influence of Disease, Sprays, Dusts, and Waxes on Transpiration Rate:— Numerous workers have recently concerned themselves with the

TABLE 47.— *Water requirement in Zea as affected by nutrition* *(data of DESAI, 1937)* : —

TREATMENT	FRESH WEIGHT		TOP ROOT RATIO	AMOUNT OF WATER LOST IN 3 WEEKS	WATER REQUIREMENT PER UNIT FRESH WT.	
	Top	Root			Top	Root
	gm.	gm.		gm.		
Full nutrient	81.60	24.38	3.34	377.33	4.624	15.47
Potassium—deficient	68.33	36.13	1.88	413.00	6.044	11.43
Phosphorus—deficient ...	11.82	9.60	1.22	145.66	12.323	15.17
Nitrogen—deficient	7.27	6.43	1.13	181.00	24.896	28.15

effect of disease and the application of sprays, dusts, and wax dips on the rate of water loss from plants.

Studies of the effect of nutrient deficiency (lack of N, P, and K) on stomatal behavior of a number of plants, including bean, corn, and tobacco have indicated that a disruption of the general metabolism of the plant is reflected in sluggish stomatal response to changing environment. Subnormal stomatal behavior is accompanied by an increased water requirement and a decreased yield and size (TABLE 47) (DESAI, 1937). This result is in agreement with observations that application of fertilizers to infertile soils reduces the water requirements of plants growing on them (KIESSELBACH, 1916).

Increased water requirements and rates of transpiration are usually observed in plants suffering from fungus diseases. This is not always true (REED and COOLEY, 1913), as the fungus may occasionally actually obstruct water loss from the leaf. Frequently the effect of the fungus is most strongly manifested through a disruption of the normal diurnal transpiration curve (GRAF-MARIN, 1934; YARWOOD, 1936; GASSNER and GOEZE, 1936; and JOHNSTON, 1940). Rupture of the cuticle or altered stomatal response may cause a greatly increased rate of transpiration, especially at night when the cuticular influence would normally be most manifest, and the amount of water lost directly through the mycelium of the fungus may be considerable. Alteration in permeability caused by secretory products of the fungus has also been suggested as a cause of accelerated water loss (WEAVER, 1916).

Although many conflicting results have been obtained on the effect of insecticides on transpiration, it seems certain that insecticides may alter the rate of transpiration, either mechanically or chemically. The mechanical action may cause a reduction in transpiration through physical interference with water vapor diffusion from the leaf, or it may cause an increase due to the presence of minute dust particles wedging in the stomata preventing closure. This latter effect was observed by BEASLEY (1942) when fine inert dusts were applied to the stomatal bearing surfaces of leaves; night water loss was increased.

Chemically, the specific effects of the insecticides may alter the permeability of the cuticle, or stomatal sensitivity. Copper sprays have been shown to increase transpiration by increasing cuticular transpiration (WILSON and RUNNELS, 1933; KRAUSCHE and GILBERT, 1937; FOSTER and TATMAN, 1940); other investigators have been unable to find significant effects on transpiration by treatment with Bordeaux sprays (CHILDERS, 1936; MILLER, 1938; LOUSTALOT, 1944).

Excessive water loss during transplanting and storage of nursery stock coupled with the great reduction of absorbing roots left on the plant largely determines the production of new roots and the plant's survival. Seven common practices listed by ERICKSON (1945) are employed to keep the water loss below the absorption. These are 1) hardening of the plants, 2) retention of as many roots as possible, 3) removal of part of the top, 4) avoidance of drying between digging and planting, 5) planting in moist soil and watering immediately, 6) protection from wind and sunshine, and 7) planting during cool, humid weather.

The work of MORRIS (1921), NEILSON (1928, 1931), TUKEY and BRASE (1931), and MANEY (1931), has been particularly influential in making commercially practicable the use of melted wax in the treatment of nursery stock to prevent excessive water loss during transplanting and storage. Wax emulsions, because of their ease of application, are now largely replacing the earlier melted wax treatment (EMERSON and HIL-DRETH, 1933; MILLER, NIELSON, and BANDEMER, 1937). A technique of evaluation, through use of controlled environment and infra-red photography, of foliar injury caused by wax and oil emulsions has been described by COMAR and BARR (1944).

Physiological Effects of Water Deficits:— A condition of water deficit in the plant, whether brought about by low soil moisture, high solute concentration in the soil solution, or desiccating atmospheric conditions, greatly modifies the transpirational, photosynthetic, assimilatory, respirational, and reproductive activities of the plant. A more thorough study of the changes which take place in the colloidal properties of cell protoplasm upon the withdrawal of water as a consequence of freezing or desiccation is necessary in order to understand the physicochemical and biochemical reactions that take place during drought and freezing, and to learn why in some cells such changes lead to irreversible coagulation of the protoplasm and death, whereas other cells are able to withstand such changes.

Emphasis of early work on drought resistance was laid particularly on an ecological consideration of xeromorphism and is adequately reviewed in MAXIMOV's work (1929a). Xeromorphic structure is characterized anatomically by 1) a decrease in dimensions of cells including guard cells, 2) a greater number of stomata per unit area, 3) a denser network of veins, 4) a thickening of the cuticle, and 5) a greater density of hair covering. All or part of these anatomical features may be induced or intensified by continued mild exposure to drought conditions. Physiologically, a xeromorphic condition is characterized by 1) a more intense assimilation; the chloroplasts function only part time because of a restriction of their activity during periods of water deficit, and 2) an increase in stomatal transpiration but a decrease in cuticular transpiration. In spite of SEY-BOLD's (1929) attempt to revive the earlier view of SCHIMPER that xerophytes have a lower transpiration due to their structure, it is generally agreed that this is not the case when the stomata are open and, in fact, under these conditions xeromorphy is often characterized by more intense transpiration (MAXIMOV, 1931; VASSILIEV, 1930).

Recently BENNET-CLARK (1945) has suggested that the anatomical features which had formerly been considered as helping to reduce the transpiration rates of xerophytes (*i.e.,* hairs, sunken stomata, and leaf roll) actually benefit the plant, tending to prevent stomatal closure by maintaining a higher humidity at the leaf surface. This increases the duration of active photosynthesis by allowing gaseous exchange to continue.

Current studies stress the effects of drought on biochemical reactions. MAXIMOV (1941) has reviewed the course of hydrolytic enzyme reactions that take place under dry conditions. He has noted their effect on photosynthesis and has discussed theories of water-supply relations and starvation with special reference to transpiration, respiration, and dry matter production. The effects of withholding water as a means of hardening plants to withstand drought is also discussed.

Enzymatic activity is greatly affected by the water balance of the plant cell. Catalase and reductase activity is high during all phases of water deficit as is also the velocity of the hydrolytic activity of amylase. The content of reducing sugars was found under these conditions also to be high (GOLOVINA, 1939). Loss of 30 to 40% of the water from leaves decreases the synthetic and increases the hydrolytic power of phosphatase. Monophosphatase and diphosphatase do not, however, respond identically to the same water deficit (SISAKIAN and KOBIAKOVA, 1940).

The net rate of protein formation from amino acids decreases with reduced water content or in other words the net rate of hydrolyses increases (PETRIE and WOOD, 1938). While the synthetic activity of invertase and protease is particularly low in drought-susceptible varieties (SISAKIAN, 1939, 1940; GOLOVINA, 1939; KURSANOV, 1941). The periodicity in the rhythm of invertase and protease activity is lost in non-drought-resistant wheat on wilting (SISAKIAN and KOBIAKOVA, 1941). Generally, then, the hydrolytic processes in the cell are accelerated and the synthetic process decreased during drought. This usually results in injury. SISAKIAN believes that such disturbances in the enzymic equilibrium are the principal causes of the death of plants from drought.

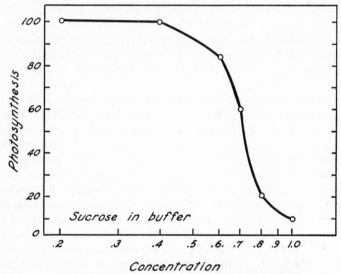

FIG. 55.—The effect of DPD of *Chlorella* cells upon photosynthesis. The cells were immersed in sucrose solutions of the indicated molal concentrations. Photosynthetic activity was greatly reduced as the concentration increased above 0.4 mol. Data of GREENFIELD (1942).

The effect of desiccation on photosynthesis cannot be attributed directly to the fact that water is a reactant in the process but must be due to the physico-chemical changes which occur in protoplasm, the altered action of enzymes, and the stomatal response which takes place with changing water supply. Protoplasmic dehydration may be brought about either directly by drying or indirectly by the use of hypertonic solutions. The results of these two types of experiments are not always the same (CHRELASHVILI, 1941).

Investigations using hypertonic solutions have shown that photosynthesis is very sensitive to changes in the colloidal state of protoplasm; perhaps more so than respiration (WALTER, 1928, 1929; RABINOWITCH, 1945).

Studies on the relation of water supply to photosynthetic activity show that desiccation brought about by growing *Chlorella* cells in solutions of varying osmotic concentration may affect the process through the dark or enzymatic reaction rather than through the light reaction (GREENFIELD, 1941, 1942). Desiccation had little effect in subdued light but profoundly affected photosynthesis in strong light where the dark reaction is limiting. FIGURE 55 from GREENFIELD (1942) shows the effect of such physiological desiccation on photosynthesis.

Plasmolysis inhibits the production of chlorophyll, and soil moisture content may affect pigment production (FURLINGER, 1938; BECK, 1942).

Slight dehydration may cause an increase in photosynthesis. Maximum photosynthesis was found by CHRELASHVILI (1941) to take place ·in all plants with slight dehydration but this action varied in different plants and with different conditions. In *Allium,* for instance, the photosynthetic activity increases up to a certain sugar concentration; in *Primula* no such upper limit was observed under the experimental conditions. In *Zea* an increase in carbohydrates caused a depression in photosynthesis and an increase in respiration (BRILLIANT, 1924; ALEXEEV, 1935; CHRELASHVILI, 1941). Here, again, the effect appears to be found only in relatively high light intensities (BRILLIANT and CHRELASHVILI, 1941). With considerable dehydration, photosynthetic activity decreases and finally ceases in both strong and weak light (DASTUR, 1924, 1925; VASSILIEV, 1927; TUMANOV, 1929; SKVORTZOV, 1931; DASTUR and DESAI, 1933; HEINICKE and CHILDERS, 1935; BRILLIANT and CHRELASHVILI, 1941; LOUSTALOT, 1945).

An excellent treatment of the carbohydrate changes which occur in wheat during wilting can be found in the work of VASSILIEV (1931) and VASSILIEV and VASSILIEV (1936). The dynamics of sugar transformations depend to a high degree on the water supply; hydrolysis predominates during water deficit, condensation when the water supply improves. When a wheat plant undergoes wilting, four stages can be noted: *1*) a decrease in the amount of monosaccharides and sucrose due to reduced photosynthesis before wilting is evident; *2*) on wilting of the lower leaves there is an intense hydrolysis of insoluble carbohydrates and an accumulation of sucrose. This process gradually spreads to the upper leaves, stem, and fruit; *3*) beginning again at the lower leaves, sucrose decreases and monosaccharides accumulate; *4*) finally, with the disappearance of sucrose and monosaccharides, the plant is well on its way to complete desiccation. The lower leaves are the first to lose sugars. Here the role of sugars in drought seems to be the same as in freezing; in both cases sugars protect the plants against adverse desiccation. A similar trend in carbohydrates was observed in lucerne by HENRICI (1943, 1945); starch was the dominant reserve carbohydrate instead of hemicellulose, as found in wheat.

Investigations on the acceleration of starch dissolution due to a decrease

TABLE 48. — *The effect of decrease in water content on the amylolytic activity and starch dissolution of sunflower leaves kept in the dark for 18 hours* (data of SPOEHR and MILNER, 1939) : —

CONDITIONS	% STARCH DECREASE	ORIGINAL pH	FINAL pH	% CHANGE IN RELATIVE AMYLOLYTIC ACTIVITY
Leaves in water, 22° C.	17	6.83	6.90	— 4.8
Leaves without water, 22° C. .	69	6.85	6.87	+44.8

in water content of leaves have also been carried out by Rywosch (1908), Molisch (1921), Schroeder and Horn (1922), Tollenaard (1925), and Collorio (1928). That this conversion of starch is associated with the increase of amylolytic activity during water deficit and apparently not with a pH shift was shown by the quantitative investigations of Spoehr and Milner (1939), Table 48.

In spite of adequate soil moisture, the desiccating effects of hot dry winds may halt the accumulation of dry substance due at least in part to the closure of the stomata. The previous conditions under which a plant has been grown will influence this response. Thus stomatal closure in wheat grown in soil at 70% of its water-retaining capacity was evidenced when water reached 40 to 50 per cent of this value. Stomata of wheat grown in soil at 40 per cent of its water-retaining capacity were always open (Vassiliev, 1929; Kondo, 1931). The difficulty of maintaining a soil at any moisture content below field capacity throws doubt upon the results of such experiments (Veihmeyer, 1927). Kransosselsky-Maximov (1930) found redistribution of water from the inflorescence to leaves in plants subjected to artificial dry wind even when they were growing in well watered soil. Stomatal closure also occurred.

Several workers have found that water deficit *per se* tends to cause stomatal closure (Iljin, 1923; Stålfelt, 1932; Scarth, 1932). In the guard cells dehydration tends to cause conversion of sugar to starch, according to the work of Iljin (1922b) and Steinberger (1922). This is in harmony with the observations of Spoehr on the carbohydrate ratio in cacti but contrary to the general trend of increased hydrolytic amylolytic activity during drying found in most plants. It appears, however, that turgor loss induces a pH reduction in guard cells, which condition is conducive to the sugar-to-starch transformation.

Huber (1937) has emphasized the profound influence that water has on the life processes of plants. In the field of genetics he refers to the work of Oehlkers (1937), and Kisch (1937). Oehlkers and his co-workers have shown that water deficiency during the conjugating phase of reduction division decreases the number of the terminal junctions and chiasmata, as shown in Table 49.

TABLE 49. — *Influence of water absorption on meiosis in Oenothera (data of* Kisch *and* Oehlkers *after* Huber, *1937) : —*

Treatment	Osmotic value of inflorescence atm.	Decrease in chiasma frequence in %
Normal	6.5	4.71
3 days dry	9.4	4.60
5 days dry	9.7	13.42
7 days dry	12.6	20.31

Huber also points out that at least part of the effect of low temperature in inhibiting conjugation may be attributed to water deficiency as the effect vanishes when water is supplied in sufficient quantities.

Subaqueous Transpiration:— It is commonly agreed that water movement through the xylem system results either from root pressure or transpiration pull. In a normally transpiring plant water loss causes a diffusion pressure deficit in the wall colloids of the mesophyll, sufficient to explain water movement to the highest tree tops. Such movement is not generally considered to utilize respirational energy except as it is required to maintain the normal structure of the cells.

The first demonstration of water movement through submerged plants was made by UNGER in 1862 (THUT, 1932b). In this experiment a *Potamogeton crispus* plant was placed with its roots in one vessel and its tops in another with both submerged. In eight days the vessel containing the tops had gained 1.6 grams. Similar experiments on water movement in submerged plants were performed by SNELL (1886), SAUVAGEAU (1891), HOCHREUTINER (1896), DIXON (1898), POND (1903), and THODAY and SYKES (1909). Such experiments utilized rooted plants, and cut shoots.

Experiments on rooted plants (UNGER, 1862; THUT, 1932b) need not be considered here for, as Thut has explained, root pressure may account for the water movement. Observations of water movement through submerged cut shoots are of great interest here for such movement cannot be caused by root pressure nor by transpiration pull.

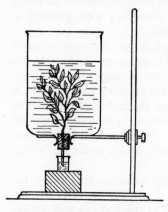

FIG. 56.—Experimental conditions for demonstrating subaqueous transpiration. Redrawn from DIXON (1938a).

DIXON, the champion of the cohesion theory through many stormy years, was forced to resort to water secretion to explain subaqueous transpiration (DIXON, 1898, 1914, 1938b; DIXON and BARLEE, 1940). Secretion was called on to account for the rise of eosin through the xylem in the experiment illustrated in FIGURE 56 (DIXON, 1938a).

THODAY and SYKES (1909) attached small glass bulbs containing eosin to the cut ends of submerged branches of *Potamogeton lucens* and found a rapid rise (5.7 to 9.5 cm. per minute) of eosin in the stems. When the apex of the branch was removed, movement slowed down and when the leaves were removed little or no movement occurred. From these observations they concluded that the leaves were the organs responsible for movement.

SMITH, DUSTMAN, and SHULL (1931) criticised the early experiments of Dixon and others, maintaining that proper precautions were not taken to ensure complete water saturation. They argued that the ascent of the transpiration stream is caused by evaporation from cell wall colloids of the mesophyll and is not dependent upon secretion or respirational energy. When they took proper precautions to completely saturate their experimental plant materials they found no rise of eosin into completely submerged shoots.

In a later paper, SHULL (1939) answers VAN DER PAAUW's (1935) criticism, that adsorption of eosin might have been responsible for SMITH, DUSTMAN, and SHULL's negative results, by the postulation that slow solution of gases might explain water movement in his (VAN DER PAAUW's) experiments. Neither advanced any support for DIXON's secretion theory. Nor was WILSON (1947) able to demonstrate the existence of continued movement of the material in a transpiration stream in completely submerged cut shoots of *Ranunculus fluitans*. Some short time absorption of eosin by these shoots was explained on the basis of internal water adjust-ments and certain observed stimulative effects of added salts seem best explainable on their action on the osmotic nature of the cells of the shoot.

In later work, DIXON (1938b) and DIXON and BARLEE (1940) satu-rated test plants by submersion for 24 hours and still found that eosin rose from 15 to 69 centimeters. Oxygen and light favored the movement which was very slight in the dark.

CRAFTS (1939d) confirmed the fact that subaqueous transpiration oc-curs only in the light and suggested that rise of water results from osmotic uptake by the phloem according to the mechanism of MÜNCH (1930). In the light photosynthesis in leaves and utilization of foods in the growing and respiring or storing cells causes a transport of osmotically active solutes via the phloem. By mass flow this would be accompanied by a certain move-ment of water. When one branch of a forked *Syringa vulgaris* stem was ringed and the whole shoot submerged, upward movement of eosin was more rapid in the xylem of the unringed branch in which, presumably, some phloem transport was taking place.

The importance of this work would seem to justify more research, for if subaqueous transpiration can be satisfactorily explained without resort to a secretory mechanism, upward movement of water through the xylem may be accounted for on a physical basis. On the other hand, if water secretion is involved, experimentation in this field is greatly complicated, for such an activity is difficult to measure and control. For anyone inter-ested in this work, it is suggested that chlorotic or albino plants may prove useful in an experimental approach to the problem.

Conclusions:— In the tremendous literature on transpiration, only a portion of which has been presented here, the emphasis has been largely on the effect of purely physical factors upon rate and volume of water loss. And, though physiological processes have been studied in relation to trans-piration, the active functions of plant cells have received little attention. Likewise the structure and unique nature of water have been neglected.

The high surface tension of water and the hydrophilic nature of cell walls and protoplasm are essential to the development of transpiration pull in leaves. The strong coordinating forces that cause water to adhere to the conducting elements are vital to the maintenance of the continuous water columns. The strong bonding forces between water molecules and solutes enable the cells to retain their aqueous contents in competition with desiccat-ing factors of the soil and atmosphere. It seems that the very ability of plants to leave their aquatic environments and invade the land depends not alone upon the adaptive nature of the plants but also upon the peculiar char-acter of the water too.

The active control of water by plants is a fairly new subject of in-vestigation. Though the "vital" forces involved may elude direct study, they must all be explainable eventually in terms of physical and chemical laws. Because of the intimate relation between such forces and the proces-ses of metabolism, studies on cell energy relations should offer an advan-tageous point of attack. In this relation it is encouraging that many cur-rent researches in plant physiology are concerned with active processes of water and salt absorption.

The essential role of water involves its contribution to the stature and elemental composition of the plant, its place in metabolism, its function in the congregation of solutes at the absorbing surfaces of the roots, and its aid in the transport of these solutes throughout the vascular system and in their final distribution by various mechanisms of translocation, both primary and secondary.

From results presented, it is evident that water deficits may have profound effects upon plants. Studies on energy absorption by leaves indicate there is no lack of available energy for photosynthesis and the transport of water, particularly during full sunlight. Work on the state of water in the conducting tracts indicates furthermore that the mechanism of translocation breaks down only after the occurrence of severe wilting. The problem of the plant's water supply then seems to resolve itself into a question of the relation of the rate of absorption by roots to the rate of loss from the leaves. Though certain leaf structures may prevent the loss of the vapor cloud from the leaf surface and hence conserve moisture, most leaves during still weather and all leaves during wind lose large amounts of water if the stomates are open so that photosynthesis may go on. Consequently, most plants require large amounts of water from the soil reservoir. In many soils around one half of the water held against the force of gravity is available for plants and in light to medium textured soils the movement of such moisture through the soil to the roots and the growth of roots through the soil are rapid enough so that plants do not suffer from lack of moisture until the permanent wilting percentage is approached. In a heavy soil, on the other hand, ALDRICH, et al. (1940) found that pear trees began to suffer when only one half of the so-called available moisture had been used. Apparently movement of water through such a soil was so slow that even though the average moisture content was well above the PWP the soil immediately around the roots became dry during the day and was not replenished during the night and root growth was not sufficient to counter-balance this effect.

Plants exhibit many means for meeting conditions of drought. Leaf and stem modifications have been mentioned as have biochemical transformations within the plant. Diverse root forms, tap roots for deep soils, fibrous roots for shallow or claypan soils, branching roots, and root hairs have all been resorted to to enable the plant to obtain adequate water from the soil. However, there is a limit to root extension. Carbohydrate supply, the concentrations and proportions of mineral nutrients, soil oxygen, and even genetic factors control the size and form of roots of a given plant. And in plant populations, particularly crops, competition may severely limit the extent to which any one root system may profitably grow into its water supply. For these various reasons there is a definite limit determined by immutable physical laws that regulates the production of plants in a given environment. This limit is related to the ability of the plant to adjust itself to a low water supply and at the same time absorb CO_2 for photosynthesis.

Certain drought-resistant plants may endure long periods of permanent wilting but though they survive they grow very little while wilted. Succulent plants may close their stomata and carry on an internal economy that enables them to survive drought but they, too, grow very little in the process. Other plants, such as the bunch grasses, space themselves so that they have enough moisture to carry them through the dry periods and still others dry up and die, leaving only seeds to carry on when moisture is again available.

Many studies have pointed out the relations of plant distribution to moisture supply and the almost innumerable adaptations by which plants have left their original aquatic environment and moved across valleys and over mountains and into the remotest wastes of the deserts and frozen arctic regions. One wonders if during the ages of development, plants, by the many ways described in these pages, have not about exhausted the possible means of adaptation. This would impose a definite limit on the extent to which man may be able by plant breeding or other technical means, to increase production in the absence of available moisture. Though plant exploration may find plants better able to survive drought, and hybridization may result in plants with more extensive root systems, it seems that the most promise lies in the possibility of conserving and utilizing our existing supplies of water more fully. As forests become depleted, oil reserves fail, and agricultural lands run short, it may become profitable to harvest cellulose and other plant products from the vast desert regions that still remain relatively unoccupied. Production on such areas, however, must remain slow. More hopeful seems to be the efficient utilization of our productive agricultural lands through control of pests, effective use of fertilizers, advanced methods of culture and harvest and, at least in our semi-arid regions where irrigation is practiced, the most effective possible use of our water resources.

In many lands the impounding and distribution of flood waters and conservation of all available supplies keynote the current developments in agriculture.

Summary:— A favorable water balance is essential to growth and development of plants. Considerable energy may be expended in the absorption of water from the soil; however, there are definite limits of DPD of water in the plant above which the plant cannot operate normally.

Transpiration may be essential in the transport and distribution of mineral nutrients throughout the plant; it usually exceeds by far the proportions required for their function; it has been termed a necessary evil for it is an inevitable consequence of the gaseous exchange necessary for photosynthesis. Water conservation is important in the economy of most plants and many of the mechanisms considered in studies on transpiration serve a vital role in water retention.

Transpiration may be stomatal or cuticular. Much of the regulation of water loss is effected by stomatal movements.

Studies on evaporation and factors controlling it have aided in an understanding of transpiration. Evaporation follows definite physical laws and is affected by osmotic concentration of the solution, temperature, dryness of the air, atmospheric pressure, and wind velocity.

Many methods have been devised for measuring transpiration such as loss of weight, water absorption, and various measurements on water vapor given off. All of these involve restriction of some type upon the natural activity of the plant or the creation of artificial conditions. The greatest problem in such studies is interpretation of the results.

The cuticle of plants is a wax-like coating that may vary widely in composition and thickness. Cuticular transpiration may make up an appreciable portion of the total water loss of some shade plants. It may be negligible in desert succulents.

Fluctuations in transpiration may be related to wall structure, physical resistance of the root system to absorption, osmotic properties of cells, internal surface, stomatal number and distribution, and other internal factors as well as the many external factors of the environment that govern evaporation.

Opening and closing of stomata have been studied by many methods. Such studies show that the stomatal mechanism plays an essential role in regulating transpiration but that the laws are complex and difficult to interpret. Mineral nutrients may affect transpiration through their osmotic effects upon the DPD of the soil solution, their tendency to increase the concentration within plant cells, and through secondary effects such as prevention of deficiency diseases, water permeability, stomatal movement, leaf abscission, and the like.

Disease may disrupt metabolism and result in sluggish stomatal response to changing environment; increased transpiration may result. Insecticides may reduce transpiration by interfering with diffusion, or increase it by wedging the stomata open. Copper sprays increase transpiration by increasing the permeability of the cuticle.

Excessive water loss by nursery stock may be prevented by hardening the plants, coating with wax, and avoiding any conditions tending to enhance rapid evaporation.

Water deficits affect the physiology of plants by stimulating hydrolysis and inhibiting condensation reactions. These responses are brought about by the effect of water balance on enzymatic activity. Starch dissolution during wilting is a common reaction of this type. Water deficit may also affect reproductive processes.

Subaqueous transpiration has been explained as due to faulty experimental technic, water secretion by leaf cells, and the functioning of the mass-flow mechanism of phloem transport.

Transpiration is important in the physiology of plants as it relates to movement of mineral and organic nutrients, to the supply of water for metabolic needs, and to its secondary effects upon growth and development as these integrate the complex relations of the plants' physical environment. Under many conditions the health of plants, and hence the well-being of man, depends upon the efficient utilization of the available supply of water.

BIBLIOGRAPHY

A.A.A.S. 1940: The cell and protoplasm. Publication No. 14, 205 pp. (Science Press, Lancaster, Pa.).

AAMODT, O. S., and W. H. JOHNSTON 1936: Studies on drought resistance in spring wheat (Canad. Jour. Res. *14*C: 122-152).

ADAMS, F., F. J. VEIHMEYER, and L. N. BROWN 1942: Cotton irrigation investigations in San Joaquin Valley, California 1926-1935 (Calif. Agric. Expt. Sta. Bull. 668).

ADOLPH, E. F. 1930: Living water (Quart. Rev. Biol. *5*: 51-67).

AGAMOV, S. 1927: Ueber die cuticulare Transpiration (Bull. Jard. Bot. de Leningrad *26*: 576-594).

AKERMAN, A. 1917: Untersuchungen über die Aggregation in den Tentakeln von *Drosera rotundifolia* (Bot. Notiser (1917): 145-192).

ALDRICH, W. W., M. R. LEWIS, R. A. WORK, A. L. RYALL, and F. C. REIMER 1940: Anjou pear responses to irrigation in a clay adobe soil (Oregon Agric. Exp. Sta. Bull. 374).

ALEXEEV, A. M. 1935: Zur Frage über den Einfluss des Wassergehaltes der Blätter auf die Kohlensäureassimilation (Jour. Botany USSR *20*: 227-241).

ALTAR, W. 1937: A study of the liquid state (Jour. Chem. Physics *5*: 577-586).

ARCICHOVSKIJ, V. 1931: Untersuchungen über die Saugkraft der Pflanzen, I. Über die Methoden der Saugkraftmessungen (Planta *14*: 517-527).

——, and N. ARCICHOVSKAJA 1931: *Ibid.*, II. Die gravimetrische Methode der Saugkraftmessungen an den Blättern (Planta *14*: 528-532).

——, N. KISSELEW, N. KRASSULIN, E. MENJINSHAJA, and A. OSSIPOV 1931: *Ibid.*, III. Die Saugkraft der Bäume. Saugkraftmessungen nach der Potometer-Methode (Planta *14*: 533-544).

——, and A. OSSIPOV 1931*a*: *Ibid.*, IV. Saugkraftmessungen nach der Schlierenmethode (Planta *14*: 545-551).

——, and —— 1931*b*: *Ibid.*, V. Die Saugkraft der baumartigen Pflanzen der zentralasiatischen Wüsten, nebst Transpirationsmessungen am Saxaul (*Arthrophytum haloxylon* Litw.) (Planta *14*: 552-565).

ARENS, K. 1939: Bestimmung des Turgordruckes an einer Einzelzelle mit der Manometer (Planta *30*: 113-117).

——, and F. DE LAURO 1946: Contribuição para o estudo da contração vacuolar (Summa Bras. Biol. *1*: 45-48).

ARMSTRONG, H. E., and others 1908: Studies of the processes operative in solutions, VI to X (Proc. Roy. Soc. London *A81*: 80-140).

ARNDT, C. H. 1929: The movement of sap in *Coffea arabica* L. (Amer. Jour. Bot. *16*: 179-190).

ARTHUR, J. M., and W. D. STEWART 1933: Transpiration of tobacco plants in relation to radiant energy in the visible and infra-red (Contrib. Boyce Thompson Inst. *5*: 483-501).

ASHBY, E. 1931: Comparison of two methods of measuring stomatal aperture (Plant Physiol. *6*: 715-719).

——, and R. WOLF 1947: A critical examination of the gravimetric method of determining suction force (Ann. Bot. *11*: 261-268).

ASKENASY, E. 1895: Ueber das Saftsteigen (Bot. Cent. *62*: 237-238).

BABBITT, J. D. 1942: On the adsorption of water vapor by cellulose (Canad. Jour. Res. *20A*: 143-172).

BAILEY, I. W. 1938: Cell wall structure of higher plants (Indus. Engin. Chem. *30*: 40-47).

BAKER, H., and W. O. JAMES 1933: The behavior of dyes in the transpiration stream of sycamores (*Acer pseudoplatanus*) (New Phytol. *32*: 245-260).

BAKKE, A. L. 1914: Studies on the transpiring power of plants as indicated by the method of standardized hygrometric paper (Jour. Ecology *2*: 145-173).

—— 1918: Determination of wilting (Bot. Gaz. *66*: 81-116).

BALÁZS, E. 1943: Plasmolysis experiments on plant epidermal cells (Botanikai közlemények (Budapest) *40*: 382-391).

BALDES, E. J. 1939: Theory of the thermo-electric measurement of osmotic pressure (Biodynamica *2* [No. 46]: 1-8).

——, and A. F. JOHNSON 1939: The thermo-electric osmometer; its construction and use (Biodynamica *2* [No. 47]: 1-11).

BANCROFT, W. D., and H. L. DAVIS 1928: Osmotic pressures of concentrated solutions (Jour. Phys. Chem. *32*: 1-43).

——, and L. P. GOULD 1934: The hydrols (*Ibid.* 38: 197-211).

BANGHAM, D. H., and F. J. LEWIS 1937: Wettability of the cellulose walls of the mesophyll in the leaf (Nature *139*: 1107-1108).

BARGER, G. 1904: A microscopical method of determining molecular weights (Jour. Chem. Soc. *85*: 286-324).

—— 1924: Eine mikroskopische Methode zur Bestimmung des Molekulargewichtes (Handb. d. biolog. Arb. Meth. von E. Abderhalden, Abt. III, Teil a 1, Heft 4, p. 729).

BARNES, C. R. 1902: The significance of transpiration (Science *15*: 460).

BARNES, T. C., and T. L. JAHN 1934: Properties of water of biological interest (Quart. Rev. Biol. *9*: 292-341).

BARTELL, F. E. 1923: Membrane potentials and their relation to anomalous osmose (Colloid Sympos. Monograph *1*: 120-144).

BARTHOLOMEW, E. T. 1926: Internal decline of lemons, III. Water deficit in lemon fruit caused by excessive leaf evaporation (Amer. Jour. Bot. *13*: 102-117).

—— 1931: Certain phases of citrus leaf transpiration (*Ibid.* 18: 765-783).

BAUMGARTNER, A. 1934: Thermoelektrische Untersuchungen über die Geschwindigkeit des Transpirationsstromes (Zeitschr. Bot. *28*: 81-136).

BEADLE, L. C. 1934: Osmotic regulation in *Gunda ulvae* (Jour. Exp. Biol. *11*: 382-396).

BEAL, J. M. 1944: Some telemorphic effects induced in sweet pea by application of 4-chlorophenoxyacetic acid (Bot. Gaz. *105*: 471-474).

BEASLEY, E. W. 1942: Effects of some chemically inert dusts upon the transpiration rate of yellow Coleus plants (Plant Physiol. *17:* 101-108).

BECK, W. A. 1927: Cane sugar and potassium nitrate as plasmolysing agents (Protoplasma *1:* 15-72).

—— 1928: Osmotic pressure, osmotic value, and suction tension (Plant Physiol. *3:* 413-440).

—— 1942: Effect of drought on the production of plant pigments (*Ibid.* 17: 487-491).

BECK, W. A. and B. ANDRUS 1943: The osmotic quantities of the cells in the hypocotyl of *Helianthus annuus* seedlings (Bull. Torrey Bot. Club *70:* 563-598).

BENEDICT, H. M. 1927: Application of Bose's theory of sap rise to ten species of trees (Amer. Jour. Bot. *14:* 623).

BENNETT, C. W. 1937: Correlation between movement of the curly top virus and translocation of food in tobacco and sugar beet (Jour. Agr. Res. *54:* 479-502).

—— 1940a: Relation of food translocation to movement of virus of tobacco mosaic (Jour. Agr. Res. *60:* 361-390).

—— 1940b: The relation of viruses to plant tissues (Bot. Rev. *6:* 427-473).

——, E. CARSNER, G. H. COONS, and E. W. BRANDES 1946: The Argentine curly top of sugar beet (Jour. Agr. Res. *72:* 19-48).

BENNETT, J. P. 1931: The treatment of lime-induced chlorosis with iron salts (Calif. Agr. Expt. Sta. Circ. *321:* 1-12).

——, and A. SNELL 1939: Transport and distribution of radioactive potassium in the pear tree (Mss. Private communication).

BENNET-CLARK, T. A. 1945: Adaptation to drought (London, Royal College of Science, Scientific Journal *15:* 99-102).

——, and D. BEXON 1940: Water relations of plant cells, II (New Phytol. *39:* 337-361).

——, and —— 1943: *Ibid.,* III. The respiration of plasmolysed tissues (*Ibid. 42:* 65-92).

——, and —— 1946: *Ibid.,* IV. Diffusion effects observed in plasmolysed tissues (*Ibid. 45:* 5-17).

——, A. D. GREENWOOD, and J. W. BARKER 1936: Water relations and osmotic pressures of plant cells (*Ibid. 35:* 277-291).

BERKELEY, Earl of, and E. G. J. HARTLEY 1906: On the osmotic pressure of some concentrated aqueous solutions (Phil. Trans. Roy. Soc. London *A206:* 481-507).

——, and —— 1916: Further determinations of direct osmotic pressures (Proc. Roy. Soc. London *A92:* 477-492).

——, ——, and C. V. BURTON 1919: On osmotic pressures derived from vapor-pressure measurements: aqueous solutions of cane sugar and methyl glucoside (Phil. Trans. Roy. Soc. London *A218:* 295-349).

BERL, E., O. HEFTER, F. RAU, G. S. DIANG, and H. UMSTÄTTER 1940: Über eine Abänderung der Molekulargewichtbestimmungsmethode nach Barger (Liebig's Ann. d. Chem. *478:* 235-246).

BERNAL, J. D. 1937: An attempt at a molecular theory of liquid structure (Trans. Far. Soc. *33:* 27-40).

—— 1940: Structural units in cellular physiology (A.A.A.S. The Cell and Protoplasm. Publication No. 14: 189-205. Science Press, Lancaster, Pa.)

——, and R. H. FOWLER 1933: A theory of water and ionic solution, with particular reference to hydrogen and hydroxyl ions (Jour. Chem. Phys. *1:* 515-548).

BIALE, J. B. 1941: Periodicity in transpiration of lemon cuttings under constant environmental conditions (Proc. Amer. Soc. Hort. Sci. *38:* 70-74).

BIDDULPH, O. 1940: Absorption and movement of radiophosphorus in bean seedlings (Plant Physiol. *15:* 131-136).

—— 1941: Diurnal migration of injected radiophosphorus from bean leaves (Amer. Jour. Bot. *28:* 348-352).

——, and J. MARKLE 1944: Translocation of radiophosphorus in the phloem of the cotton plant (Amer. Jour. Bot. *31:* 65-70).

BLACKMAN, V. H. 1921: Osmotic pressure, root pressure, and exudation (New Phytol. *20:* 106-115).

BLANCHARD, K. C. 1940: Water, free and bound (Cold Spring Harbor Symposia on Quant. Biol. *8:* 1-8).

BLEGEN, E., and P. BRANDT REHBERG 1938: Method for the determination of the osmotic pressure of biological fluids (Skand. Arch. Physiol. *80:* 40-45).

BODE, H. R. 1923: Beiträge zur Dynamik der Wasserbewegung in den Gefässpflanzen (Jahrb. wiss. Bot. *62:* 92-127).

BOEHM, J. A. 1892: Ueber einer eigenthümlichen Stammdruck (Ber. deut. bot. Ges. *10:* 539-544).

BONNER, J. 1942: Transport of thiamin in the tomato plant (Amer. Jour. Bot. *29:* 136-142).

—— 1944: Accumulation of various substances in girdled stem of tomato plants (*Ibid. 31:* 551-555).

——, and R. DORLAND 1943: Some observations concerning riboflavin and pantothenic acid in tomato plants (*Ibid. 30:* 414-418).

BOON-LONG, T. S. 1941: Transpiration as influenced by osmotic concentration and cell permeability (*Ibid. 28:* 333-343).

BOSE, J. C. 1923: The physiology of the ascent of sap, 277p. (Longmans, Green and Co., London).

—— 1928: The motor mechanism of plants, 429 p. (Longmans, Green and Co., London).

BOUILLENNE, R. 1932: Contribution à l'étude des phénomènes d'osmose dans les cellules végétales (Archives de l'Institut de Botanique de l'Université de Liége *9:* 1017-1026).

BOURDILLON, J. 1939: An apparatus for the rapid and accurate determination of low osmotic pressures (Jour. Biol. Chem. *127:* 617-625).

BOUSFIELD, W. R. 1914: Note on osmotic pressure (Proc. Roy. Soc. London *A90:* 41-5).

—— 1917: Osmotic pressure in relation to the constitution of water and the hydration of the solute (Trans. Far. Soc. *13:* 141-155).

——, and T. M. LOWRY 1910: Liquid water a ternary mixture; solution volumes in aqueous solutions (*Ibid. 6:* 85-104).

BOUYOUCOS, G. J. 1911: Transpiration of wheat seedlings as affected by soils, by solutions of different densities, and by various chemical compounds (Jour. Amer. Soc. Agron. *3:* 130-191).

BRAUNER, L. 1931: Eine neue automatische Transpirationswage (Jahrb. wiss. Bot. *75:* 295-303).

—— 1932: Das kleine pflanzenphysiologische Praktikum, II. Die physikalische Chemie der Pflanzenzelle (Fischer, Jena).

——, and M. BRAUNER 1940: Further studies of the influence of light upon the water intake and output of living plant cells (New Phytol. *39:* 104-128).

——, and —— 1943a: The relations between water intake and oxybiosis in living plant-tissues, II. The tensility of the cell wall (Istanbul Universitesi fen Facültesi Mecmuasi. *B/8:* 30-75).

——, and —— 1943b: Studies in the relations between water permeability and electric charge in membrane models and in living plant cells (*Ibid. B/8:* 264-310).

——, and M. HASMAN 1946: Untersuchungen über die anomale Komponents des osmotischen Potentials lebender Pflanzenzellen (*Ibid. B/11:* 1-37).

——, and —— 1947: Weitere Untersuchungen über die anomale Komponente des osmotischen Potentials lebender Pflanzenzellen (*Ibid. B/12:* 210-254).

BRETT, P. G. C. 1943: The downward movement of sap produced by rapid killing of the leaves (So. African Jour. Sci. *39:* 126-138).

BRIGGS, D. R. 1932: Water relations in colloids, II. Bound water in colloids (Jour. Phys. Chem. *36:* 367-386).

BRIGGS, L. J., and H. L. SHANTZ 1912: The wilting coefficient for different plants and its indirect determination (U. S. Dept. Agri. Bur. Plant Ind. Bull. *230:* 1-83).

——, and —— 1913: The water requirement of plants, I-II (U. S. Dept. Agri. Bur. Plant Ind. Bulls. *284:* 1-49; *285:* 1-96).

——, and —— 1915: An automatic transpiration scale of large capacity for use with freely exposed plants (Jour. Agr. Res. *5:* 117-132).

——, and —— 1916: Daily transpiration during the normal growth period and its correlation with the weather (*Ibid. 7:* 155-213).

BRILLIANT, B. 1924: La teneur en eau dans les feuilles et l'énergie assimilatrice (Compt. Rend. *178:* 2122-2125).

BRILLIANT, V. A., and M. N. CHRELASHVILLI 1941: The relation of photosynthesis in light and darkness to the degree of dehydration of the assimilating tissues (Trudy Botan. Inst. Acad. Sci. USSR, Ser. IV (Exptl. Botany) *5:* 88-100).

BROOKS, S. C. 1929: The accumulation of ions in living cells—a non-equilibrium condition (Protoplasma *8:* 389-412).

—— 1938: The penetration of radioactive potassium chloride into living cells (Jour. Cell. Comp. Physiol. *11:* 247-252).

—— 1940: The standardization of osmotic pressure as a term (Science *92:* 428-429).

—— 1945: Permeability (Ann. Rev. Physiol. *7:* 1-33).

——, and M. M. BROOKS. 1941: The permeability of living cells, 395 p. (Borntraeger, Berlin).

BROWN, A. J. 1909: The selective permeability of the coverings of the seeds of *Hordeum vulgare* (Proc. Roy. Soc. London *B.81:* 82-93).

BROYER, T. C. 1939: Methods of tissue preparation for analysis in physiological studies with plants (Bot. Rev. *5:* 531-545).

—— 1946: The movement of materials into plants, Part I. Osmosis and the movement of water in plants (Bot. Rev. *13:* 1-58).

——, and A. H. FURNSTAL 1941: A press for recovery of fluids from plant tissues (Plant Physiol. *16:* 419-421).

BUHMANN, A. 1935: Kritische Untersuchungen über vergleichende plasmolytische und kryoskopische Bestimmungen des osmotischen Wertes bei Pflanzen (Protoplasma *23:* 579-612).

BULL, H. B. 1943: Physical biochemistry, 347 p. (Wiley and Sons, New York)

BÜNNING, E. 1935: Zellphysiologische Studien an Meeresalgen (Protoplasma *22:* 444-456).

BURGERSTEIN, A. 1920: Die Transpiration der Pflanzen, zweiter Teil (Fischer, Jena).

BURIAN, R., and K. DRUCKER 1909: Gefrierpunktsmessungen an kleinen Flüssigkeitsmengen (Zentralbl. Physiol. *23:* 772-777).

CALLENDAR, H. L. 1908: On the vapor pressure and osmotic pressure of concentrated solutions (Proc. Roy. Soc. London *A80:* 466-500).

CAPUS, G. 1883: Sur l'observation directe du mouvement de l'eau dans les plantes (Compt. Rend. *97:* 1087).

CARRICK, D. B. 1930: Some cold-storage and freezing studies on the fruit of the Vinifera grape (Cornell Univ. Agr. Expt. Sta. Memoir *131:* 1-37).

CHADWELL, H. M. 1927: The molecular structure of water (Chem. Rev. *4:* 375-398).

CHAMBERS, R. 1944: Some physical properties of protoplasm (*In Alexander*, J. ed. Colloid Chemistry *5:* 864-875. Reinhold, New York).

CHANDLER, W. H. 1914: Sap studies with horticultural plants (Missouri Agr. Expt. Sta. Res. Bull. 14, pp. 491-552).

CHANDLER, R. C. 1941: Nature of bound water in colloidal systems (Plant Physiol. *16:* 273-291).

CHATFIELD, C., and G. ADAMS 1940: Proximate composition of American food materials (U. S. Dept. Agric. Circ. *549:* 1-91).

CHIBNALL, A. C. 1923: A new method for the separate extraction of vacuole and protoplasmic material from leaf cells (Jour. Biol. Chem. *55:* 333-342).

CHILDERS, N. F. 1936: Some effects of sprays on the growth and transpiration of tomatoes (Proc. Amer. Soc. Hort. Sci. *33:* 532-535).

CHRELASHVILI, M. N. 1941: The influence of water content and carbohydrate accumulation on the energy of photosynthesis and respiration (Trudy Botan. Inst. Acad. Sci. USSR, Ser. IV [Exptl. Botany] *5:* 101-137, p. 136-37 Eng. sum.).

CHU, CHIEN-REN 1936: Der Einfluss des Wassergehaltes der Blätter der Waldbäume auf ihre Lebensfähigkeit, ihre Saugkräfte und ihren Turgor (Flora *130:* 384-437).

CHUNG, C. H. 1935: A study of certain aspects of the phenomenon of transpiration periodicity (Ph.D. Dissert., The Ohio State University).

CLARK, D. G., H. HECHT, O. F. CURTIS, and J. I. SHAFER, JR. 1941: Stomatal behavior in inbred and hybrid maize (Amer. Jour. Bot. *28:* 537-541).

CLEMENTS, H. F. 1934a: Translocation of solutes in plants (Northwest Sci. *8(4):* 9-21).

—— 1934b: Significance of transpiration (Plant Physiol. *9:* 165-172).

—— 1940: Movement of organic solutes in the sausage tree, *Kigelia africana* (Plant Physiol. *15:* 689-700).

——, and C. J. ENGARD 1938: Upward movement of inorganic solutes as affected by a girdle (Plant Physiol. *13:* 103-122).

COLLANDER, R. 1939: Permeabilitätsstudien an Characeen, III. Die Aufnahme und Abgabe von Kationen (Protoplasma *33:* 215-257).

——, and H. BÄRLUND 1933: Permeabilitätsstudien an *Chara ceratophylla*, II. Die Permeabilität fur Nichtelektrolyte (Acta Bot. Fenn. No. *11:* 1-114).

COLLORIO, H. M. 1928: Untersuchungen über die Beziehungen zwischen der Wasserabgabe der Pflanzen und ihrer Atmungsgrösse (Planta *5:* 1-27).

COLWELL, R. N. 1942: The use of radioactive phosphorus in translocation studies (Amer. Jour. Bot. *29:* 798-807).

COHN, E. J. 1936: Influence of the dielectric constant in biochemical systems (Chem. Rev. *19:* 241-273).

COMAR, C. L., and C. G. BARR 1944: Evaluation of foliage injury and water loss in connection with use of wax and oil emulsions (Plant Physiol. *19:* 90-104).

COMMONER, B., S. FOGEL, and W. H. MULLER 1943: The mechanism of auxin action. The effect of auxin on water absorption by potato tuber tissue (Amer. Jour. Bot. *30:* 23-28).

——, and K. V. THIMANN 1941: On the relation of growth and respiration in the *Avena* coleoptile (Jour. Gen. Physiol. *24:* 279-296).

CONRAD, J. P., and F. J. VEIHMEYER 1929: Root development and soil moisture (Hilgardia *4:* 113-134).

COOIL, B. J. 1941: Significance of phloem exudate of *Cucurbita pepo* with reference to translocation of organic materials (Plant Physiol. *16:* 61-84).

COPELAND, E. B. 1902: The rise of the transpiration stream: an historical and critical discussion (Bot. Gaz. *34:* 161-193, 260-283).

CRAFTS, A. S. 1931: Movement of organic material in plants (Plant Physiol. *6:* 1-42).

—— 1932: Phloem anatomy, exudation, and transport of organic nutrients in cucurbits (*Ibid. 7:* 183-225).

—— 1933*a*: The use of arsenical compounds in the control of deep-rooted perennial weeds (Hilgardia *7:* 361-372).

—— 1933*b*: Sulfuric acid as a penetrating agent in arsenical sprays for weed control (*Ibid. 8:* 125-147).

—— 1935: Physiological problems connected with the use of sodium chlorate in weed control (Plant Physiol. *10:* 699-711).

—— 1936: Further studies on exudation in cucurbits (*Ibid. 11:* 63-79).

—— 1937: The acid-arsenical method in weed control (Jour. Amer. Soc. Agron. *29:* 934-943).

—— 1938: Translocation in plants (Plant Physiol. *13:* 791-814).

—— 1939*a*: The relation between structure and function of the phloem (Amer. Jour. Bot. *26:* 172-177).

—— 1939*b*: Movement of viruses, auxins, and chemical indicators in plants (Bot. Rev. *5:* 471-504).

—— 1939*c*: The protoplasmic properties of sieve tubes (Protoplasma *33:* 389-398).

—— 1939*d*: Solute transport in plants (Science *90:* 337-338).

——, and T. C. BROYER 1938: Migration of salts and water into xylem of the roots of higher plants (Amer. Jour. Bot. *25:* 529-535).

——, and P. B. KENNEDY 1930: The physiology of *Convolvulus arvensis* (morning glory or bindweed) in relation to its control by chemical sprays (Plant Physiol. *5:* 329-344).

——, and O. A. LORENZ 1944*a*: Fruit growth and food transport in cucurbits (*Ibid. 19:* 131-138).

——, and —— 1944*b*: Composition of fruits and phloem exudate of cucurbits (*Ibid. 19:* 326-337).

CURRIER, H. B. 1943: Water relations of root cells of *Beta vulgaris* L. (Ph.D. Dissert. Univ. of Calif.).

—— 1944*a*: Water relations of root cells of *Beta vulgaris* (Amer. Jour. Bot. *31:* 378-387).

—— 1944*b*: Cryoscopy of small amounts of expressed tissue sap (Plant Physiol. *19:* 544-550).

CURTIS, C. C. 1902: Some observations on transpiration (Bull. Torrey Bot. Club *29:* 360-373).

CURTIS, L. C. 1944: The exudation of glutamine from lawn grass (Plant Physiol. *19:* 1-5).

CURTIS, O. F. 1926: What is the significance of transpiration? (Science *63:* 267-271).

—— 1935: The translocation of solutes in plants (McGraw-Hill, New York).

——, and H. T. SCOFIELD 1933: A comparison of osmotic concentrations of supplying and receiving tissues and its bearing on the Münch hypothesis of the translocation mechanism (Amer. Jour. Bot. *20:* 502-512).

DALTON, J. 1802: Experimental essays on the constitution of mixed gases; on the force of steam or vapor from water and other liquids in different temperatures, both in a Torricellian vacuum and in air; on evaporation; and on the expansion of gases by heat (Mem. Manchester Lit. Phil. Soc. *V:* 535-602).

DARWIN, F., and D. F. M. PERTZ 1911: On a new method of estimating the aperture of stomata (Proc. Roy. Soc. London *B84:* 136-154).

DASTUR, R. H. 1924: Water content, a factor in photosynthesis (Ann. Bot. *38:* 779-788).

—— 1925: The relation between water content and photosynthesis (Ann. Bot. *39:* 769-786).

——, and B. L. DESAI 1933: The relation between water-content, chlorophyll content, and the rate of photosynthesis in some tropical plants at different temperatures (Ann. Bot. *47:* 69-88).

DAVIS, A. R., and D. R. HOAGLAND 1928: An apparatus for the growth of plants in a controlled environment (Plant Physiol. *3:* 277-292).

DAVIS, C. H. 1940: Absorption of soil moisture by maize roots (Bot. Gaz. *101:* 791-805).

DAVSON, H., and J. F. DANIELLI 1943: The permeability of natural membranes, 361 p. (Cambridge. Univ. Press, Cambridge, Eng.).

DEBYE, P. 1936: Dielectric properties of pure liquids (Chem. Rev. *19:* 171-182).

DELF, E. M. 1912: Transpiration in succulent plants by measurement of rate of shrinkage of turgid tissues (Ann. Bot. *26:* 409-442).

—— 1916: Studies of protoplasmic permeability (Ann. Bot. *30:* 283-310).

DENNY, F. E. 1917: Permeability of certain plant membranes to water (Bot. Gaz. *63:* 373-397).

DESAI, M. C. 1937: Effect of certain nutrient deficiencies on stomatal behavior (Plant Physiol. *12:* 253-283).

DIETRICH, M. 1925: Die Transpiration der Schatten- und Sonnen-pflanzen in ihren Beziehungen zum Standort (Jahrb. f. wiss. Bot. *65:* 98-194).

DIXON, H. H. 1898: Transpiration into a saturated atmosphere (Proc. Roy. Irish Acad. III, *4:* 627-635).

—— 1911: A thermo-electric method of cryoscopy (Proc. Roy. Dubl. Soc. *XIII:* 49-63).

—— 1914: Transpiration and the ascent of sap in plants, 216 p. (Macmillan, New York).

—— 1924: The transpiration stream, 80 p. (Univ. of London Press, Ltd., London).

—— 1933: Bast-sap (Sci. Proc. Roy. Dublin Soc. *20:* 487-494).

—— 1937: The convection of heat and materials in the stem of a tree (Notes from the Botanical School, Trinity College, Dublin, *4:* 269-278).

—— 1938*a*: Transportation of substances in plants (*Ibid. 4:* 279-304).

—— 1938*b*: Subaqueous transpiration (Sci. Proc. Roy. Dublin Soc. *22:* 55-57).

——, and W. R. G. ATKINS 1912: Changes in the osmotic pressure of the sap of the developing leaves of *Syringa vulgaris* (*Ibid. 13:* 219-222).

——, and —— 1913: Osmotic pressures in plants, I. Methods of extracting sap from plant organs (*Ibid. 13:* 422-433).

——, and —— 1916: Osmotic pressure in plants, VI. On the composition of the sap in the conducting tracts of trees at different levels and at different seasons of the year (*Ibid. 15:* 51-62).

——, and J. S. BARLEE 1940: Further experiments on transpiration into a saturated atmosphere (*Ibid. 22:* 211-222).

——, and J. JOLY 1894: On the ascent of sap (Ann. Bot. *8:* 468-470).

DONEEN, L. D. 1934: Method for the preparation of green plant material for the extraction of juices (Plant Physiol. *9:* 839-843).

DORSEY, N. E. 1940: Properties of ordinary water-substance, 673 p. (Reinhold, New York).

DRUCKER, C., and E. SCHREINER 1913: Mikrokryoskopische Versuche (Biolog. Zentralbl. *33:* 99-103).

DUTROCHET, R. J. H. 1827: Nouvelles observations sur l'endosmose, et sur la cause de ce double phénomène (Annales Chim. Phys. *35:* 393-400).

EATON, F. M. 1941. Water uptake and root growth as influenced by inequalities in the concentration of the substrate (Plant Physiol. *16:* 545-564).

—— 1943: The osmotic and vitalistic interpretations of exudation (Amer. Jour. Bot. *30:* 663-674).

EDLEFSEN, N. E. 1941: Some thermodynamic aspects of the use of soil-moisture by plants (Amer. Geophys. Union Trans. of 1941, part III, *22:* 917-926).

——, and A. B. C. ANDERSON 1943: Thermodynamics of soil moisture (Hilgardia *15:* 31-298).

ELAZARI-VOLCANI, T. 1936: The influence of a partial interruption of the transpiration stream by root pruning and stem incisions on the turgor of citrus trees (Palestine Jour. Bot. Hort. Sci. *1:* 94-96).

ELEY, D. D. 1944: The structure of water in aqueous solutions (Trans. Far. Soc. *40:* 184-194).

ELFORD, W. J. 1937: Principles governing the preparation of membranes having graded porosities. The properties of "Gradocol" membranes as ultrafilters (*Ibid. 33:* 1094-1104).

EMERSON, J. L., and A. C. HILDRETH 1933: Preliminary report on reducing transpiration of transplanted evergreens (Science 77: 433-434).

ENGARD, C. J. 1939*a*: Translocation of carbohydrates in the Cuthbert raspberry (Bot. Gaz. *100:* 439-464).

—— 1939*b*: Translocation of nitrogenous substances in the Cuthbert raspberry (*Ibid. 101:* 1-34).

ERICKSON, L. C. 1945: The water factor in transplanting guayule (Amer. Jour. Bot. *32:* 634-643).

ERNEST, E. C. M. 1931: Suction-pressure gradients and the measurement of suction pressure (Ann. Bot. *45:* 717-731).

—— 1934*a*: Studies in the suction pressure of plant cells, II (*Ibid. 48:* 293-305).

—— 1934*b*: The effect of intercellular pressure on the suction pressure of cells (*Ibid. 48:* 915-918).

—— 1934*c*: The water relations of the plant cell (Jour. Linn. Soc. [London] Bot. *49:* 495-502).

—— 1935. Factors rendering the plasmolytic method inapplicable in the estimation of osmotic values of plant cells (Plant Physiol. *10:* 553-558).

EWELL, R. H., and H. EYRING 1937: Theory of the viscosity of liquids as a function of temperature and pressure (Jour. Chem. Phys. *5:* 726-736).

EYSTER, H. C. 1940: A standardization of osmotic pressure as a term (Science *92:* 171-172).

—— 1943: Osmosis and osmotic pressure (Bot. Rev. *9:* 311-324).

FARR, W. K. 1944: Plant cell membranes (*In* ALEXANDER, J., Colloid Chemistry *5:* 611-667. Chemical Catalog Co., New York).

FERRI, M. G. 1945: Preliminary observations on the translocation of synthetic growth substances (Contrib. Boyce Thompson Inst. *14:* 51-68).

FINBAK, C. and H. VIERVOLL 1943: The structure of liquids, II. The structure of liquid water (Tids. Kjemi, Bergvesen Met. *3:* 36-40).

FINDLAY, A. 1919: Osmotic pressure, 116 p. (Longmans, Green and Co., London).

FISCHER, M. H. 1921: Oedema and nephritis, 3rd. ed., 209 p. (Wiley, New York).

—— 1923: On the theory of the lyophilic colloids and the behavior of protoplasm (Colloid Sympos. Monograph *1:* 244-264).

FITTING, H. 1917: Untersuchungen über isotonische Koeffizienten und ihren Nutzen für Permeabilitätsbestimmung (Jahrb. wiss. Bot. *57:* 553-612).

FOGG, G. E. 1944: Diurnal fluctuation in a physical property of leaf cuticle (Nature *154:* 515).

FOSTER, A. C., and E. C. TATMAN 1940: Effect of certain fungicides and environmental factors on the rate of transpiration of tomato plants (Jour. Agr. Res. *61:* 721-735).

FRAZER, J. C. W., and R. T. MYRICK 1916: The osmotic pressure of sucrose solutions at 30° (Jour. Amer. Chem. Soc. *38:* 1907-1922).

FREEMAN, G. F. 1908: A method for the quantitative determination of transpiration in plants (Bot. Gaz. *46:* 118-129).

FREY-WYSSLING, A. 1938: Submikroskopische Morphologie des Protoplasmas und seiner Derivate, 317 p. (Borntraeger, Berlin).

—— 1939: The submicroscopic structure of cell walls (Science Progress *34:* 249-262).
—— 1940: The submicroscopic structure of the cytoplasm (J. Roy. Microscop. Soc. *60:* 128-139).
FRITSCH, F. E. 1922: The moisture relations of terrestrial algae, I. Some general observations and experiments (Ann. Bot. *36:* 1-20).
FÜRLINGER, H. 1938: Plasmolyse verhindert Ergrünen (Protoplasma *30:* 328-333).
FURR, J. R., and E. S. DEGMAN 1932: Relation of moisture supply to stomatal behavior of the apple (Proc. Amer. Soc. Hort. Sci. *28:* 547-551).
——, and J. O. REEVE 1945: Range of soil-moisture percentages through which plants undergo permanent wilting in some soils from semiarid irrigated areas (Jour. Agr. Res. *71:* 149-170).
——, and C. A. TAYLOR 1935: The apparent growth rate of lemon fruits as an index of the moisture supply of the tree (Amer. Soc. Hort. Sci. Proc. *33:* 70).
——, and —— 1939: Growth of lemon fruits in relation to moisture content of the soil (U. S. Dept. Agr. Tech. Bull. *640:* 1-72).

GAIL, F. W. 1926: Osmotic pressure of cell sap and its possible relation to winter killing and leaf fall (Bot. Gaz. *81:* 434-445).
——, and W. H. CONE 1929: Osmotic pressure pH measurements on cell sap of *Pinus ponderosa* (Bot. Gaz. *88:* 437-441).
GALLENKAMP, W. 1919: Versuche über den Zusammenhang von Verdunstungsmenge und Grösse der verdunstenden Flächen (Meteorol. Zeitschr. *36:* 16-22).
GASSER, R. 1942: Zur Kenntnis der Aenderung der Saugkraft bei Grenzplasmolyse durch Wasserunter- und -überbilanz (Ber. schweiz. botan. Ges. *52:* 47-110).
GASSNER, G., and G. GOEZE 1936: Einige Versuche über die Physiologische Leistungsfähigkeit rostinfizierter Getreideblätter (Phytopath. Zeitschr. *9:* 371-386).
GÄUMANN, E. 1942: Über die pflanzliche Transpiration. 1. Die kutikulare Transpiration (Zeitschrift für Botanik 38: 225-327).
GEHENIO, P. M. 1941: The freezing points of living and dead myxomycetes (Biodynamica *3:* 348-352).
GÉNEAU DE LAMARLIÈRE, L. 1892: Recherches physiologiques sur les feuilles, développées à l'ombre et au soleil, VI. Transpiration (Rev. Gén. Bot. *4:* 529).
GETMAN, F. H., and F. DANIELS 1943: Outlines of Theoretical Chemistry, 691 p. (John Wiley and Sons, New York).
GIBBS, R. D. 1935: Studies of wood, II. The water content of certain Canadian trees, and changes in the water-gas system during seasoning and flotation (Canad. Jour. Res. *12:* 727-760).
GICKLHORN, J., and F. WEBER 1926: Über Vakuolenkontraktion und Plasmolyseform (Protoplasma *1:* 427-432).
GLASSTONE, S. 1940: Textbook of physical chemistry, 1289 p. (D. Van Nostrand, New York).
GODLEWSKI, E. 1884: Zur Theorie der Wasserbewegung in den Pflanzen (Jahrb. wiss. Bot. *15:* 569-630).
GOLDSMITH, G. W., and J. H. C. SMITH 1926: Some physico-chemical properties of spruce sap and their seasonal and altitudinal variation (Colorado Col. Pub. Sci. Ser. *13:* 13-71).
GOLOVINA, A. S. 1939: The effect of drought on the biochemical processes of plants (Voronezh. Gosudarst. Univ., Nauch. Raboty Studentov [1939]: 51-58).
GORTNER, R. A. 1938: Outlines of biochemistry, 1017 p. (Wiley and Sons, New York).
——, and J. A. HARRIS 1914: Notes on the technique of the determination of the depression of the freezing point of vegetable saps (Plant World *17:* 49-53).
——, J. V. LAWRENCE, and J. A. HARRIS 1916: The extraction of sap from plant tissues by pressure (Biochem. Bull. *5:* 139-142).
GRAFE, V. 1924: Messung der Gas- und Wasserbewegung (Handbuch der biolog. Arb. Meth. von E. Abderhalden, Abt. XI, Teil *2:* 105-186).
GRAF-MARIN, A. 1934: Studies on powdery mildew of cereals (N. Y. [Cornell] Agr. Expt. Sta. Mem. *157:* 1-48).
GREENFIELD, S. S. 1941: Differential inhibition of photochemical and dark reactions in photosynthesis by inorganic compounds (Science *93:* 550-551).
—— 1942: Inhibitory effects of inorganic compounds on photosynthesis in *Chlorella* (Amer. Jour. Bot. *29:* 121-131).
GREGORY, F. G., and PEARSE, H. L. 1934: The resistance porometer and its application to the study of stomatal movement (Proc. Roy. Soc. *B.114:* 477-493).
GROSS, F. 1934: Zur Biologie und Entwicklungsgeschichte von *Noctiluca miliaris* (Arch. Protistenk. *83:* 178-196).
—— 1940: The osmotic relations of the plankton diatom *Ditylum brightwelli* (West.) (Jour. Mar. Biol. Assn. U. K. *24:* 381-415).
GROSSENBACHER, K. A. 1938: Diurnal fluctuation in root pressure (Plant Physiol. *13:* 669-676).
—— 1939: Autonomic cycle of rate of exudation of plants (Amer. Jour. Bot. *26:* 107-109).
GUILLIERMOND, A. 1941: The cytoplasm of the plant cell, 247 p. (Chronica Botanica Co., Waltham, Mass.).
GUYE, P. A. 1910: The chemical nature of molecular association (Trans. Far. Soc. *6:* 78-85).
GYÖRFFY, B. 1941: Untersuchungen über den osmotischen Wert polyploider Pflanzen (Planta *32:* 15-37).

HAAN, I. DE 1933: Protoplasmaquellung und Wasserpermeabilität (Recueil des Travaux botaniques Néerlandais *30:* 234-335).
HABERLANDT, G. 1914: Physiological plant anatomy. Translation from the 4th German edition by M. DRUMMOND, 777 p. (Macmillan and Co., New York).
HAINES, F. M. 1935: Observations on the occurrence of air in conducting tracts (Ann. Bot. *49:* 367-379).
HALDANE, J. S. 1918: The extension of the gas laws to liquids and solids (Biochem. Jour. *12:* 464-498).
HALES, S. 1738: Vegetable staticks, Vol. 1, 3rd ed., 376 p. (London).
HALKET, A. C. 1913: On various methods for determining osmotic pressures (New Phytol. *12:* 164-176).

HALL, W. H. 1940: Suggestions regarding a proposed standardization of osmotic pressure as a term (Science *92:* 334).

HALMA, F. F., and A. R. C. HAAS 1928: Effect of sunlight on sap concentration of citrus leaves (Bot. Gaz. *86:* 102-106).

HAMNER, K. C., and J. BONNER 1938: Photoperiodism in relation to hormones as factors in floral initiation and development (*Ibid. 100:* 388-431).

HANDLEY, W. R. C. 1939: The effect of prolonged chilling on water movement and radial growth in trees (Ann. Bot. *3:* 803-813).

HANNIG, E. 1912: Untersuchungen über die Verteilung des osmotischen Druckes in der Pflanze in Hinsicht auf die Wasserleitung (Ber. deut. bot. Ges. *30:* 194-204).

HANSTEEN-CRANNER, B. 1914: Über das Verhalten der Kulturpflanzen zu den Bodensalzen, III (Jahrb. wiss. Bot. *53:* 536-602).

HARKENS, W. D. 1926: Surface energy and surface tension (*In* ALEXANDER, J., Colloid Chemistry *1:* 192-264. Chemical Catalog Company, New York).

HARNED, H. S., and B. B. OWEN 1943: The physical chemistry of electrolytic solutions, 611 p. (Reinhold, New York).

HARRIS, J. A. 1915: An extension to 5.99° of tables to determine the osmotic pressure of expressed vegetable saps from the depression of the freezing point (Amer. Jour. Bot. *2:* 418-419).

—— 1934: The physico-chemical properties of plant saps in relation to phytogeography, 339 p. (Univ. Minnesota Press, Minneapolis).

——, and R. A. GORTNER 1914: Notes on the calculation of the osmotic pressure of expressed vegetable saps from the depression of the freezing point, with a table for the values of P for Δ = 0.001° to Δ = 2.999° (Amer. Jour. Bot. *1:* 75-78).

——, J. V. LAWRENCE, and R. A. GORTNER 1916: The cryoscopic constants of expressed vegetable saps as related to local environmental conditions in the Arizona deserts (Physiol. Res. *2:* 1-49).

HARTER, L. L. 1908: The influence of a mixture of soluble salts, principally sodium chlorid, upon the leaf structure and transpiration of wheat, oats, and barley (U. S. Dept. Agric. Bur. Plant Ind. Bull. *134:* 1-22).

HARTMAIR, V. 1937: Über Vakuolenkontraktion in Pflanzenzellen (Protoplasma *28:* 582-592).

HARTSUIJKER, K. 1935: Kritische Bemerkungen ueber einige der wichtigsten Methoden zur Ermittlung des Oeffnungszustandes der Spaltoeffnungen (Rec. trav. botan. Néerland. *32:* 516-542).

HARVEY, E. B. 1917: A physiological study of specific gravity and of luminescence in *Noctiluca,* with special reference to anesthesia (Publ. Carnegie Inst. 11, p. 237-253).

HÄUSERMANN, E. 1944: The amount of wetting of mesophyllic intercellular spaces (Ber. schwez. boton. Ges. *54:* 541-578).

HASMAN, M. 1943: A study of the shape of the determinant curve in measurements of the suction potential in plant tissues (Istanbul Universitesi fen Facultesi Mecmuasi. *B/8:* 167-200).

HASSELBRING, H. 1914: The relation between the transpiration stream and the absorption of salts (Bot. Gaz. *57:* 72-73).

HAYWARD, H. E., and W. B. SPURR 1944: Effects of isosmotic concentrations of inorganic and organic substrates on entry of water into corn roots (Bot. Gaz. *106:* 131-139).

HEATH, O. V. S. 1941: Experimental studies of the relation between carbon assimilation and stomatal movement, II. The use of the resistance porometer in estimating stomatal aperture and diffuse resistance. (Ann. Bot. N.S. *5:* 455-500).

HEINICKE, A. J., and N. F. CHILDERS 1935: The influence of water deficiency in photosynthesis and transpiration of apple leaves (Proc. Amer. Soc. Hort. Sci. *33:* 155-159).

HENDERSON, L. J. 1924: The fitness of the environment, 317 p. (Macmillan, New York).

HENDRICKSON, A. H., and F. J. VEIHMEYER 1941: Moisture distribution in soil containers (Plant Physiol. *16:* 821-826).

——, and —— 1942: Irrigation experiments with pears and apples (Calif. Agr. Exp. Sta. Bull. 667).

——, and —— 1945: Permanent wilting percentages of soils obtained from field and laboratory trials (Plant Physiol. *20:* 517-539).

HENRICI, M. 1943: Data on the sugar and starch content of some fodder plants under different physiological conditions (So. African Jour. Sci. *40:* 157-161).

—— 1945: The effect of wilting on the direct assimilates of lucerne and other fodder plants (*Ibid. 41:* 204-212).

HERMANS, P. H., and A. WEIDINGER 1946: The hydrates of cellulose (Jour. Colloid Sci. *1:* 185-193).

HERRICK, E. M. 1933: Seasonal and diurnal variations in the osmotic values and suction tension values in the aerial portions of *Ambrosia trifida* (Amer. Jour. Bot. *20:* 18-34).

—— 1934: A three wire thermocouple system for use in cryoscopic investigations (*Ibid. 21:* 673-687).

HEUSER, E. 1944: The chemistry of cellulose, 660 p. (Wiley, New York).

HEYN, A. N. J. 1940: The physiology of cell elongation (Bot. Rev. *6:* 515-574).

HIBBARD, R. P., and O. E. HARRINGTON 1913: Depression of the freezing point in triturated plant tissues and the magnitude of this depression as related to soil moisture (Physiol. Res. *1:* 441-454).

HIESEY, W. M. 1940: A critical study of transpiration rates of alpine and lowland forms of *Potentilla gracilis* (Ph.D. Dissert., Univ. of California).

HILDEBRAND, E. M. 1942: Rapid transmission techniques for stone-fruit viruses (Science *95:* 52).

——, and O. F. CURTIS 1942: A darkening technique for inducing virus symptoms in mature as well as in growing leaves (Science *95:* 390).

HILDEBRAND, J. H. 1924: Solubility (Amer. Chem. Soc. Monograph Ser., 206 p., Chem. Catalog. Co., New York).

—— 1936: Solubility of non-electrolytes, 2nd ed., 303 p. (Reinhold, New York).

—— 1937: Intermolecular forces in solutions (Trans. Far. Soc. *33:* 144-151).

HILL, A. V. 1930: A thermal method of measuring the vapour pressure of aqueous solutions (Proc. Roy, Soc. London *A127:* 9-19).

HIRSCHFELDER, J., D. STEVENSON, and H. EYRING 1937: A theory of liquid structure (Jour. Chem. Physics *5:* 896-912).

HOAGLAND, D. R. 1944: Lectures on the inorganic nutrition of plants, 226 p. (Chronica Botanica Co., Waltham, Mass.)

——, and T. C. BROYER 1936: General nature of the process of salt accumulation by roots with description of experimental methods (Plant Physiol. *11:* 471-507).

——, and —— 1942: Accumulation of salt and permeability in plant cells (Jour. Gen. Physiol. *25:* 865-880).

——, and A. R. DAVIS 1923*a:* The composition of the cell sap of the plant in relation to the absorption of ions (*Ibid.* 5: 629-646).

——, and —— 1923*b:* Further experiments on the absorption of ions by plants, including observations on the effect of light (*Ibid.* 6: 47-62).

——, and —— 1929: The intake and accumulation of electrolytes by plant cells (Protoplasma *6:* 610-626).

HÖBER, R. 1945: Physical chemistry of cells and tissues, 676 p. (Blakiston, Philadelphia).

HOCHREUTINER, G. 1896: Physiologie des plantes aquatiques du Rhône et du Port de Genève (Rev. Gén. Bot. *8:* 158-167).

HOFFMANN, C. 1932: Zur Frage der osmotischen Zustandsgrössen bei Meeresalgen (Planta *17:* 805-809).

HÖFLER, K. 1917: Die plasmolytisch-volumetrische Methode und ihre Anwendbarkeit zur Messung des osmotischen Wertes lebender Pflanzenzellen (Ber. deut. bot. Ges. *35:* 706-726).

—— 1920: Ein Schema für die osmotische Leistung der Pflanzenzelle (*Ibid.* *38:* 288-298).

—— 1930: Das Plasmolyse-Verhalten der Rotalgen (Zeitschr. f. Bot. *23:* 570-588).

—— 1931: Hypotonietod und osmotische Resistenz einiger Rotalgen (Oesterr. Bot. Zeitschr. *80:* 51-71).

—— 1939: Kappenplasmolyse und Ionenantagonismus (Protoplasma *33:* 545-578).

HOFMEISTER, L. 1940*a:* Mikrurgische Studien an Borraginoideen-Zellen, I. Mikrodissektion (Protoplasma *35:* 65-94).

—— 1940*b: Ibid.,* II. Mikroinjektion und mikrochemische Untersuchung (*Ibid.* *35:* 161-186).

HOFMEISTER, W. 1862: Über Spannung, Ausflussmenge und Ausflussgeschwindigkeit von Säften lebender Pflanzen (Flora *45:* 97-108).

HOLLE, H. 1915: Untersuchungen ueber Welken, Vertrocknen und Wiederstraffwerden (Flora, N. F. *8:* 73-126).

HOMAN, C., T. F. YOUNG, and C. A. SHULL 1934: Evaporation in its thermodynamic relation to the cohesion theory and to imbibitional and osmotic pressures of cell constituents (Plant Physiol. *9:* 653-661).

HOUSKA, H. 1941: Beiträge zur Kenntnis der Kappenplasmolyse (Protoplasma *36:* 11-51).

HUBER, B. 1923: Transpiration in verschiedener Stammhöhe, I. *Sequoia gigantea* (Zeitschr. f. Bot. *15:* 465-501).

—— 1932: Beobachtung und Messung pflanzlicher Saftströme (Ber. deut. bot. Ges. *50:* 89-109).

—— 1933: Beiträge zur Kenntnis der Wasserpermeabilität des Protoplasmas (*Ibid.* *51:* 53-64).

—— 1937: Wasserumsatz und Stoffbewegungen (Fortschitte der Botanik *7:* 197-207).

——, and K. HÖFLER 1930: Die Wasserpermeabilität des Protoplasmas (Jahrb. f. wiss. Bot. *73:* 351-511).

——, and E. SCHMIDT 1936: Weitere thermoelektrische Untersuchungen über den Transpirationsstrom der Baüme (Tharandter Forstl. Jahrb. *87:* 369-412).

——, and —— 1937: Eine Kompensationsmethode zur thermoelektrischen Messung langsamer Saftströme (Ber. deut. bot. Ges. *55:* 514-529).

——, ——, and H. JAHNEL 1937: Untersuchungen über den Assimilatstrom, I (Tharandter Forstl. Jahrb. *88:* 1017-1050).

HUMPHREYS, W. J. 1940: Physics of the air, 676 p. (McGraw-Hill, New York).

ILJIN, W. S. 1922*a:* Wirkung der Kationen von Salzen auf den Zerfall und die Bildung von Stärke in den Pflanzen (Biochem. Zeitschr. *132:* 494-510).

—— 1922*b:* Ueber den Einfluss des Welkens der Pflanzen auf die Regulierung der Spaltöffnungen (Jahrb. f. wiss. Bot. *61:* 670-697, 698-712).

—— 1923: Der Einfluss des Wassermangels auf die Kohlenstoffassimilation durch die Pflanzen (Flora *116:* 360-378).

International Critical Tables 1933 (McGraw-Hill, New York).

IVANOV, L. A. 1924: Ueber die Transpiration der Holzgewächse im Winter, I u. II (Ber. deut. bot. Ges. *42:* 44-49, 210-218).

—— 1928: Zur Methodik der Transpirationsbestimmung am Standort (*Ibid.* *46:* 306-310).

JACCARD, P., and A. FREY-WYSSLING 1934: Über Versuche zur Bestimmung der Zellsaftkonzentration in der Kambialzone beim exzentrischen Dickenwachstum, I (Jahrb. f. wiss. Bot. *79:* 655-680).

JANSE, J. M. 1913: Die Wirkung des Protoplasten in den Zellen welche bei der Wasserbewegung beteiligt sind (Jahrb. f. wiss. Bot. *52:* 603-621).

JEFFREYS, H. 1918: Some problems of evaporation (Phil. Mag. *35:* 270-280).

JENNY, H., and R. OVERSTREET 1939: Cation interchange between plant roots and soil colloids (Soil Science *47:* 257-272).

JOHNSTON, C. O. 1940: Modification of diurnal transpiration in wheat by infections of *Puccinia triticina* (Jour. Agr. Res. *61:* 427-444).

KAISERLEHNER, E. 1939: Über Kappenplasmolyse und Entmischungsvorgänge im Kappenplasma (Protoplasma *33:* 579-601).

KAMP, H. 1930: Untersuchungen über Kutikularbau und kutikuläre Transpiration von Blättern (Jahrb. f. wiss. Bot. *72:* 403-465).

KATZOFF, S. 1934: X-ray studies on the molecular arrangement in liquids (Jour. Chem. Physics *2:* 841-851).

KENDALL, J. 1937: Pure liquids and liquid mixtures (Trans. Far. Soc. *33:* 2-7).

KENNEDY, P. B., and A. S. CRAFTS 1927: The application of physiological methods to weed control (Plant Physiol. *2:* 503-506).

——, and —— 1931: The anatomy of *Convolvulus arvensis,* wild morning glory or field bindweed (Hilgardia *5:* 591-623).

KENNY, I. J., and D. R. PORTER 1941: Relative rind toughness among watermelon varieties (Proc. Amer. Soc. Hort. Sci. *38:* 537-540).

KERR, T., and D. B. ANDERSON 1944: Osmotic quantities in growing cotton bolls (Plant Physiol. *19:* 338-349).

KESSLER, W., and W. RUHLAND 1938: Weitere Untersuchungen über die inneren Ursachen der Kälteresistenz (Planta *28:* 159-204).

KEYS, A. 1932: The mechanism of adaption to varying salinity in the common eel and the general problem of osmotic regulation in fishes (Proc. Roy. Soc. London *B112:* 184-199).

KIESSELBACH, T. A. 1916: Transpiration as a factor in crop production (Nebraska Agr. Exp. Sta. Res. Bull. *6:* 1-214).

KINCAID, J. F., H. EYRING, and A. E. STEARN 1941: The theory of absolute reaction rates and its application to viscosity and diffusion in the liquid state (Chem. Rev. *28:* 301-365).

KIRKWOOD, J. G. 1936: Statistical mechanics of liquid solutions (Chem. Rev. *19:* 275-307).

KISCH, R. 1937: Die Bedeutung der Wasserversorgung für den Ablauf der Meiosis (Jahrb. f. wiss. Bot. *85:* 450-484).

KISSER, J. 1927: Untersuchungen über den Einfluss der Nährsalze auf die Wasserabgabe, Wasseraufnahme, relative Spross- und Wurzelmasse und die Blattstruktur (Planta *3:* 562-577).

KITCHING, J. A. 1938: Contractile vacuoles (Biol. Rev. *13:* 403-444).

KNIGHT, R. C. 1922: Further observations on the transpiration, stomata, leaf water-content, and wilting of plants (Ann. Bot. *36:* 361-383).

KNIGHT, T. A. 1801: Account of some experiments on the ascent of sap in trees (Phil. Trans. Roy. Soc. London *91:* 333-353).

KOHL, F. G. 1886: Die Transpiration der Pflanzen und ihre Einwirkung auf die Ausbildung pflanzlicher Gewebe, 124 p. (H. Braunschweig, Brünn).

KONDO, I. N. 1931: The influence of external factors as well as of the stages of development on the resistance of plants to dehydration (Bull. Applied Bot. of Genetics and Plant Breeding, Trudy *27:* 129-156).

KORSTIAN, C. F. 1924: Density of cell sap in relation to environmental conditions in the Wasatch mountains of Utah (Jour. Agr. Res. *28:* 845-907).

KOTTE, H. 1915: Turgor und Membranquellung bei Meeresalgen (Wiss. Meeresunters., Abt. Kiel, N. F. Bd. *17:* 115-167).

KRAMER, P. J. 1933: The intake of water through dead root systems and its relation to the problem of absorption by transpiring plants (Amer. Jour. Bot. *20:* 481-492).

—— 1939: The forces concerned in the intake of water by transpiring plants (*Ibid. 26:* 784-791).

—— 1944: Soil moisture in relation to plant growth (Bot. Rev. *10:* 525-559).

—— 1945: Absorption of water by plants (Bot. Rev. *11:* 310-355).

KRASNOSSELSKY-MAXIMOV, T. A. 1931: Physiological analysis of windburn by means of artificial dry wind (Bull. Applied Bot. of Genetics and Plant Breeding, Trudy *25:* 3-44).

KRAUSCHE, K. K., and B. E. GILBERT 1937: Increase of transpiration rates of tomato leaves due to copper sprays (Plant Physiol. *12:* 853-860).

KROGH, A. 1939: Osmotic regulation in aquatic animals, 242 p. (Cambridge Univ. Press).

—— 1946: The active and passive exchange of inorganic ions through the surfaces of living cells and through living membranes generally (Proc. Roy. Soc. London *B133:* 140-200).

KURSANOV, A. L. 1941: The physiological role of enzymes in plants (Collection of papers on plant physiology in memory of K. A. TIMIRYAZEV, Acad. Sci. USSR, Inst. Plant Physiol. in the name of K. A. TIMIRYAZEV 1941, 131-169).

KÜSTER, E. 1928: Über die Gewinnung nackter Protoplasten (Protoplasma *3:* 223-233).

—— 1929: Beobachtungen an verwundeten Zellen (*Ibid. 7:* 150-170).

—— 1935: Die Pflanzenzelle, 672 p. (Gustav Fischer, Jena).

—— 1940: Neue Objekte für die Untersuchung der Vakuolenkontraktion (Ber. deut. bot. Ges. *58:* 413-416).

LATSHAW, W. L., and E. C. MILLER 1924: Elemental composition of the corn plant (Jour. Agr. Res. *27:* 845-859).

LEICK, E. 1939: Bestimmung der Transpiration und Evaporation mit Rücksicht auf die Bedürfnisse der Ökologie (Handb. d. biolog. Arb. Meth. von E. Abderhalden, Abt. XI, Teil *4:* 1573-1735).

LEIGHLY, J. 1937: A note on evaporation (Ecology *18:* 180-198).

LEITCH, J. L. 1934: The water exchanges of living cells, II. Non solvent volume determinations from swelling and analytical data (Jour. Cell. Comp. Physiol. *4:* 457-473).

LEPESCHKIN, W. W. 1936: The "Vitaids." A theory of the fundamental substances of living matter (Biodynamica *1* [No. 19]: 1-6).

—— 1937: Zell-Nekrobiose und Protoplasma-Tod, 198 p. (Borntraeger, Berlin).

—— 1938: Kolloidchemie des Protoplasmas, 244 p. (Steinkopff, Dresden).

LEVITT, J. 1941: Frost killing and hardiness of plants, 211 p. (Burgess Publ. Co., Minneapolis, Minn.).

—— 1946: Osmotic pressure determinations with isolated protoplasmic proteins (Plant Physiol. *21:* 562-572).

—— 1947: The thermodynamics of active (non-osmotic) water absorption (*Ibid. 22:* 514-525).

——, and G. W. SCARTH 1936: Frost hardening studies with living cells (Canad. Jour. Res. *C14:* 267-305).

——, ——, and R. D. GIBBS 1936: Water permeability of isolated protoplasts in relation to volume change (Protoplasma *26:* 237-248).

LEWIS, F. J. 1945: Physical conditions of the surface of the mesophyll cell walls of the leaf (Nature *156:* 407-490).

——, and G. M. TUTTLE 1920: Osmotic properties of some plant cells at low temperatures (Ann. Bot. *34:* 405-416).

LEWIS, G. N. 1908: The osmotic pressure of concentrated solutions, and the laws of the perfect solution (Jour. Amer. Chem. Soc. *30:* 668-683).

—— 1916: The atom and the molecule (*Ibid. 38:* 762-785).

——, and M. Randall 1923: Thermodynamics and the free energy of chemical substances, 653 p. (McGraw-Hill, New York).

Li, T. T. 1929: Effect of climatic factors on suction force (Quart. Rev. Biol. *4:* 401-414).

Livingston, B. E. 1903: The rôle of diffusion and osmotic pressure in plants, 149 p. (Univ. of Chicago Press, Chicago).

—— 1906: The relation of desert plants to soil moisture and to evaporation (Carnegie Inst. of Washington Publ. No. 50: 1-78).

—— 1913: The resistance offered by leaves to transpirational water loss (Plant World *16:* 1-35).

——, and E. B. Shreve 1916: Improvements in the method for determining the transpiring power of plant surfaces by hygrometric paper (*Ibid. 19:* 287-309).

Livingston, L. G., and B. M. Duggar 1934: Experimental procedures in a study of the location and concentration within the host cell of the virus of Tobacco Mosaic (Biol. Bull. *67:* 504-512).

Lloyd, D. J., and W. B. Pleass 1927: The absorption of water by gelatin (Biochem. Jour. *21:* 1352-1367).

Lloyd, F. E. 1908: The physiology of stomata (Carnegie Inst. Wash. Publ. *82:* 1-142).

—— 1912: The relation of transpiration and stomatal movements to the water content of the leaves of *Fouquieria splendens* (Plant World *15:* 1-14).

—— 1913: Leaf water and stomatal movement in *Gossypium* and a method of direct visual observation of stomata *in situ* (Bull. Torrey Bot. Club. *40:* 1-26).

Loehwing, W. F. 1938: Locus and physiology of photoperiodic perception in plants (Proc. Soc. Expt. Biol. Med. *37:* 631-634).

Loftfield, J. V. G. 1921: The behavior of stomata (Publ. Carnegie Inst. Wash. No. 314: 1-104).

London, F. 1937: A general theory of molecular forces (Trans. Far. Soc. *33:* 8-26).

—— 1942: On centers of van der Waals attraction (Jour. Phys. Chem. *46:* 305-316).

Longinescu, G. G. 1929: Molecular association (Chem. Rev. *6:* 381-418).

Loomis, W. E. 1935: The translocation of carbohydrates in maize (Iowa State Col. Jour. Sci. *9:* 509-520).

—— 1945: Translocation of carbohydrates in maize (Science *101:* 398-400).

Loustalot, A. J. 1944: Apparent photosynthesis and transpiration of pecan leaves treated with Bordeaux mixture and lead arsenate (Jour. Agr. Res. *68:* 11-20).

—— 1945: Influence of soil moisture conditions on apparent photosynthesis and transpiration of pecan leaves (Jour. Agr. Res. *71:* 519-532).

Lucké, B., and M. McCutcheon 1932: The living cell as an osmotic system and its permeability to water (Physiol. Rev. *12:* 68-139).

Lundegårdh, H. 1940: Investigations as to the absorption and accumulation of inorganic ions (Reprint from The Annals of the Agricultural College of Sweden *8:* 233-404).

—— 1946: Transport of water and salts through plant tissues (Nature *157:* 575-577).

Lutman, B. F. 1919: Osmotic pressures in the potato plant at various stages of growth (Amer. Jour. Bot. *6:* 181-202).

Luyet, B. J., and P. M. Gehenio 1937: The double freezing point of living tissues (Biodynamica *1* (30): 1-23).

——, and —— 1939: The physical states of protoplasm at low temperatures. Review and critical study (*Ibid. 2*(48): 1-128).

——, and G. Galos 1940: The effect of the rate of cooling on the freezing point of living tissue (*Ibid. 3*(65): 157-169).

Lyon, C. J. 1936: Analysis of osmotic relations by extending the simplified method (Plant Physiol. *11:* 167-172).

—— 1940: Improvements in the simplified method for osmotic measurements (*Ibid. 15:* 561-562).

—— 1941: Osmotic pressure for the plant physiologist (Science *93:* 374-375).

—— 1942: A non-osmotic force in the water relations of potato tubers during storage (Plant Physiol. *17:* 250-266).

MacDougal, D. T. 1925: Reversible variations in volume, pressure, and movement of sap in trees (Carnegie Inst. Wash. Publ. 365).

—— 1926: The hydrostatic systems of trees (*Ibid. 373:* 1-125).

——, and J. B. Overton 1927: Sap flow and pressure in trees (Science *65:* 189-190).

——, ——, and G. B. Smith 1929: The hydrostatic-pneumatic system of certain trees: movement of liquids and gases (Carnegie Inst. Wash. Publ. No. 397: 1-99).

MacLeod, D. B. 1937: The compressibility of liquids and a method of obtaining the compressibility of molecules (Trans. Far. Soc. *33:* 694-707).

Magistad, O. C. 1945: Plant growth relations on saline and alkali soils (Bot. Rev. *11:* 181-230).

——, and R. F. Reitemeier 1943: Soil solution concentrations at the wilting point and their correlation with plant growth (Soil Sci. *55:* 351-360).

Mair, B. J., A. R. Glasgow, and F. D. Rossini 1941: Determination of freezing points and amounts of impurity in hydrocarbons from freezing and melting curves (Jour. of Research *26:* 591-620).

Mallery, T. D. 1934: Comparison of the heating and freezing methods of killing plant material for cryoscopic determinations (Plant Physiol. *9:* 369-375).

Malpighi, M. 1675 (1901): Die Anatomie der Pflanzen, 163 p. (Engelmann, Leipzig).

Maney, T. J. 1931: An apparatus for spraying plants with melted paraffin or other waxes (Proc. Amer. Soc. Hort. Sci. *28:* 496-497).

Mark, H. 1944: Cellulose: physical evidence regarding its constitution (*In* Wise, L. E., Wood Chemistry, pages 106-136. Reinhold, New York).

Markley, K. S., and C. E. Sando 1931: Progressive changes in the waxlike coating on the surface of the apple during growth and storage (Jour. Agr. Res. *42:* 705-722).

Marsh, F. L. 1940: Water content and osmotic pressure of certain prairie plants in relation to environment (Nebraska University Studies, Vol. 40, No. 3: 3-44).

—— 1941: Water content and osmotic pressure of sun and shade leaves of certain woody prairie plants (Bot. Gaz. *102:* 812-814).

Martens, P. 1931: Phénomènes cúticulaires et phénomènes osmotiques dans les poils staminaux de *Tradescantia* (La Cellule *41:* 15-48).

MARTIN, E. V. 1943: Studies of evaporation and transpiration under controlled conditions (Carnegie Inst. Wash. Publ. No. 550: 1-48).

MARTIN, J. H. 1927: Comparative studies of winter hardiness in wheat (Jour. Agr. Res. *35:* 493-535).

—— 1930: The comparative drought resistance of sorghums and corn (Jour. Amer. Soc. Agron. *22:* 993-1003).

MASKELL, E. J., and T. G. MASON 1929: Studies on the transport of nitrogenous substances in the cotton plant, I. Preliminary observations on the downward transport of nitrogen in the stem (Ann. Bot. *43:* 205-231).

MASON, T. G., and E. J. MASKELL 1928a: Studies on the transport of carbohydrates in the cotton plant, I. A study of diurnal variation in the carbohydrates of leaf, bark, and wood, and the effects of ringing (*Ibid. 42:* 189-253).

——, and —— 1928b: Studies on the transport of carbohydrates in the cotton plant, II. The factors determining the rate and the direction of movement of sugars (*Ibid. 42:* 571-636).

——, and —— 1931: Further studies on transport in the cotton plant, I. Preliminary observations on the transport of phosphorus, potassium, and calcium (*Ibid. 45:* 125-173).

——, and E. PHILLIS 1937: Migration of sclutes (Bot. Rev. *3:* 47-71).

——, and —— 1939: Experiments on the extraction of sap from the vacuole of the leaf of the cotton plant and their bearing on the osmotic theory of water absorption by the cell (Ann. Bot. *3:* 531-544).

MAXIMOV, N. A. 1914: Experimentelle und kritische Untersuchungen über das Gefrieren und Erfrieren der Pflanzen (Jahrb. f. wiss. Bot. *53:* 327-420).

—— 1929a: The plant in relation to water. Transl. by R. H. YAPP, 451 p. (Allen and Unwin, London).

—— 1929b: Internal factors of frost- and drought resistance of plants (Bull. Applied Bot. of Genetics and Plant Breeding, Trudy *22:* 3-41).

—— 1931: Physiological significance of xeromorphic structure (*Ibid. 25:* 152-162).

—— 1941: The influence of drought on the physiological processes in plants, p. 299-309. Collection of papers on plant physiology in memory of K. A. TIMIRYAZEV (Acad. Sci. USSR, Inst. Plant Physiol. in the name of K. A. Timiryazev, 1941).

——, and T. A. KRASNOSSELSKY-MAXIMOV 1924: Wilting of plants in its connection with drought resistance (Jour. Ecology *12:* 95-110).

——, and T. LOMINADZE 1916: Contributions à l'étude de la pression osmotique chez les plantes (Jour. Soc. Bot. de Russ. *1:* 166-178).

——, and L. V. MOZHAEVA 1944: Age variations of colloid-chemical properties of protoplasm in vegetable cells (Acad. des Sci. URSS Compt. Rend. [Dok.] *42:* 229-232, 277-280).

McDERMOTT, J. J. 1945: The effect of the moisture content of the soil upon the rate of exudation (Amer. Jour. Bot. *32:* 570-574).

McNAB, W. R. 1871: Experiments on the transpiration of watery fluid by leaves (Trans. Bot. Soc. Edinburgh *11:* 45-65).

MENDEL, K. 1945: Orange leaf transpiration under orchard conditions (Palestine Jour. Bot., Rehovot Series *5:* 59-85).

MENDIOLA, N. B. 1922: Effect of different rates of transpiration on the dry weight and ash content of the tobacco plant (Philippine Jour. Sci. *20:* 639-655).

MER, C. L. 1940: The factors determining the resistance to the movement of water in the leaf (Ann. Bot. *4:* 397-401).

MEYER, B. S. 1928: Seasonal variations in the physical and chemical properties of the leaves of the pitch pine, with especial reference to cold resistance (Amer. Jour. Bot. *15:* 449-472).

—— 1929: Some critical comments on the methods employed in the expression of leaf saps (Plant Physiol. *4:* 103-112).

—— 1931: Effects of mineral salts upon the transpiration and water requirement of the cotton plant (Amer. Jour. Bot. *18:* 79-93).

—— 1932: Further studies on cold resistance in evergreens, with special reference to the possible role of bound water (Bot. Gaz. *94:* 297-321).

—— 1938: The water relations of plant cells (Bot. Rev. *4:* 531-547).

—— 1945: A critical evaluation of the terminology of diffusion phenomena (Plant Physiol. *20:* 142-164).

——, and D. B. ANDERSON 1939: Plant Physiology, 696 p. (D. Van Nostrand Co., New York).

——, and A. M. WALLACE 1941: A comparison of two methods of determining the diffusion pressure deficit of potato tuber tissues (Amer. Jour. Bot. *28:* 838-843).

MIGAHID, A. M. 1945: Binding of water in xerophytes and its relation to osmotic pressure (Bull. Fac. Sci. Fouad I Univ. *25:* 83-92).

MILLER, E. C. 1938: Plant Physiology, 2d. ed., 1201 p. (McGraw-Hill, New York).

MILLER, E. J., J. A. NEILSON, and S. L. BANDEMER 1937: Wax emulsions for spraying nursery stock and other plant materials (Michigan Agr. Exp. Sta. Special Bull. *282:* 5-39).

MINCKLER, L. S. 1936: A new method of measuring transpiration (J. Forestry *34:* 36-39).

MITCHELL, J. W., and J. W. BROWN 1946: Movement of 2, 4-dichlorophenoxyacetic acid stimulus and its relation to the translocation of organic food materials in plants (Bot. Gaz. *107:* 393-407).

MOLISCH, H. 1912: Das Offen- und Geschlossensein der Spaltoeffnungen, veranschaulicht durch eine neue Methode (Infiltrationsmethode) (Zeitschr. f. Bot. *4:* 106-122).

—— 1921: Über den Einfluss der Transpiration auf das Verschwinden Stärke in den Blättern (Ber. deut. bot. Ges. *39:* 339-344).

—— 1928: The movement of sap in plants (Nature *122:* 168-169).

—— 1929: The movement of sap in plants (Science *69:* 217-218).

MOLZ, F. J. 1926: A study of suction force by the simplified method, I. Effect of external factors. II. Periodic variations and the influence of habitat (Amer. Jour. Bot. *13:* 433-501).

MONTEMARTINI, L. 1943: Il bilancio idrico delle piante (Soc. Anonima Editrice D. Alighieri, Genoa).

MONTERMOSO, J. C., and A. R. DAVIS 1942. Preliminary investigation of the rhythmic fluctuations in transpiration under constant environmental conditions (Plant Physiol. *17:* 473-480).

MORGAN, J., and B. E. WARREN 1938: X-ray analysis of the structure of water (Jour. Chem. Physics 6: 666-673).

MORRIS, R. T. 1921: Nut growing (Macmillan Co., New York).

MORSE, H. N. 1914: The osmotic pressure of aqueous solutions (Carnegie Inst. Wash. Publ. No. 198: 1-222).

MOSEBACH, G. 1936: Kryoskopisch ermittelte osmotische Werte bei Meeresalgen (Beitr. Biol. Pflanzen 24: 113-137).

—— 1940: Ein Mikroverfahren zur kryoskopischen Untersuchung saftreicher Gewebe (Ber. deut. bot. Ges. 58: 29-40).

MOSHKOV, B. S. 1939: Transfer of photoperiodic reaction from leaves to growing points (Compt. Rend. [Dok.] Acad. Sci. URSS 24: 489-491).

MUENSCHER, W. C. 1922: The effect of transpiration on the absorption of salts by plants (Amer. Jour. Bot. 9: 311-329).

MÜLLER-THURGAU, H. 1880: Über das Gefrieren und Erfrieren der Pflanzen (Landw. Jahrb. 9: 133-189).

—— 1886: Ibid. 15: 453-610.

MÜNCH, E. 1930: Die Stoffbewegungen in der Pflanze, 234 p. (Fischer, Jena).

NADEL, M. 1938: Sur la mesure de l'ouverture des stomates (Thesis, University Paris).

NEILSON, J. A. 1928: Parafine wax—an aid to growth in transplanted trees and shrubs (Proc. North. Nut Grow. Assn. 19: 44-51).

—— 1931: Reducing storage and transplanting losses in nursery stock (Florida Exch. and Hort. Trade World 78: 27, 35).

NERNST, W. 1910: The specific heat of ice, water, and water vapor (Trans. Far. Soc. 6: 117-119).

NEWTON, R. 1924: Colloidal properties of winter wheat plants in relation to frost resistance (Jour. Agric. Sci. 14: 178-191).

——, W. R. BROWN, and W. M. MARTIN 1926: The extraction of plant tissue fluids and their utility in physiological studies Plant Physiol. 1: 57-65).

NIGAM, B. S. 1934: Effect of excessive humidity on the resistance of citrus plant to sun scorch (Amer. Jour. Bot. 21: 351-354).

NOLLET, M. l'Abbé 1748: Recherches sur les causes du Bouillonnement des Liquides (Acad. Roy. des Sciences Mémoires, p. 57-104).

NORDHAUSEN, M. 1916: Ueber die Saugkraft transpirierender Sprosse (Ber. deut. bot. Ges. 34: 619-639).

—— 1917: Zur Kenntnis der Saugkraft und der Wasserversorgung transpirierender Sprosse (Jahrb. f. wiss. Bot. 58: 295-335).

—— 1921: Weitere Beiträge zum Saftsteigeproblem (Jahrb. f. wiss. Bot. 60: 307-353).

NORTHERN, H. T. 1942: Relationship of dissociation of cellular proteins by auxins to growth (Bot. Gaz. 103: 668-683).

OEHLKERS, F. 1937: Neue Versuche über zytologisch-genetische Probleme (Biol. Zbl. 57: 126-149).

OPPENHEIMER, J. D. 1926: Researches on the changes in the opening of stomata which occur in different species of Citrus (Agric. Records No. 1 of the P. Z. E. Inst. of Agric. and Nat. Hist. Tel-Aviv., 9-30).

OPPENHEIMER, H. R. 1930a: Kritische Betrachtungen zu den Saugkraftmessung von Ursprung und Blum (Ber. deut. bot. Ges. 48: 130-140).

—— 1930b: Dehnbarkeit und Turgordehnung der Zellmembran (Ibid. 48: 192-206).

—— 1932a: Über Zuverlässigkeit und Anwendungsgrenzen der üblichsten Methoden zur Bestimmung der osmotischen Konzentration pflanzlicher Zellsäfte (Planta 16: 467-517).

—— 1932b: Untersuchungen zur Kritik der Saugkraftmessungen (Planta 18: 525-549).

—— 1936: Remarks on two recent critical contributions concerning methods used in plant physiology (Palestine Jour. Bot. and Hort. Sci. 1: 84-93).

——, and K. MENDEL 1939: Orange leaf transpiration under orchard conditions (Agric. Res. Sta., Rehovot, Bull. 25: 1-82).

OSTERHOUT, W. J. V. 1913: Protoplasmic contractions resembling plasmolysis which are caused by pure distilled water (Bot. Gaz. 55: 446-451).

—— 1922: Some aspects of selective absorption (Jour. Gen. Physiol. 5: 225-230).

—— 1936: The absorption of electrolytes in large plant cells (Bot. Rev. 2: 283-315).

—— 1943: Studies of the inner and outer protoplasmic surfaces of large plant cells, I. Plasmolysis due to salts (Jour. Gen. Physiol. 27: 139-142).

—— 1945: Water relations in the cell (Ibid. 29: 73-78).

—— 1947a: The absorption of electrolytes in large plant cells, II. (Bot. Rev. 13: 194-215).

—— 1947b: Some aspects of secretion, I. Secretion of water (Jour. Gen. Physiol. 30: 439-447.

——, and E. S. HARRIS 1927: Protoplasmic asymmetry in Nitella as shown by bioelectric measurements (Jour. Gen. Physiol. 11: 391-406).

——, and J. W. MURRAY 1940: Behavior of water in certain heterogeneous systems (Ibid. 23: 365-390).

OVERBECK, F. 1930: Mit welchen Druckkräften arbeitet der Schleudermechanismus der Spritzgurke (Zeitschr. f. wiss. Biol. Abt. E 10: 138-169).

OVERTON, E. 1902: Beiträge zur allgemeinen Muskel- und Nervenphysiologie (Pflüger's Archiv. 92: 115-280).

PAGLIANI, S. 1920: The compressibility and viscosity of water and its solutions and its polymerization (Gazzeta Chim. Ital. 50, I, 186-194).

PALLADIN, V. I. 1923: Plant physiology, 360 p., 2nd American edition, ed. by B. E. LIVINGSTON (P. Blakiston, Philadelphia).

PALVA, P. 1939: Die Wasserpermeabilität der Zellen von Tolypellopsis Stelligera (Protoplasma 32: 265-271).

PAULING, L. 1939: The nature of the chemical bond, 429 p. (Cornell Univ. Press, Ithaca, N. Y.).

PEIRCE, G. J. 1936a: Are living cells involved in the ascent of sap? (Amer. Jour. Bot. 23: 159-162).

—— 1936b: The state of water in ducts and tracheids (Plant Physiol. 11: 623-628).

PENNYCUICK, S. W. 1928: The structure of water (Jour. Phys. Chem. 32: 1681-1696).

PETERS, J. P. 1942: Water metabolism (Ann. Rev. Physiol. *4:* 89-114).

PETRIE, A. H. K., and WOOD, J. G. 1938: Studies on the nitrogen metabolism of plants, I. The relation between the content of proteins, amino-acids, and water in the leaves (Ann. Bot. N. S. *2:* 33-60).

PFEFFER, W. F. P. 1877: Osmotische Untersuchungen, 236 p. (W. Engelmann, Leipzig).

PFITZER, E. 1878: Ueber die Geschwindigkeit der Wasserströmung in der Pflanze (Jahrb. f. wiss. Bot. *11:* 177-217).

PHILLIS, E., and T. G. MASON 1941: On the expression of sap by low pressure (Ann. Bot. *5:* 15-23).

——, and —— 1945: Studies on foliar hydration in the cotton plant; gel theory of water relations (*Ibid. 9:* 297-334).

PICKEN, L. E. R. 1936: A note on the mechanism of salt and water balance in the heterotrichous ciliate, *Spirostomum ambiguum* (Jour. Exp. Biol. *13:* 387-392).

PIENIAZEK, S. A. 1944: Physical characters of the skin in relation to apple fruit transpiration (Plant Physiol. *19:* 529-536).

PISEK, A., and E. CARTELLIERI 1931: Zur Kenntnis des Wasserhaushaltes der Pflanzen, I. Sonnenpflanzen (Jahrb. f. wiss. Bot. *75:* 195-251).

——, and —— 1932: *Ibid.,* II. Schattenpflanzen (*Ibid. 75:* 643-678).

——, and —— 1939: *Ibid.,* IV. Baume und Sträucher (Jahrb. f. wiss. Bot. *88:* 22-68).

POND, R. H. 1903: The biological relation of aquatic plants to the substratum (Contributions to the Biology of the Great Lakes. Report U. S. Fish Comm. 483-526).

PONDER, E. 1944: The osmotic behavior of crenated red cells (Jour. Gen. Physiol. *27:* 273-285).

PORTER, A. W. 1917: The kinetic theory of osmotic pressure (Trans. Far. Soc. *13:* 123-132).

PRÁT, S. 1927: The toxicity of tissue juices for cells of the tissue (Amer. Jour. Bot. *14:* 120-125).

—— 1934: Stimulation plasmolysis on marine algae (Acta Adriat. No. 4: 1-20).

PRESTON, R. D. 1938: The contents of the vessels of *Fraxinus americana* L., with respect to the ascent of sap (Ann. Bot. *2:* 1-22).

PRIESTLEY, J. H. 1920: The mechanism of root pressure (New Phytol. *19:* 189-200).

—— 1935: Sap ascent in the tree (Science Progress *30:* 42-56).

PRINGSHEIM, E. G. 1906: Wasserbewegung und Turgorregulation in welkenden Pflanzen (Jahrb. f. wiss. Bot. *43:* 89-144).

—— 1931: Untersuchungen über Turgordehnung und Membrangeschaffenheit (*Ibid. 74:* 749-796).

RABIDEAU, G. S., and G. O. BURR 1945: The use of the C[13] isotope as a tracer for transport studies in plants (Amer. Jour. Bot. *32:* 349-356).

RABINOVICH, A. I. 1922: Negative viscosity (Jour. Amer. Chem. Soc. *44:* 954-964).

RABINOWITCH, E. I. 1945: Photosynthesis and related processes, Vol. I (Interscience Publishers, New York).

RAO, I. R. 1934: The constitution of water in different states (Proc. Roy. Soc. London *A145:* 489-508).

RAOULT, F. M. 1885: Sur le point de congélation des dissolutions salines (Ann. de Chim. et de Physique, Ser. 6, *4:* 401-430).

REED, H. S. 1910: The effect of certain chemical agents upon the transpiration and growth of wheat seedlings (Bot. Gaz. *49:* 81-109).

—— 1942: A short history of the plant sciences (Chronica Botanica, Waltham, Mass.)

——, and J. S. COOLEY 1913: The transpiration of apple leaves infected with *Gymnosporangium* (Bot. Gaz. *55:* 421-430).

REIN, H. 1928: Die Thermo-Stromuhr. Ein Verfahren, welches mit etwa ± 10 Procent Genauigkeit die umblutige langdauernde Messung der mittleren Durchflussmengen an gleichzeitig Gefässen gestattet (Zeitschr. f. Biol. *87:* 394-418).

—— 1929: Die Thermo-Stromuhr, II. Mitteilung der Arbeitsbedingungen und Arbeitsmöglichkeiten im Tierversuch (*Ibid. 89:* 195-201).

REINDERS, D. E. 1938: The process of water-intake by discs of potato tuber tissue (Kon. Nederl. Akadamie van Wetenschappen, Proceedings Sect. Sci. *41:* 820-831).

—— 1942: Intake of water by parenchymatic tissue (Rec. trav. botan. Néerland. *39:* 1-140).

REMICK, A. E. 1943: Electronic interpretations of organic chemistry, 474 p. (Wiley, New York).

RENNER, O. 1910: Beiträge zur Physik der Transpiration (Flora *100:* 451-547).

—— 1911*a:* Experimentelle Beiträge zur Kenntnis der Wasserbewegung (*Ibid. 103:* 171-247).

—— 1911*b:* Zur Physik der Transpiration (Ber. deut. bot. Ges. *29:* 125-132).

—— 1912: Versuche zur Mechanik der Wasserversorgung, I. Der Druck in den Leitungsbahnen von Freilandpflanzen (*Ibid. 30:* 576-580).

—— 1915*a:* Die Wasserversorgung der Pflanzen (Handwörterbuch Naturwiss. *10:* 538-557).

—— 1915*b:* Theoretisches und Experimentelles zur Kohäsionstheorie der Wasserbewegung (Jahrb. f. wiss. Bot. *56:* 617-667).

—— 1932: Zur Kenntnis des Wasserhaushalts javanischer Kleinepiphyten (Planta *18:* 215-287).

RESÜHR, B. 1935: Hydrations- und Permeabilitätsstudien an unbefruchteten Fucus-Eiern (*Fucus vesiculosus* L.) (Protoplasma *24:* 531-586).

RICHARDS, L. A. 1941: A pressure-membrane extraction apparatus for soil solution (Soil Sci. *51:* 377-386).

——, and L. R. WEAVER 1944: Moisture retention by some irrigated soils as related to soil-moisture tension (Jour. Agr. Res. *69:* 215-235).

RICHARDS, T. W., and H. M. CHADWELL 1925: The densities and compressibilities of several organic liquids and solutions and the polymerization of water (Jour. Amer. Chem. Soc. *47:* 2283-2302).

——, and S. PALITZSCH 1919: Compressibility of aqueous solutions, especially of urethane, and the polymerization of water (Jour. Amer. Chem. Soc. *41:* 59-69).

RIEDL, H. 1937: Bau und Leistungen des Wurzelholzes (Jahrb. f. wiss. Bot. *85:* 1-75).

ROACH, W. A. 1938: Plant injection for diagnostic and curative purposes (Imperial Bur. Hort. and Plant Crops Tech. Comm. *10:* 1-78).

—— 1939: Plant injection as a physiological method (Ann. Bot. *3:* 155-226).

——, and W. O. ROBERTS 1945: Further work on plant injection for diagnostic and curative purposes (Imperial Bur. Hort. and Plant Crops Tech. Comm. *16:* 1-12).

ROBBINS, W. W., A. S. CRAFTS, and R. N. RAYNOR 1942: Weed control (McGraw-Hill, New York).

ROBERTS, O., and S. A. STYLES 1939: An apparent connection between the presence of colloids and the osmotic pressures of conifer leaves (Sci. Proc. Roy. Dublin Soc. 22: 119-125).

ROEPKE, R. R. 1942: The thermoelectric method of measuring vapor pressure (J. Phys. Chem. 46: 359-366).

RÖNTGEN, W. C. 1892: Ueber die Constitution des flüssigen Wassers (Ann. Physik. u. Chemie. N. F. 45: 91-97).

ROSENE, H. F. 1941: Control of water transport in local root regions of attached and isolated roots by means of the osmotic pressure of the external solution (Amer. Jour. Bot. 28: 402-410).

ROUSCHAL, E. 1941: Untersuchungen über die Protoplasmatik und Funktion der Siebröhren (Flora 35: 135-200).

RUDOLPH, K. 1925: Epidermis und epidermale Transpiration (Bot. Arch. 9: 49-94).

RYWOSCH, S. 1908: Zur Stoffwanderung im Chlorophyllgewebe (Bot. Zeitung 66: 121-130).

SABININ, D. A. 1925: On the root system as an osmotic apparatus (Bull. Inst. Rech. Biol. Univ. Perm 4: [suppl. 2] 1-136).

SALISBURY, E. J. 1927: On the causes and ecological significance of stomatal frequency, with special reference to the woodland flora (Phil. Trans. Roy. Soc. B216: 1-65).

SAUVAGEAU, C. 1891: Sur les feuilles de quelques monocotylédones aquatiques (Ann. Sci. Nat. Bot. VII, 13: 103-296).

SAVASTANO, G. 1934: Ricerche fisiologiche sul raggrinzimento delle drupe dell 'olivo (Boll. R. Staz. Patol. Veg. 14: 79-116).

SAYRE, J. D. 1926: Physiology of stomata of Rumex patientia (The Ohio Jour. of Sci. 26: 233-266).

——, and V. H. MORRIS 1932: Use of expressed sap in determining the composition of corn tissue (Plant Physiol. 7: 261-272).

SCARTH, G. W. 1923: Adhesion of protoplasm to cell wall and the agents which cause it (Transact. Roy. Soc. Canada 17: 137-143).

—— 1932: Mechanism of the action of light and other factors on stomatal movement (Plant Physiol. 7: 481-504).

—— 1941: Dehydration injury and resistance (Ibid. 16: 171-179).

—— 1944: Cell physiological studies of frost resistance: a review (New Phytol. 43: 1-12).

SCATCHARD, G. 1936: Concentrated solutions of strong electrolytes (Chem. Rev. 19: 309-327).

——, and L. F. EPSTEIN 1942: The calculation of the thermodynamic properties and the association of electrolyte solutions (Chem. Rev. 30: 211-226).

SCHMIDT, C. L. A. 1938: The chemistry of the amino acids and proteins, 1031 p. (C. C. Thomas, Springfield, Illinois).

SCHNEIDER, G. W., and N. F. CHILDERS 1941: Influence of soil moisture on photosynthesis, respiration, and transpiration of apple leaves (Plant Physiol. 16: 565-583).

SCHRATZ, E. 1931: Vergleichende Untersuchungen über den Wasserhaushalt von Pflanzen im Trockengebiete des südlichen Arizona (Jahrb. f. wiss. Bot. 74: 153-290).

SCHROEDER, H., and T. HORN 1922: Das gegenseitige Mengenverhältnis der Kohlenhydrate im Laubblatt in seiner Abhängigkeit vom Wassergehalt (Biochem. Zeit. 130: 165-198).

SCHORN, M. 1929: Untersuchungen ueber die Verwendbarkeit der Alkoholfixierungs- und Infiltrationsmethode zur Messung von Spaltoeffnungs-weiten (Jahrb. f. wiss. Bot. 71: 783-840).

SCOFIELD, H. T., and L. E. YARMAN 1943: Some investigations of the water relations of lichens (Ohio Jour. Sci. 43: 139-146).

SEIFRIZ, W. 1928: New material for microdissection (Protoplasma 3: 191-196).

—— 1938: The physiology of plants, 315 p. (Wiley, New York).

—— 1942: A symposium on the structure of protoplasm, 283 p. (Iowa State College Press, Ames).

SEYBOLD, A. 1929: Die physikalische Komponente der pflanzlichen Transpiration, 214 p. (Monogr. a. b. Gesamtg. Wissensch. Bot., 2, Julius Springer, Berlin).

SHAFER, J. 1942: Water loss from excised leaves (Amer. Jour. Bot. 29: 89-91).

SHREVE, E. B. 1916: Analysis of the causes of variations in the transpiring power of cacti (Physiol. Res. 2: 73-127).

—— 1931: The role of sap concentration in transpiration (Carnegie Inst. Wash. Yearbook 30: 262-263).

SHULL, C. A. 1913: Semipermeability of seed coats (Bot. Gaz. 56: 169-199).

—— 1924: Imbibition in relation to absorption and transportation of water in plants (Ecology 5: 230-240).

—— 1939: Atmospheric humidity and temperature in relation to the water system of plants and soils (Plant Physiol. 14: 401-422).

SIDGWICK, N. V. 1936: Dipole moment and molecular structure (Chem. Rev. 19: 183-194).

SIERP, H., and A. SEYBOLD 1927: Untersuchungen zur Physik der Transpiration (Planta 3: 115-168).

SIFTON, H. B. 1945: Air-space tissue in plants (Bot. Rev. 11: 108-143).

SIGNER, R. 1930: Über eine Abänderung der Moleculargewichtsbestimmungsmethode nach Barger Justus Liebig's Ann. Chem. 478: 246-266).

SISAKIAN, N. M. 1939: The biochemical characteristics of the drought resistance of plants (Sbornik Akad. Nauk, Prezidentu Akad. Nauk SSSR Akad. V. L. Komarovw (1939): 707-719).

—— 1940: The character of enzyme action in connection with the drought resistance of plants (Trudy Moskov. Doma Uchenykhi Inst. Biokhim. Akad. Nauk SSSR (1940), No. 4: 29-38).

——, and A. KOBIAKOVA 1940: The behavior of enzymes as an index of drought resistance in crop plants, IV. The effect of wilting upon the trend of esterification and hydrolysis of phosphoric esters in plants (Biokhimiia 5: 225-233).

——, and —— 1941: The prevailing direction of enzyme action as an index of drought resistance in cultivated plants, V. The diurnal rhythm of the trend of enzyme action in withering (Ibid. 6: 103-112).

SKOOG, F. 1938: Absorption and translocation of auxin (Amer. Jour. Bot. 25: 361-372).

——, T. C. BROYER, and K. A. GROSSENBACHER 1938: Effects of auxin on rates, periodicity, and osmotic relations in exudation (Amer. Jour. Bot. 25: 749-759).

SKVORTZOV, S. S. 1931: On the influence of desiccating winds on photosynthesis (Bull. Applied Bot. of Genetics and Plant Breeding, Trudy, *25*, No. 3: 45-68).

SMITH, F., R. B. DUSTMAN, and C. A. SHULL 1931: Ascent of sap in plants (Bot. Gaz. *91*: 395-410).

SMITH, H. B. 1941: Variation and correlation of stomatal frequency and transpiration rate in *Phaseolus vulgaris* (Amer. Jour. Bot. *28*: 722-725).

SNELL, H. 1886: Untersuchungen über die Nahrungsaufnahme der Wasserpflanzen (Flora *98*: 213-249).

SÖLLNER, K. 1930: Zur erklärung der abnormen Osmose an nicht quellbaren Membranen, I. Teil (Ztschr. f. Elektrochemie und angewandte physikalische Chemie *36*: 36-47).

—— 1930: Zur erklärung der abnormen Osmose an nicht quellbaren Membranen, II. Teil (*Ibid. 36*: 234-241).

——, I. ABRAMS, and C. W. CARR 1941: The structure of the collodion membrane and its electrical behavior, II. The activated collodion membrane (Jour. Gen. Physiol. *25*: 7-27).

——, and A. GROLLMAN 1932: Zur erklärung der abnormen osmose an nichtquellbaren membranen, III. Teil (Ztschr. f. Elektrochemie und angewandte physikalische Chemie *38*: 274-282).

SPOEHR, H. A., and H. W. MILNER 1939. Starch solution and amylolytic activity in leaves (Proc. Amer. Phil. Soc. *81*: 37-78).

SPONSLER, O. L. 1940: Molecular structure in protoplasm (*In* A. A. A. S. The Cell and Protoplasm. Publication No. 14: 166-187. Science Press, Lancaster, Pa.).

——, and J. D. BATH 1942: Molecular structure in protoplasm (*In* SEIFRIZ, W. 1942: The Structure of Protoplasm. Iowa State College Press, Ames, pp. 41-79).

——, ——, and J. W. ELLIS 1940: Water bound to gelatin as shown by molecular structure studies (Jour. Phys. Chem. *44*: 996-1006).

STAHL, E. 1894: Einige Versuche ueber Transpiration und Assimilation (Bot. Zeit. *52*: 117-145).

STÅLFELT, M. G. 1929: Neuere Methoden zur Ermittlung des Öffnungszustandes der Stomata (Handb. d. biolog. Arb. Meth. von E. Abderhalden, Abt. XI, Teil *4*: 167-192).

—— 1932: Der stomatare Regulator in der pflanzlichen Transpiration (Planta *17*: 22-85).

STAMM, A. J. 1936: Colloid chemistry of cellulosic materials (U. S. Dept. Agric. Misc. Publ. *240*: 1-90).

—— 1944: Surface properties of cellulosic materials (*In* WISE, L. E., ed.: Wood Chemistry, pp. 449-550. Reinhold, New York).

STEFAN, J. 1873: Versuche über die Verdunstung (Sitzungsber. Akad. Wiss. Wien *68*: 385-428).

—— 1881: Über die Verdampfung aus einem kreisförmig odor elliptisch begrenzten Becken (*Ibid. 83*: 943-954).

STEIN, E. 1912: Bemerkungen zu der Arbeit von MOLISCH: Das Offen- und Geschlossensein der Spaltoeffnungen veranschaulicht durch eine neue Methode (Ber. deut. bot. Ges. *30*: 66-68).

STEINBERGER, A. L. 1922: Über Regulation des osmotischen Wertes in den Schliesszellen von Luft- und Wasserspalten (Biol. Centralb. *42*: 405-419).

STERN, K. 1933: Pflanzenthermodynamik (Springer, Berlin).

STEWARD, F. C. 1928: The maintenance of semi-permeability in the plant cell during leaching experiments (Proc. Leeds Phil. Soc. *1*: 258-270).

—— 1932: The absorption and accumulation of solutes by living plant cells, I. Experimental conditions which determine salt absorption by storage tissue (Protoplasma *15*: 29-58).

——, and J. A. HARRISON 1939: *Ibid.*, IX. The absorption of Rubidium bromide by potato discs (Ann. Bot. *3*: 427-453).

——, W. E. BERRY, C. PRESTON, and T. K. RAMAMURTI 1943: *Ibid.*, X. Time and temperature effects on salt uptake by potato discs and the influence of storage conditions of the tubers on metabolism and other properties (Ann. Bot. *7*: 221-260).

——, P. R. STOUT, and C. PRESTON 1940: The balance sheet of metabolites for potato discs showing the effect of salts and dissolved oxygen on metabolism at 23° C. (Plant Physiol. *15*: 409-447).

STEWART, G. W. 1939: The variation in the structure of water in ionic solutions (Jour. Chem. Phys. *7*: 869-877).

—— 1943: *Ibid.* II (Jour. Chem. Phys. *11*: 72-74).

—— 1944: Physical concepts of ionic and other aqueous solutions (Amer. Jour. Physics *12*: 321-323).

STILES, W. 1937: The constitution of plant cell membranes (Trans. Far. Soc. *33*: 923-930).

——, and I. JORGENSEN 1917: Studies in permeability, V. The swelling of plant tissue in water and its relation to temperature and various dissolved substances (Ann. Bot. *31*: 415-434).

STOCKING, C. R. 1943: Continuity, tensions, and redistribution of water in plants (Ph.D. Dissert. Univ. of California).

—— 1945: The calculation of tensions in *Cucurbita pepo* (Amer. Jour. Bot. *32*: 126-134).

—— 1948: Recovery of turgor by cut shoots after wilting (Plant Physiol. *23*: 152-155).

STODDART, L. A. 1935: Osmotic pressure and water content of prairie plants (Plant Physiol. *10*: 661-680).

STOUT, M. 1945: Translocation of the reproductive stimulus in sugar beets (Bot. Gaz. *107*: 86-95).

STOUT, P. R., and D. R. HOAGLAND 1939: Upward and lateral movement of salt in certain plants as indicated by radioactive isotopes of potassium, sodium and phosphorus absorbed by roots (Amer. Jour. Bot. *26*: 320-324).

STRASBURGER, E. 1891: Ueber den Bau und die Verrichtungen der Leitungsbahnen in den Pflanzen, Vol. 3 (Gustav Fischer, Jena).

STRUGGER, S. 1934: Beiträge zur Physiologie des Wachstums, I. Zur protoplasma physiologischen Kausalanalyse des Streckungs-Wachstums (Jahrb. f. wiss. Bot. *79*: 406-471).

—— 1935: Praktikum der Zell- und Gewebephysiologie der Pflanze (Borntraeger, Berlin).

—— 1943: Der aufsteigende Saftstrom in der Pflanze (Naturwiss. *31*: 181-192).

SUTHERLAND, W. 1900: The molecular constitution of water (Phil. Mag. 5th Ser. *50*: 460-489).

—— 1902: The electric origin of molecular attraction (Phil. Mag. [6] *4*: 625-645).

—— 1910: The constitution of water (Trans. Far. Soc. *6*: 105-116).

TAGAWA, T. 1934: The relation between the absorption of water by plant root and the concentration and nature of the surrounding solution (Jap. Jour. Bot. *7*: 33-60).

—— 1936: The influence of light on the stomatal opening (Jap. Jour. Bot. *8*: 95-112).

TAMIYA, H. 1938: Zur Theorie der Turgordehnung und über den funktionellen Zusammenhang zwischen den einzelnen osmotischen Zustandsgrössen (Cytologia *8:* 542-562).

THODAY, D. 1918: On turgescence and the absorption of water by the cells of plants (New Phytol. *17:* 108-113).

——, and M. G. SYKES 1909: Preliminary observations on the transpiration current in submerged water-plants (Ann. Bot. *23:* 635-637).

THOMAS, N., and A. FERGUSON 1917a: On the reduction of transpiration observations (Ann. Bot. *31:* 241-255).

——, and —— 1917b: On evaporation from a circular water surface (Phil. Mag. *34:* 308-321).

THREN, R. 1934: Jahreszeitliche Schwankungen des osmotischen Wertes verschiedener ökologischer Typen in der Umgebung von Heidelberg. Mit einem Beitrag zur Methodik der Pressaftuntersuchung (Zeitschr. f. Bot. *26:* 449-526).

THUT, H. F. 1932a: Demonstrating the lifting power of transpiration (Amer. Jour. Bot. *19:* 358-364).

—— 1932b: The movement of water through some submerged plants (*Ibid. 19:* 693-709).

TINKER, F. 1917: The colloidal membrane: its properties and its function in the osmotic system (Trans. Far. Soc. *13:* 133-140).

TOLLENAARD, D. 1925: Omzettingen van Koolhydratenin het Blad van *Nicotiana tabacum* L. (Dissert., H. Veenman and Zonen, Wageningen).

TRAUBE, M. 1867: Experimente zur Theorie der Zellbildung und Endosmose (Archiv. Anat. Physiol. und wiss. Medicin, p. 87-165).

TUMANOV, I. I. 1929: Wilting and drought resistance (Bull. of Applied Bot. of Genetics and Plant Breeding, Trudy *22,* No. 1: 107-146).

TUKEY, H. B., and K. BRASE 1931: The effect of paraffining, pruning and other storage treatments upon the growth of roses and cherry trees (Proc. Amer. Soc. Hort. Sci. *28:* 489-495).

TURRELL, F. M. 1936: The area of the internal exposed surface of dicotyledon leaves (Amer. Jour. Bot. *23:* 255-264).

—— 1944: Correlation between internal surface and transpiration rate in mesomorphic and xeromorphic leaves grown under artificial light (Bot. Gaz. *105:* 413-425).

UNGER, F. 1854: Beiträge zur Physiologie der Pflanzen, I. Bestimmung der in den Interzellulargängen der Pflanzen enthaltenen Luftmenge (Kön. Akad. Wiss. Wien Math.-Natw. *12:* 367-378).

—— 1862: Neue Untersuchungen über die Transpiration der Pflanzen (Sitzb. K. Akad. Wissensch. [Wien] *44:* 181-217).

URQUHART, A. R. 1929: The mechanism of the adsorption of water by cotton (Jour. Text. Inst. *20:* T125-T132).

URSPRUNG, A. 1915: Über die Kohäsion des Wassers im Farnannulus (Ber. deut. bot. Ges. *33:* 153-162).

—— 1923: Zur Kenntnis der Saugkraft, VII. Eine neue vereinfachte Methode zur Messung der Saugkraft (*Ibid. 41:* 338-343).

—— 1935: Osmotic quantities of plant cells in given phases (Plant Physiol. *10:* 115-133).

—— 1938: Die Messung der osmotischen Zustandsgrössen pflanzlicher Zellen und Gewebe (Handb. d. biolog. Arb. Meth. von E. Abderhalden, Abt. XI, Teil 4, Heft 7, pp. 1109-1572).

——, and G. BLUM 1916a: Über die Verteilung des osmotischen Wertes in der Pflanze (Ber. deut. bot. Ges. *34:* 88-104).

——, and —— 1916b: Zur Methode der Saugkraftmessung (*Ibid. 34:* 525-539).

——, and —— 1927: Eine Methode zur Messung der Saugkraft von Hartlaub (Jahrb. wiss. f. Bot. *67:* 334-348).

——, and —— 1930: Zwei neue Saugkraft-Messmethoden (*Ibid. 72:* 254-334).

VAN LAAR, J. J. 1917: Communication to the symposium on osmotic pressure (Trans. Far. Soc. *13:* 171-173).

VAN ORSTRAND, C. E., and F. P. DEWEY 1915: Preliminary report on the diffusion of solids (U. S. Geol. Survey Profess. Paper 95-G: 83-96).

VAN OVERBEEK, J. 1942: Water uptake by excised root systems of the tomato due to non-osmotic forces (Amer. Jour. Bot. *29:* 677-683).

—— 1944: Auxin, water uptake and osmotic pressure in potato tissue (*Ibid. 31:* 265-269).

VAN DER PAAUW, F. 1935: The entrance of water into cut leafy shoots under conditions which prevent transpiration (Rec. trav. bot. Neérl. *32:* 293-310).

VAN'T HOFF, J. H. 1887: Die Rolle des osmotischen Drucke in der Analogie zwischen Lösungen und Gasen (Z. Phys. Chem. *1:* 481-508).

—— 1888: The function of osmotic pressure in the analogy between solutions and gases (Phil. Mag. Ser. 5, *26:* 81-105).

VASSILIEV, I. M. 1929: The investigation of drought-resistance in wheat (Bull. Applied Bot. of Genetics and Plant Breeding, Trudy *22:* No. 1: 147-218).

—— 1930: The water relations of plants of the sand desert South Eastern Kara-Kum (*Ibid. 25,* No. 3: 185-272).

—— 1931: Effect of drought on the carbohydrate transformation in wheats (*Ibid. 27,* No. 5: 47-69).

—— 1932: Plant physiology in relation to drought control (Soc. Zern. Khoz. *1-2:* 10-12).

——, and M. G. VASSILIEV 1936: Change in carbohydrate content of wheat plants during the process of hardening for drought resistance (Plant Physiol. *11:* 115-125).

VEIHMEYER, F. J. 1927: Some factors affecting the irrigation requirements of deciduous orchards (Hilgardia *2:* 125-284).

—— 1938: Effect of organic matter on the infiltration of water into soils (Amer. Geophysical Union Trans. 19, Pt. *1:* 326-342).

——, and N. E. EDLEFSEN 1936: Water in soils and its movement (Union Géodésique et Géoph. Internat. Assoc. Internat. d'Hydr. Sci. Bull. *22:* 355-365).

——, and —— 1937: Interpretation of soil moisture problems by means of energy changes (Amer. Geophysical Union Trans. 18, Pt. *2:* 302-308).

——, ——, and A. H. HENDRICKSON 1943: Use of tensiometers in measuring availability of water to plants (Plant Physiol. *18:* 66-78).

——, and A. H. HENDRICKSON 1927: The relation of soil moisture to cultivation and plant growth (Proc. First Int. Cong. Soil Sci. Wash. *3:* 498-513).

——, and —— 1934: Some plant and soil moisture relations (Amer. Soil Survey Assoc. Bull. *15:* 76-80).

——, and —— 1938: Soil moisture as an indication of root distribution in deciduous orchards (Plant Physiol. *13:* 169-177).

——, and —— 1943: Essentials of irrigation and cultivation of orchards (Calif. Agr. Ext. Serv. Circ. 50).

——, and —— 1946: Soil density as a factor in determining the permanent wilting percentage (Soil Sci. *62:* 451-456).

VERNON, H. M. 1891: On the maximum density of water (Phil. Mag. 5th Ser. *31:* 387-392).

VERSCHAFFELT, E., and J. VERSCHAFFELT 1890: De transpiratie der planten in koolzuurvrije lucht (Bot. Jaarboek, witgegeven door het Kruidkundig Genootschap Dodonaea te Gent, *2:* 305).

VESQUE, J. 1883: Sur l'interprétation d'une expérience de Hales concernant le rôle des vaisseaux Compt. Rend. *97:* 1085-1087).

VRIES, H. DE 1884: Eine Methode zur Analyse der Turgorkraft (Jahrb. wiss. Bot. *14:* 427-601).

—— 1888: Osmotische Versuche mit lebenden Membranen (Zeitschr. f. Physik. Chem. *2:* 415).

—— 1918: Opera e periodicis collata v. 1-2. Collected works of HUGO DE VRIES published in Utrecht by A. Oosthoek.

WADLEIGH, C. H., and A. D. AYERS 1945: Growth and biochemical composition of bean plants as conditioned by soil moisture tension and salt concentration (Plant Physiol. *20:* 106-132).

——, H. G. GAUCH, and V. DAVIES 1943: The trend of starch reserves in bean plants before and after irrigation of a saline soil (Proc. Amer. Soc. Hort. Sci. *43:* 201-209).

WALKER, J. 1910: Summary of symposium (Trans. Far. Soc. *6:* 122-123).

WALTER, H. 1925: Die Verdunstung von Wasser in bewegter Luft und ihre Abhängigkeit von der Grösse der Oberfläche (Ztschr. f. Bot. *18:* 1-47).

—— 1928: Die Bedeutung des Wassersättigungszustandes für die CO_2-Assimilation der Pflanzen (Ber. deut. bot. Ges. *46:* 530-539).

—— 1929: Plasmaquellung und Assimilation (Protoplasma *6:* 113-156).

—— 1931a: Die kryoskopische Bestimmung des osmotischen Wertes bei Pflanzen (Handb. d. biolog. Arb. Meth. von E. Abderhalden, Abt. XI, Teil 4, Heft 2, pp. 353-371).

—— 1931b: Die Hydratur der Pflanze, 174 p. (Fischer, Jena).

——, and O. WEISMANN 1935: Über die Gefrierpunkte und osmotischen Werte lebender und toter pflanzlicher Gewebe (Jahrb. f. wiss. Bot. *82:* 273-310).

WANN, F. B. 1943: Water relations of the plant cell (Mimeographed correspondence).

WASHBURN, E. W. 1921: An introduction to the principles of physical chemistry, 516 p. (McGraw-Hill, New York).

WEAVER, J. E. 1916: The effect of certain rusts upon the transpiration of their hosts (Minnesota Bot. Studies *4:* 379-406).

WEAVER, R. J., and H. R. DEROSE 1946: Absorption and translocation of 2, 4-dichlorophenoxyacetic acid (Bot. Gaz. *107:* 509-521).

WEBER, F. 1923: Zur Physiologie der Spaltoeffnungsbewegungen (Österr. bot. Zeitschr. *72:* 43-57).

—— 1924: Plasmolyseform und Protoplasmaviskosität (*Ibid. 73:* 261-266).

—— 1925: Plasmolyseform und Kernform funktionierender Schliesszellen (Jahrb. f. wiss. Bot. *64:* 687-701).

—— 1929a: Plasmolysezeit und Lichtwirkung (Protoplasma *7:* 256-258).

—— 1929b: Plasmolyse in verdünntem Gewebesaft (*Ibid. 8:* 437-439).

WEIDLICH, H. 1930: Die Bewegungsmechanik der Variationsgelenke (Bot. Archiv. *28:* 219-254).

WEINMANN, H., and M. LE ROUX 1945: A critical study of the torsion balance for measuring transpiration (South African Jour. of Science *42:* 147-153).

WEISMANN, Otto 1938: Eine Theoretische und Experimentelle Kritik der "Bound Water-Theorie" (Protoplasma *31:* 27-68).

WENT, F. W. 1944: Plant growth under controlled conditions, III. Correlation between various physiological processes and growth in the tomato plant (Amer. Jour. Bot. *31:* 597-618).

——, and M. CARTER 1945: Wounding and sugar translocation (Plant Physiol. *20:* 457-460).

WHITE, P. R. 1938: Cultivation of excised roots of dicotyledonous plants (Amer. Jour. Bot. *25:* 348-356).

—— 1942: "Vegetable Staticks" (Amer. Scientist *30:* 119-136).

WHITING, H. 1884: Theory of cohesion (Harvard University, Cambridge, Mass.).

WHITMAN, W. C. 1941: Seasonal changes in bound water content of some prairie grasses (Bot. Gaz. *103:* 38-63).

WILDERVANCK, L. S. 1932: Osmotic adaptation of *Nitella translucens* Agardh (Rec. trav. bot. Neérl. *29:* 227-378).

WILLIAMS, W. T. 1947: Shock-induced stomatal movements (Nature *160:* 364-365).

WILSON, J. D., and H. A. RUNNELS 1933: Some effects of Bordeaux mixture on transpiration (Ohio Agr. Exp. Sta. Bimonthly Bull. *165:* 147-151).

WILSON, K. 1947: Water movement in submerged aquatic plants, with special reference to cut shoots of *Ranunculus fluitans* (Ann. Bot. N. S. *9:* 91-122).

WISE, L. E. ed. 1944: Wood chemistry, 900 p. (Reinhold Publ. Co., New York).

WITHROW, A. P., and R. B. WITHROW 1943: Translocation of the floral stimulus in *Xanthium* (Bot. Gaz. *104:* 409-416).

WRIGHT, K. E. 1939: Transpiration and the absorption of mineral salts (Plant Physiol. *14:* 171-174).

WYLIE, R. B. 1938: Concerning the conductive capacity of the minor veins of foliage leaves (Amer. Jour. Bot. *25:* 567-572).

WYMAN, J. 1936: The dielectric constant of solutions of dipolar ions (Chem. Rev. *19:* 213-239).

YARWOOD, C. E. 1936: The diurnal cycle of the powdery mildew *Erysiphe polygoni* (Jour. Agr. Res. *52:* 645-657).

ZALENSKI, V. 1904: Materials for the study of the quantitative anatomy of different leaves of the same plant (Mém. Polytech. Inst. Kiev. *4:* 1-203).

ZEEUW, J. DE 1939: On water exosmosis in *Chaetomorpha linum* (Müll.) Kütz. (Rec. trav. botan. Néerland. *36:* 268-346).

ZIEGENSPECK, H. 1945: Fluoroskopische Versuche an Blättern, über Leitung, Transpiration und Abscheidung von Wasser (Biol. Gen. [Vienna] *18:* 254-326).

ZIRKLE, C. 1937: The plant vacuole (Bot. Rev. *3:* 1-30).

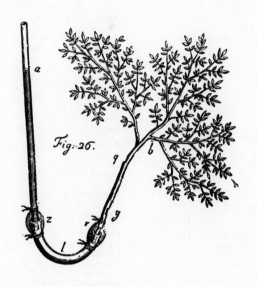

Fig. 26.

INDICES

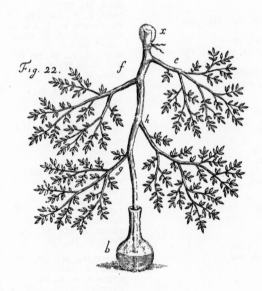

Fig. 22.

SUBJECT INDEX

A (see Intercellular pressure), 107
Absorption, forces involved, 138
Absorption of water, 148-154
  active, 149-151
  at permanent wilting, 152
  "induced," 138
  passive, 151
  "primary," 138
Accumulation, solute, 79, 126, 138
  water (see Active water relations)
Acer, gas in stem of, 161
Acid-arsenical method, of weed control, 157
"Activated diffusion," theory of translocation, 174
"Active pressure," 129
Active water relations, 111-147
  diffusion pressure deficits and, 131-132
  evidence from animal physiology, 136-138
  evidence from frost and drought resistance, 132-136
  mechanisms proposed for, 141-146
  solute accumulation, relation to, 138-139
Active water uptake, auxin and, 127-131
Activity, defn., 41, 77
  freezing pt. detn. of, 93
Adhesion, cytoplasm to wall, 83-85, 114-115
  water movement and, 154-155
Aesculus, gas in stem of, 161
Alfalfa, 2,4-D movement in, 177
Algae, osmotic detns., 85, 127
  vacuolar sap of, 70
  vacuolization in, 68
Alkalinity, effect on growth, 148
Alliaria officinalis, water continuity in, 163
Allium (see also Onion), photosyn. and sug. conc., 201
Alnus, gas in stem of, 161
Aloe, expressed sap of, 119
Amino acids, protein constituents, 66
  in protein synthesis, 129
Ammonia, thermal properties of, 4
Ammonium thiocyanate, translocation of, 157
Amylase, hydrolytic activity of, 200, 202, 203
Anaphoresis, 141
Anatomy, root structure and absorption, 149
Anguilla vulgaris, water regulation in, 137
Animal physiology, evidence for active water relations, 136-138
Anion accumulation, 139
Anomalous osmosis, 141, 142, 143
Anomalous plasmolytic behavior, 124
Anthocyanin, as indicator of cell injury, 84, 118, 125
Apple, water content of fruit, 62
Aquatic animals, osmoregulatory processes in, 136
Arsenic, weed control and, 157
Arthrophytum haloxylon, DPD of, 166
  DP gradient in, 164, 165
  transpiration of, 165
Ash tree, gas in, 157
Association factor, of water, 37
Atmospheric moisture, relative humidity, 56
  vapor pressure, 56
  DPD of, 56
Atmospheric pressure, DPD base line, 48
  and sap rise, 156
  effect on evaporation, 181-182
Atoms, forces between, 20
Atriplex confertifolia, OP sap of, 99
Auxin, active water relations and, 127-131
  effect on cell, 140
  effect on exudation, 150
  effect on respiration, 124
  translocation of, 175

Barger-Halket method, OP by, 96
Barley, water content of, 62
Bean, water content of, 62
  2,4-D movement in, 177
  water absorption by, 153
Beet (see Beta)
Begonia rex, plas.-cryos. discrepancy in, 112
Bellis perennis, DPD of, 106
Benzene, phys. properties of, 4
  stomatal detns. with, 197
  wettability of cell wall by, 193
Berberis nervosa, internal leaf surface in, 195
Bergenia cordifolia, adhesion pressure, 83
  OP values of, 114-115
Beta vulgaris, adhesion in, 84
  flower stimulation in, 176
  freezing pt. of sap of, 112, 115, 116, 118, 120, 126, 134
  plas.-cryosc. discrep. in, 112, 115, 118
  plastic stretching of walls, 84
Bioelectric forces, in plant cells, 144
Birch, rate of sap flow in, 171
Blood, thermoelectric detn. of rate of movement, 170
Bombardment theory, of OP, 33
Bonds (see also Forces), and hydration, 29
  hydrogen, 22, 29
  ionic, 22, 29
Boraginaceae, colloids in vacuoles of, 69
Bordeaux spray, effect on transpiration, 199
Bound water, 24-26
  calorimetric method for, 121, 122
  definitions of, 24
  frost resistance and, 135
Boundary layer, evaporation and, 183
Boyle's law, 32
Brassica napobrassica, plas.-cryos. discrepancy, 112
Brassica sinapis, wettability of cuticle, 187
Bryophyllum calicynum, internal leaf surface of, 195
Buckeye, gas in stem, 159
Butyl alcohol, leaf penetration by, 193
Buxus sempervirens, expressed sap of, 120

Cabbage, water content of, 62
Caladium bicolor, plas.-cryos. discrepancy, 112
Calcium, salt effect on leaves, 198
Calcium chloride, electroosmosis and, 131, 144
  moisture detn. with, 186
  plasmolyzing agent, 83
  water requirement and, 198
Calcium ferrocyanide, OP of solutions, 38, 39
Callithamnion roseum, cell walls of, 85
Calorimetric method, 121, 122
Cambium, OP of, 100
  water movement and activity of, 154, 156
Camphora officinalis, air space in leaves of, 194
Capillarity, and liquid in xylem, 162
Capillary force, and injection into xylem, 157
Capillary tubes, in OP detns., 96, 97
Carbohydrates, translocation of, 175
Carbon: nitrogen ratio, in phloem exudate, 175
Carbon dioxide, physical properties, 4
Carbon disulfide, physical properties, 4
Carbon tetrachloride, physical properties, 4
Carrot, water content of, 62
Castor bean, gas in stem of, 159
Castor oil, in infiltration method, 197
Catalase activity, water deficit and, 200
Catalpa, protoplasmic volume in, 135
Catalpa speciosa, internal leaf surface of, 195
Cell method for diffusion pressure deficit, 102-103
Cell sap, (see also Sap) cryoscopic value of entire, 118